THE ECOLOGY OF SOIL FUNGI

THE ECOLOGY OF
Soil Fungi

AN INTERNATIONAL SYMPOSIUM

Edited by

D. PARKINSON

AND

J. S. WAID

LIVERPOOL UNIVERSITY PRESS
1960

PUBLISHED BY
LIVERPOOL UNIVERSITY PRESS
123 GROVE STREET · LIVERPOOL 7

FIRST PUBLISHED 1960

PRINTED IN GREAT BRITAIN BY
HAZELL WATSON AND VINEY LTD
AYLESBURY AND SLOUGH

CONTRIBUTORS

BARTON, R., Department of Cryptogamic Botany, University of Manchester.

BOULTER, D., Department of Botany, The University of Liverpool.

BRIAN, P. W., Akers Research Laboratories, Imperial Chemical Industries, Ltd., Welwyn.

BURGES, N. A., Department of Botany, University of Liverpool.

BYWATER, J., University College of North Wales.

CHESTERS, C. G. C., Department of Botany, University of Nottingham.

DOBBS, C. G., University College of North Wales.

GARRARD, E. H., Department of Bacteriology, Ontario Agricultural College, Guelph, Canada.

GUILLEMAT, J., École Nationale d'Agriculture de Grinon, France.

HARLEY, J. L., Department of Agriculture, University of Oxford.

HENDERSON, M. E., The Macaulay Institute for Soil Research, Craigiebuckler, Aberdeen.

HINSON, W. H., University College of North Wales, Bangor.

HURST, H. M., Department of Botany, The University of Liverpool.

JACKSON, R. M., Rothamsted Experimental Station, Hertfordshire.

KATZNELSON, H., Microbiology Research Institute, Ottawa, Canada.

KENDRICK, W. B., Department of Botany, University of Liverpool.

LATTER, P. M., Department of Botany, The University of Liverpool.

MALISZEWSKA, I. U. N. G., Pulawy, Poland.

MAYAUDON, J., Centre de Microbiologie du Sol, Université de Louvain.

MONTÉGUT, J., École Nationale d'Horticulture, France.

MOREAU, R., École Nationale de Medicine et de Pharmacie, Besançon, France.

NICOT, J., Laboratoire de Cryptogamie du Museum, Paris.

PARK, D., Department of Cryptogamic Botany, University of Manchester.

PARKINSON, D., Department of Botany, University of Liverpool.

PEUSS, H., Botanische Abt. Madaus, Köln-Merheim, Germany.

PUGH, G. J. F., Department of Botany, University of Nottingham.

SCHÖNBECK, F., Botanische Abt. Madaus, Köln-Merheim, Germany.

SEWELL, G. W. F., East Malling Research Station.

SIMONART, P., Centre de Microbiologie du Sol, Université de Louvain, Belgium.

THORNTON, R. H., Soil Bureau, Department of Scientific and Industrial Research, Wellington, New Zealand.

TRIBE, H. T., School of Agriculture, Cambridge.

WAID, J. S., Levington Research Station, Suffolk.

WARCUP, J. H., Wait Agricultural Institute, Adelaide, South Australia.

WILLOUGHBY, L. G., Freshwater Biological Association, Westmorland.

WINTER, A. G., Botanische Abt. Madaus, Köln-Merheim, Germany.

PREFACE

During the grand period of soil microbiology dominated by Winogradsky and Beijerinck, interest centred primarily on bacteria and the key parts they played in the many changes undergone by substances in the soil. The organisms associated with the nitrogen and sulphur cycles received particular attention. At this stage little thought was given to fungi and indeed so little was known of them that in 1914 Waksman found it necessary to pose and answer questions such as 'Do fungi have an active life in the soil?' His work ushered in a new phase and many studies were carried out to determine the nature of the fungal flora in different soils. Nearly all of this work was essentially floristic and except for a few investigators little attention was paid to the ecological aspects of fungal growth in soil. Recently the situation has changed considerably and the ecological aspects of soil mycology have attracted an ever growing body of adherents, particularly in England. It was not surprising therefore that when a tentative proposal was made to hold a Symposium on the Ecology of Soil Fungi, it was enthusiastically welcomed. Most of the work of organizing the symposium fell on the shoulders of Dr. D. Parkinson and Dr. J. Waid; to this has now been added the editing of the papers and seeing the volume through the press. They are to be warmly congratulated not only on the success of the symposium but also on the appearance of the printed account despite the difficulties of dealing with manuscripts from authors widely separated in different countries and the almost impossible task of condensing many vigorous discussions to short summaries which still convey the gist and the feeling of the contributions.

In many ways the present volume marks a transition in the study of soil fungi from a period in which the use of dilution plate techniques was pre-eminent and in which the species list was regarded as an end in itself, to one in which attention is focused on the habitats of the individual species and the parts they play in the biochemical changes which take place in the soil. This is reflected in many of the contributions which are concerned with new techniques. It will not be possible to judge the value of these until they have been tested by a number of workers under differing conditions. It is clear that the next few years will see big changes in soil mycology. If this volume assists the development of the subject the contributors will feel amply rewarded.

ALAN BURGES

Department of Botany
University of Liverpool

CONTENTS

CONTENTS

PHYSIOLOGY OF SOIL FUNGI

CONTENTS

METHODS FOR ISOLATION
AND ESTIMATION OF ACTIVITY OF
FUNGI IN SOIL

METHODS FOR ISOLATION
AND ESTIMATION OF ACTIVITY OF
FUNGI IN SOIL

J. H. WARCUP

Waite Agricultural Research Institute, Adelaide, South Australia

A wide range of techniques has been used in the study of soil fungi; many have been devised to study the population as a whole, others to study a single organism or group of organisms with some common property. Most general studies have depended on making a suspension of soil, and incubating a portion of it in an agar medium. Exhaustive studies have been made of the factors which influence the results of these plate-counts of fungi obtained from soil dilutions, and also the factors which must be considered in evaluating such estimates. Any colony on a plate may have arisen from a spore or a hypha, and owing to the capacity of some soil fungi for heavy sporulation, the presence of a sporing fungus in a sample collected for analysis would weigh the subsequent 'count' very heavily. Also, since the origin of colonies arising on dilution plates was unknown, it is impossible to differentiate between active mycelium and resting bodies in the soil. A further difficulty was that many fungi known to occur in soil, such as Basidiomycetes, species of *Pythium*, *Mortierella*, and a galaxy of darker Hyphomycetes (Chesters, 1949) were rarely obtained in dilution studies. Subsequent work by soil-baiting and other techniques has increased the number of fungi known to be missed.

Following the realization of the imperfections of dilution studies, many investigators have devised other methods for isolation of fungi from soil. These have attempted to minimize the advantage of heavily sporing fungi on isolation plates, to enlarge the range of species obtained, to isolate specific fungi, or to differentiate between active and inactive fungi in soil; there is, however, often a lack of critical data on their usefulness for these purposes. In this paper I wish to re-examine methods of isolation of fungi from soil, to consider their use, their limitations and particularly their use in the estimation of activity of fungi in soil; general methods and some specific ones are considered. Garrett (1955), Harley & Waid (1955), and Chesters & Thornton (1956) have all pointed out that it is fundamental for many studies to be able to differentiate active from inactive fungi, since it is only in the active mycelial condition that fungi play their part in decomposition and other soil processes.

The soil-dilution plate method

This method, the most widely used in soil mycology, has been adapted from the method originally developed for general isolation of soil bacteria (Waksman, 1927); the chief modifications have been in the use of lower dilutions on account of the lower 'numbers' of soil fungi, and in the development of different isolation media, adjusted to an acid reaction (pH 4·0) for suppression of bacteria (Garrett, 1951).

The method consists of shaking a known amount of soil in sterile water, then obtaining a progressive series of dilutions. From one or more of the dilutions, 1-ml. samples are placed in Petri dishes and dispersed with melted but cooled agar by shaking and rotating the plate before the agar solidifies. The effect of various operations on the degree of variability in estimated numbers has been studied by Brierley, Jewson & Brierley (1927).

The dilutions used, usually between 1/1000 and 1/100,000, are chosen so that the degree of interference between developing colonies on the plates through competition and antagonism can be minimized. Waksman (1944) recommended 30–100 colonies per plate. Brierley *et al.* (1927) recommended 35–45, but the average of 25 chosen by Bisby, James & Timonin (1933) appears more suitable, and has been found permissible by James & Sutherland (1939) as a result of statistical tests. Even with low numbers, Warcup (unpublished data) has found evidence of suppression, since plates from which young colonies were removed as they developed always gave significantly higher counts than plates where fungi were allowed to develop normally; both series of plates having been prepared from the same suspension. Interference is most marked if spreading colonies are present, but may also occur in their absence.

To reduce the growth of bacteria and Actinomycetes on dilution plates, Waksman (1922) and Jensen (1931) adjusted the medium with sulphuric acid to approximately pH 4·0; other acids, lactic, boric, and phosphoric, have also been used. Acid, however, is known to depress or prevent the growth of some fungi. Smith & Dawson (1944) proposed the use of rose bengal at a concentration of 1:15,000 as a bacteriostatic agent, which Dawson & Dawson (1947) found to produce no fungistatic effect other than a reduction of colony size. Martin (1950) recommended the use of a peptone-dextrose agar containing 1:30,000 rose bengal and 30 μg./ml. of streptomycin. He found that this medium gave higher numbers and types than one acidified with sulphuric acid, partly due to suppression of fungi by the acid and partly due to reduction in size of spreading colonies by the rose bengal. Some workers (Miller, Giddens & Foster, 1957) have found this medium satisfactory, others have found it necessary to increase the quantity of one or both bacteriostatic agents. Other antibiotics have been used, and Johnson (1957) reports aureomycin (chlortetracycline) at 0·5 μg./ml. to be more effective than streptomycin at 30 μg./ml.; he also found significantly more colonies with aureomycin than with streptomycin. Dulaney, Larsen & Stapley (1955) have reported on the use of a combination of antibiotics for isolating fungi. Paharia & Kommedahl (1954) reported that distributing 1 ml. of soil solution over the solidified agar surface 2–3 days after plates were poured gave more colonies than incorporating the soil dilution at the time of pouring the plates, especially in the presence of streptomycin and rose bengal.

Most soil mycologists have always considered that when this method is applied to the 'counting' of soil fungi, a serious difficulty arises owing to the fact that any given fungal colony may have originated from an active hypha or an inactive spore. Since many of the abundant fungi, *Mucor, Aspergillus, Penicillium, Trichoderma*, etc., isolated by the dilution-plate method are species that spore heavily, it has been generally considered that a major defect of the method is the substantial advantage it gives to heavily sporing fungi (Garrett, 1951). While there has long been circumstantial evidence for this view, direct evidence has recently been obtained (Warcup, 1955*b*, 1957). Dilution plates after a short incubation (18 hr.) were searched for young fungal colonies, each of which was removed in a small block of agar for direct examination. After the nature of the propagule giving rise to the young colony had been determined, the agar block was transferred to fresh medium to permit growth and identification. Plates were examined twice daily until no more colonies were obtained. By the use of this method, the majority of colonies developing on dilution plates prepared from a sample of wheat-field soil were found to have arisen from spores. Comparative studies showed that not only did dilution studies neglect a large number of fungi but that many of these were present in soil as hyphae (Warcup, 1957).

Data were also obtained that high counts obtained on dilution plates are not necessarily correlated with current activity of fungi in soil, though activity and high count may coincide. All examinations so far made show that even where high count and activity coincide, it is the spore component and not the mycelial one that is recorded on dilution plates (Warcup, unpublished data). While this may not be true in all soils or under all circumstances, it is apparent that, without further information, a high count cannot be taken as an indication of present fungal activity. Chesters (1949) had earlier expressed the opinion that a fungal count appears to be a compound of what is, what was, and what may be.

These results show that the dilution-plate method is of little use in estimating the activity of fungi in soil. Examination of the origin of colonies on dilution plates may be made and hyphae recorded, but the method is tedious and the number of hyphae found is generally low, so that it is unlikely to become a general procedure, though for specific problems it may be useful. Dilution plates, however, will always have a place in isolating fungi for soil floras or for other purposes, and for estimating the inactive component of the soil flora. It is important to remember, however, that it records only a part of the species present in soil, and not all fungal spores or other units enter into suspension or grow on the isolation plates; both hyphae and spores often remain with the organic and mineral material discarded as the residue of the soil suspension (Warcup, 1951a; Saitô, 1955).

Soil plates (Warcup, 1950)

The method was developed for an ecological study where large numbers of separate samples were to be handled; in such cases the labour of preparation and handling of water blanks for dilution plates becomes prohibitive. It had also been found that many fungi are discarded with the residue in the preparation of dilution plates, and it was considered that the use of soil would allow growth of fungi embedded in humus or attached to mineral particles.

By this method, small samples (0·005–0·015 g.) of soil are taken from the main samples by means of a sterile nichrome needle with a flattened tip, which is then used to disperse the soil aggregates in a drop of sterile water in the bottom of a sterile Petri dish. Melted and cooled agar (8–10 ml.) is then added, and the particles distributed throughout the medium by shaking and rotating the dish.

Comparison of soil plates and dilution plates showed that usually, but not always, more species of fungi were recorded by soil than dilution plates. A study of incubated and stained soil plates showed that many of the colonies which occurred on a plate developed from humus particles, but viable spores were also present, sometimes in large numbers (Warcup, 1951a).

In a further comparison between soil and dilution plates, Warcup (1957) found that both methods give essentially the same picture of the fungal flora of a wheat-field soil. While a higher total number of species were recorded from dilution than soil plates during the investigation, in any particular sample soil plates usually gave a higher number than did dilution plates. This difference in the number of species obtained was most marked with subsurface samples, where soil plates often recorded twice the number of species obtained on dilution plates, was less marked with surface samples, and if *Pythium* or *Trichoderma* was present was likely to be reversed, since both genera contain fast-growing species that may swamp other fungi, and both were isolated more frequently from soil than dilution plates. Besides these differences in the number of species obtained, several fungi, including *Absidia butleri*, *Cunninghamella*, *Penicillium* W4, *Trichoderma viride* and species of *Aspergillus*, *Pythium*, *Mucor*, and *Mortierella*, were usually more abundant on soil than dilution plates. A species of *Melanospora* that showed synergistic growth was of frequent occurrence on soil, but was absent from dilution plates. Other studies have shown that the parasitic mucorales are often more frequent on soil than dilution plates. Whether the difference in results obtained by the two methods can be attributed mainly to the difference in the dilutions used (dilution plates 1/5000, soil plates approximately 1/250), or whether other factors, such as a possible failure of some fungi to enter into soil suspensions, are important is not known. In general, the data suggest that soil plates tend to favour medium to fast-growing fungi present in soil in relatively low numbers.

While incorporation of soil with the medium should allow any hyphae present to grow, recent work suggests that this is rarely the case. Under most conditions the number of faster-growing organisms present as spores is sufficient to mask growth from any viable hyphae present. In any case, without further evidence it is impossible to tell which fungi may have developed from hyphae. Unless an analysis of the unit of origin of individual colonies is carried out, no information on the activity of fungi in soil is obtained by either the dilution- or soil-plate methods. If soil plates are to be used, some trials varying the amount of soil embedded in the agar should be made; some workers have used up to 0·2 g. of soil, which in my experience is too much, unless the number of fungi in the soil is very low.

The direct inoculation method (*Waksman*, 1916)

This method was devised by Waksman to answer a question then very controversial, viz, whether fungi actually lived and produced mycelium in the soil, or whether they were deposited there from the air as spores and remain viable but inert (Garrett, 1951). Waksman transferred lumps of soil, about 1 cm. in diameter, into sterile plates of Czapek's solution agar. After incubation at 22° C. for 24 hr., hyphal tips were removed, and Waksman remarks 'the organisms thus isolated are believed to come from the mycelium that is actually found in the soil. The period allowed for incubation was not long enough for spores to germinate and produce such a mass of mycelium'. Waksman further tested his hypothesis by examining plates of Czapek's agar inoculated with spores or mycelium after 24 hr., and found that those inoculated with mycelium had extensive growth, whereas those with spores showed only minute colonies. Waksman records *Mucor, Trichoderma, Rhizopus*, and *Zygorrhynchus* as found most abundantly by this method. Workers who have used this method (Brown, 1917; Waksman, 1927; Jensen, 1931; Park, 1954; Chesters & Thornton, 1956) have found that large lumps are not necessary, and have noted that the method is highly selective for fast-growing fungi.

Saitô (1955) using Waksman's direct inoculation method, isolated *Mucor, Rhizopus*, and *Zygorrhynchus* from garden soil. He made direct microscopic examination of the lumps and 'apart from septate fine hyphae, none of the non-septate, broad hyphae characteristic of the mucoraceous fungi could be found even by careful direct microscopic examination; therefore, the mycelia developed from the lumps of soil should be derived from spores'. A few experiments of my own have substantiated Saitô's results. Examination by the hyphal isolation method (Warcup, 1955a) of lumps which would invariably give rise to *Rhizopus* if placed on agar, failed to reveal any aseptate hyphae of this fungus. Saitô remarks that Waksman based his cultural observations on a mass of mycelium, on the one hand, and a single spore on the other; certainly my experience with spores and hyphae of *Rhizopus* obtained from soil, shows that hyphae do not invariably grow faster than spores, and that spores may grow, usually as single hyphae, for surprising distances (over 1 cm.) on weak Czapek-Dox plus yeast agar in 24 hr. While the latter medium contains accessory growth substances absent from Czapek's agar, spores in soil also have access to extra nutrients.

These results show that in some cases, at least, the fungal growth obtained by direct inoculation is derived from spores. This suggests that, in the absence of further information, this method is of no use for investigating fungal activity in soil.

Soil desiccation method (*McLennan*, 1928)

In 1928 McLennan suggested that a possible method for discriminating between fungal mycelium and spores in soil might be drying the soil in a desiccator over calcium chloride. McLennan plated out samples of moist soil and soil which had been dried over calcium chloride, and compared the number of fungal colonies obtained, a marked decrease after drying was noted. Suspensions in soil of fragmented mycelia and of a mixture of spores were in turn plated out directly and after drying; no colonies developed from the sample containing only mycelia, whereas the sample containing spores was in no way affected. McLennan suggested that the decrease obtained with natural soil was due to the desiccation of the vegetative mycelium in the soil, and since the reduction in the number of colonies per plate was pronounced, it was considered that the normal fungal constituents of the soil were present extensively in the mycelial condition.

Jensen (1934) found that, in agreement with Rossi-Cholodny slide studies, the method showed that a large proportion of the fungi in one soil were present as spores. His results also caused doubt whether McLennan's conclusion that fungi exist mainly as mycelium in soil was valid in general. While pointing out that from general evidence available spores are more resistant to desiccation than is mycelium, Garrett (1952) considered it was improbable that this treatment would affect anything approaching a complete separation of colonies derived from these two sources. Eastwood (1952) considered using the technique, but on testing it with fungi in pure culture found that while mycelium was destroyed by desiccation, there was also a reduction of about 25% in the number of spores surviving. Agnihothrudu (1955) has used the method to examine the state in which fungi occur in the rhizosphere. Harley & Waid (1955) have pointed out that methods such as this, being dependent on the dilution-plate technique, are often subject to grave errors because the cultures obtained by dilution of soil may be so preponderantly from spores that estimates of vegetatively active forms are greatly affected by variations in the number of spores. The studies (Warcup, 1955b) showing that most of the colonies on dilution plates arise from spores suggest that this view is probably correct.

Since there are contradictions in these accounts, particularly in the proportion of spores lost on drying, it was decided to investigate this method. From the wheat-field previously studied, samples of surface soil (1 in. deep) were collected in autumn and winter, when it was known that there was fungal activity in the soil (Warcup, 1957). From each sample dilution plates were prepared immediately after collection, and again after drying for 3 days over calcium chloride in a desiccator as recommended by McLennan. The origin of colonies developing on plates of both fresh and dried soil were determined by the method

TABLE 1

Total number of colonies of each fungus developing from spores, hyphae, or humus particles on dilution plates of wheat-field soil before and after desiccation over calcium chloride

Fungus	BEFORE TREATMENT				AFTER TREATMENT			
	No. of colonies developing from:				No. of colonies developing from:			
	Spores	Hyphae	Humus particles	Unclassified	Spores	Hyphae	Particles	Unclassified
Mortierella spp.	4	—	—	—	—	—	—	—
Mucor spp.	3	—	—	—	1	—	1	—
Rhizopus arrhizus	41	—	—	—	13	—	1	—
Aspergillus terreus	2	—	15	1	10	—	6	—
Penicillium W2	85	—	2	2	2	—	1	—
P. purpurogenum	13	—	—	—	2	—	1	—
P. spp.	23	—	4	3	2	—	3	—
?*Scopulariopsis* W21	23	—	—	—	1	—	3	—
Cladosporium herbarum	3	—	1	—	—	—	1	—
Chaetomium funicola	3	—	—	—	1	—	—	—
Fusarium oxysporum	9	—	6	—	—	—	3	—
Trichoderma viride	4	—	—	—	2	—	—	—
Pestalotia W67	7	—	—	—	—	—	—	—
T1 (sterile culture)	—	2	4	—	—	—	—	—
T7 (sterile culture)	—	4	8	—	—	—	—	—
T6 (sterile culture)	—	1	3	—	—	—	2	—
Other fungi	35	5	19	4	5	1	9	—
TOTALS			339				80	

previously recorded (Warcup, 1955*b*). The origin of colonies developing on 3 dilution plates from 4 different samples of fresh and dried soil are given in Table 1, which records total numbers obtained from all samples. As previously, the unit of origin is given as spore, hypha, humus particle, and 'unclassified' if the nature of the unit could not be determined. Table 1 shows that drying over calcium chloride caused a marked reduction in the number of colonies, and that this fall was mainly due to loss of spores. Some fungi, particularly species of *Penicillium*, were decimated by the drying; a high proportion of the fungi which survived grew from humus particles. One hypha was found to have survived the treatment. The effect of desiccation over calcium chloride would appear similar, though more severe, to that noted for natural drying of soil in the field during the summer dry period at Adelaide (Warcup, 1957); both cause a reduction in the number of colonies and a rise in the percentage of fungi recorded from humus particles.

The immersion-tube method (*Chesters*, 1940)

This method, described by Chesters (1940, 1948), consists of the introduction into soil of a glass tube, with 4–6 spirally arranged invaginated capillaries, filled with a nutrient agar. A soil core is removed in the field and an immersion tube inserted in its place. After 7–14 days it is removed, and fungi isolated from it by removing a core the length of the tube with a stainless-steel corer, and then cutting it into portions which are plated out.

Mueller & Durrell (1957) have described a modification of Chesters' immersion tubes, using plastic centrifuge tubes bored with $\frac{3}{16}$-in. holes and wrapped with 'Koroseal' electrical tape. In the field a large heated needle is pushed through the tape and tube perforation into the agar to make an entrance for fungal growth; after burial in soil, the tubes are taken to the laboratory and the tape unwound to allow fungal isolation.

Chesters (1948) states that the dominant genera obtained from cultivated and pasture soils by his method are *Mortierella*, *Mucor*, and *Pythium*, followed by *Rhizoctonia*, *Rhizopus*, *Zygorrhynchus*, *Fusarium* and an occasional *Armillaria mellea*. He also found that the use of differentially enriched media within the tubes influenced the type and frequency of isolation of different genera and species; *Pythium* was isolated only on maize-meal agar. Chesters says 'our view of the limits of the immersion-tube method is that it easily isolates active spreading mycelium or active localized mycelium which happens to come in contact with the capillaries. The fungi so isolated must obviously be capable of growth into and through the medium in the tube, and preliminary experiments indicate that a control of isolated fungi may be effected at this point'.

Chesters & Thornton (1956) made a comparison of the fungi isolated from a forest soil by immersion tubes and by screened immersion plates (Thornton, 1952). Discussing the results, they remark that colonization of immersion tubes by fungi depends on the ability of individuals to compete successfully with other members of the soil population for entry through capillary orifices. Also, once established the fungi must be capable of growing into the depths of the medium far enough to be isolated in the agar core. This implies tolerance of low oxygen tension resulting from sterilization of the agar during preparation. They also consider that fast-growing fungi once established may be likely to colonize the bulk of the agar within the tube, and therefore be recorded with a high frequency of isolation.

While it is generally considered that immersion tubes isolate active mycelia from soil, and the isolation of *Rhizoctonia solani* and *Armillaria* certainly substantiate this, it must be pointed out that many of the other species recorded are sporing species that are, to some extent or other, found on dilution plates. The observations of Hinson (Dobbs & Hinson, 1953) with La Touche slide traps and 'gap traps' (two slides touching at one end and kept apart with a glass fibre at the other), showing that spores germinating in water condensed between the slides provided the origin of many, at least, of the hyphae seen in the traps after burial in soil, suggest that condensation of water in the orifices of immersion tubes could also provide a habitat for spore germination.

Screened immersion plates (Thornton, 1952)

Thornton (1952) devised screened immersion plates as a development of the Rossi-Cholodny slide method, which permits isolation of micro-organisms capable of growing from the soil on to water agar placed behind a perforated screen. The agar is carried on a glass slide carried in a 'Perspex' box with a lid containing 10 spaced holes for entrance of fungal growth. After a suitable period of burial in the soil, the plates are removed, examined and fungal growth transferred to potato dextrose agar. Screened immersion plates resemble immersion tubes in that both methods attempt the isolation of mycelium from soil, and both techniques introduce an agar medium into natural soil so that the medium is exposed only at selected sites. Thornton (1956) isolated *Rhizoctonia solani* by screened immersion plates, but not on soil plates, from natural grassland soils in New Zealand.

Chesters & Thornton (1956) in their study of methods of isolation of fungi from soil, found that isolations by screened immersion plates showed close agreement with those by more direct methods (immersion tubes and Waksman's direct isolation method), and differed from those obtained by dilution and soil plates. Isolations by screened plates also exhibited a wider range and variety of species than those obtained by any other method, particularly for species of *Mortierella* and demati-aceous fungi.

In limited studies with this method at Adelaide I have encountered a practical difficulty, that of coping with soil animals. In screened immersion plates placed in grassland soil for 3–4 days (Thornton kept his in soil for 7–14 days), there is considerable movement of mites, springtails, and termites through the orifices; in some cases the agar has been cut out and removed lump by lump. While some fungi isolated belong to the sterile group obtained by the hyphal isolation method (Warcup, 1955*a*) and have developed from hyphae, with other species there was a much greater element of doubt, some originating from 'foot pads' and small particles on the agar surface; further studies on this method seem desirable.

Other immersion methods

Another method by which culture medium may be immersed in soil is the slide-trap method of La Touche (1948). In this method two standard hanging drop slides clipped together so that their concavities lie opposite one another enclose a small quantity of suitable agar medium. The moisture of condensation which collects between the slides enable growth to take place until the agar is reached.

Sewell (1956) used La Touche slide traps, but found them to be highly selective for rapidly growing species and with a few exceptions only isolated *Trichoderma viride* from surface soil. He proposed a modified slide trap, a shallow chamber of 'Perspex' covered by a glass microscope slide. He reports results similar to those obtained with immersion tubes.

The hyphal isolation method (*Warcup*, 1955*a*)

In 1955 Warcup reported a simple method for extracting and plating hyphae from soil; essentially the method depends on the observation that when a soil suspension is prepared many of the fungal hyphae remain with the heavier soil particles of the residue. Removal of the fine suspended matter from the residue also permits visual examination of the latter for the presence of hyphae, which may then be removed and grown on agar media.

In the originally described method (Warcup, 1955*a*) a sedimentation method was used to separate the heavier particles from the suspension, but sieves may also be used, a 50μ pore diameter sieve has proved very useful. The residue is examined microscopically for the presence of fungal hyphae, and individual hyphae or portions of hyphal masses are removed with fine forceps and placed in a drop of sterile water in a clean sterile isolation dish. A pair of forceps which allow hyphae to be transported in a small drop of water behind the points are more satisfactory than types which grasp the hyphae themselves. When sufficient hyphae (usually 20–50) are in the dish, it is poured with melted but cooled agar and the hyphae dispersed in the usual manner. Hyphae are then located, ringed, and numbered on the reverse of the plate. Plates are incubated at room temperature, and examined daily under a microscope for fungal growth. The location of and examination of hyphae, though tedious, is essential since hyphae may have small humus particles or occasionally spores along their surfaces, and growth may originate from these attached particles. However, with suitable precautions one may be sure that growth is from a hypha and no other fungal unit.

In the study of the fungal flora of a wheat-field by dilution plates and by hyphal isolation, Warcup (1957) found that a high proportion of the fungi obtained by hyphal isolation are species which were rare or absent from dilution plates. In contrast to dilution plates, where the most abundant fungi isolated were species of *Penicillium*, *Rhizopus*, *Mucor*, *Cladosporium*, and *Fusarium*, many fungi obtained from hyphae remain sterile in culture. Besides sterile forms, *Rhizoctonia solani*, *Ophiobolus graminis*, and several Basidiomycetes were among the fungi isolated from hyphae; also *Pythium*, *Rhizopus*, *Mortierella*, and *Fusarium* species, which also occurred on dilution plates. These results indicate that the hyphal isolation method, besides giving data on which fungi are present in a soil as mycelium, isolates a large group of fungi that have hitherto been neglected in soil fungal studies.

Warcup (1957) also considered how selective hyphal isolation may be, and concluded that the method may be selective for (*a*) hyphae of large diameter, (*b*) mycelia that do not fragment readily, and (*o*) fungi with dark-coloured hyphae. Hyphal isolation may tend to neglect (*a*) hyphae that fragment readily, (*b*) fine single hyphae, (*c*) hyphae in large humus particles or grosser organic fragments in soil, and (*d*) hyphae closely adherent to, or occurring in, plant roots. Whether any fungi occurring in soil have mycelium that fragments easily is not known; there is evidence that fine unbranched hyphae do occur in soil. Grosser organic fragments and plant roots are both important 'ecological niches' in soil which must also be investigated in any work on the activity of fungi in soil. Another selective element is that not all fungi present as hyphae in soil may be able to grow on the isolation medium, a weak Dox plus yeast agar. Some clamp-bearing hyphae, and vesicle-bearing fungi similar in appearance to the root endophyte *Rhizophagus*, have not yet been grown satisfactorily on the isolation medium or on any other medium tested; with a few other hyphae it is difficult to decide whether they are dead, or alive but incapable of growth on the medium.

A further question is whether the actual extraction of hyphae from soil may damage or kill them. It is difficult to obtain information on how important this may be; circumstantial evidence indicates that while many are extracted alive some are probably damaged. The only positive evidence of loss due to damage has been with *Pythium*. While this fungus has been successfully grown from hyphae isolated from soil, some cases have been noted where this fungus present in and on roots failed to grow from free hyphae picked from the root. Other Phycomycetes, however, including *Thraustotheca*, *Aphanomyces*, *Rhizopus*, and *Mucor*, have been grown from a considerable proportion of their hyphae isolated from soil.

While hyphae have been successfully isolated and grown from soil, evidence suggests that the presence of viable hyphae need not be synonymous with active growth in soil. Some viable hyphae have been found present when soil moisture is well below wilting point and when it seems unlikely that active growth could proceed. Also hyphae have been grown from the surface of dead roots some months after the root has died, although there is no evidence that the fungus colonizes dead roots. Perhaps 'resting hyphae' may be more common in soil than is usually considered (Hawker, 1957). Most of the fungi which circumstantial evidence suggests have resting hyphae have hyphae with dark brown or black walls. Many hyphae, however, particularly those with hyaline walls, seem undoubtedly active at the time of isolation; many such hyphae appear to lose their cell contents if not active.

Selective methods

A wide range of selective methods have been used to isolate fungi from soil, and particularly with 'baiting' methods there seems to be an infinite number of substrates that may be added to soil to encourage specific organisms or groups of organisms. Selective techniques are especially valuable when the organism is present in soil in very low numbers. It should, however, be pointed out that most selective methods give little information besides presence of fungi in soil.

A bait added to water covering a soil sample is especially useful for those organisms that form zoospores. A considerable range of baits,

'Cellophane', boiled grass leaves, pine pollen, hemp seed, shrimp chitin, insect wings, hair, and snakeskin cast, have been used for soil chytrids (Sparrow, 1957). Anderson (1951) has used pineapple stems and leaves for baiting *Phytophthora cinnamomi* and other species of *Phytophthora*; hemp seed is the usual bait for *Pythium* and 'water moulds'. Other methods have placed soil on or in plant tissue; examples are: the apple technique for *P. cinnamomi* (Campbell, 1949), the carrot method for *Thielaviopsis basicola* (Yarwood, 1946), and the potato technique of McKee & Boyd (1952) for *Fusarium caeruleum*. The use of a host as a selective method is common procedure for soil-borne pathogens. Soil plated with a cooled weak maize-meal agar has been used for isolation of nematode-destroying fungi (Duddington, 1954). Ledingham & Chinn (1955) have used an interesting flotation method by means of which spores of *Helminthosporium sativum* may be recovered from soil. Soil mixed with a small amount of mineral oil is shaken up in water. The emulsion which collects on the surface of the water contains most of the spores (80–90 %) originally in the soil.

A different approach is treating the soil with heat or chemicals before plating it out. Warcup (1951*b*) used heat treatment to show that certain Ascomycetes were more common in soil than usually suspected; Wensley (1953), Warcup (1952) and Evans (1955) have shown that soil fumigants, chloropicrin, formalin, carbon disulphide, at certain dosages may act selectively, killing most but not all soil fungi. Organisms with resistant spores, such as ascosporic species of *Aspergillus* and *Penicillium* and some species of *Thielavia*, *Chaetomium*, *Sordaria*, and *Gelasionospora*, are often obtained. This approach may be capable of further development.

Isolation from roots

Since roots, alive or dead, are one of the major substrates for fungi in soil, particularly uncultivated soil, any investigation into activity of fungi in soil needs to consider the growth of fungi on and in roots. Roots have long been examined for fungi, particularly root-disease organisms, mycorrhizal fungi, or in connexion with rhizosphere studies. The last type of investigation has mainly been made by dilution techniques so that little information on activity of fungi in soil is obtainable from them (Harley & Waid, 1955). Pathological investigations are usually made by plating out suitable pieces of material from the edge of a lesion, following some surface sterilization procedure. In some cases, and particularly with fine roots, surface sterilization may kill all organisms in the root, so washing techniques have been used. That used by

Harley & Waid (1955) in a study of the fungi on roots and decaying petioles in soil is of interest. Harley & Waid gave the material serial washings in sterile water, and checked the degree of completeness of removal of fungal units by the dilution-plate method. They found that the detachable fungal fragments were mostly removed in the first washes, and that after about 10 washes a low, fairly constant number was obtained. They found that the impression gained by studying populations growing on agar from unwashed surfaces is different from that obtained from washed surfaces, because in the former sporing Hyphomycetes are greatly over-represented, whilst Phycomycetes and more particularly slow-growing non-sporing mycelia are under-represented.

Waid (1956) has introduced a further refinement—root dissection—for studying the fungi within root tissue. Washed roots were cut into 2 mm. segments from which the outer cortex was dissected, leaving the central cylinder comprising the inner cortex and stele. Dissection was carried out in dishes of sterile water, using sterile forceps and scalpel. The fragments were plated and studied separately. Waid (1956, 1957) has used the method in a study of fungi in decomposing roots of ryegrass. He obtained sterile fungi from the inner cortex, which were rarely obtained from intact roots, presumably because they could not compete in mixed culture with such surface-inhabiting forms as *Trichoderma viride* or *Mucor* spp. He noted, however, that clamp-bearing mycelia seen in decomposing cortical tissues were rarely obtained in culture.

One of the difficulties in isolation from roots is that any root portion, even 2 mm. long, may be inhabited by more than one fungus; on plating out such material usually only the faster-growing species survive, overgrowing any other fungi. With banana roots, Stover (1953) used a Waring blender to fragment roots, and reported a greater range of fungi by this technique than from plating root segments. This method is excellent for a bulk of root material. For examination of small individual roots I have used a root-fragmentation method with success (Warcup, 1959).

Following washing, small pieces of root, about 5–15 mm. in length, the length depending on the diameter of the root, were cut off and placed in sterile water in a Petri dish. Wide roots were usually dissected into two portions, and each piece placed in a separate dish. Before pouring the plates, each root piece was dissected apart with two needles under a binocular dissecting microscope, the root fragments were then dispersed in agar. The fragments were located and ringed, and by examining fragments under a microscope it was possible in many cases to discern both the region of the root from which growth occurred and the

S.E.S.F.—2

nature of the fungal unit. To reduce the amount of scanning for root fragments, it has been found advantageous to use a 7-cm. instead of the usual 10-cm. dishes. Since many roots are heavily contaminated with bacteria a bacteriostatic agent is necessary; streptomycin has been used successfully, acid at pH 4·0 has not prevented bacterial growth and has suppressed some fungal growth.

By this method a wide range of fungi has been isolated from roots from a pasture soil. *Penicillium* and *Gliocladium roseum* have been found growing and fruiting on the surface of young roots, and *Ophiobolus graminis*, sterile fungi and several Basidiomycetes have been isolated from steles of dead roots.

Wilhelm (1956), using a different technique, has been able to demonstrate the occurrence of many root pathogens, including *Verticillium albo-atrum*, *Colletotrichum* and *Pyrenochaeta terrestris*, on healthy roots of weeds growing in strawberry fields. He surface sterilized roots, often whole root systems, with mercuric chloride, and buried them for 2–4 weeks in sterilized moist sand. Roots were then examined for resting or reproductive structures of various fungi, these were isolated for further culturing or study.

DISCUSSION

While, as has been recently re-emphasized, ability to distinguish between spores and hyphae in soil is essential for many ecological studies of soil fungi, this study shows that most of the methods which have been suggested for this purpose are unreliable. Without making an analysis of the origin of colonies arising on the plates, neither dilution- nor soil-plate studies give any information on activity of fungi in soil. If an analysis of colonies is to be carried out, the dilution-plate method should be used. Waksman's direct-inoculation method is unreliable, since colonies may originate from spores; soil desiccation, as suggested by McLennan, has been found to kill large numbers of spores besides mycelium in soil, hence it cannot be used as a basis of a differential method for detecting mycelia in soil.

The immersion methods, Chesters' immersion tubes and Thornton's screened immersion plates, where an agar medium is introduced into natural soil at selected sites, undoubtedly isolate some fungi from mycelium in soil (*Rhizoctonia* and *Armillaria*). However, the lists for these methods contain many sporing species and little mention of sterile fungi; the observations of Hinson, showing spores may germinate in drops of water condensed on glass surfaces added to soil, leave some doubt as to whether all species obtained by these methods originate from mycelium. This must not be taken to imply that sporing fungi do not have active growth in soil, but because their spores may be abundant more care needs to be taken to prove their mycelial growth than with species without spores. Until evidence is available to show otherwise, it is perhaps better to have doubts whether the majority of the sporing fungi isolated by the immersion methods do, in fact, come from hyphae. It is desirable to obtain further information on these methods.

One of the criticisms often levelled against soil fungal studies is that the methods neglect the soil Basidiomycetes. While much more needs to be known about these fungi, even about where they occur in soil, it must be pointed out that they have now been isolated from hyphae and from sclerotia obtained from soil (Warcup, 1957), from rhizomorphs and mycelial strands from soil (Levisohn, 1955; Warcup, 1959) and from plant roots, both living and dead (Warcup, 1959).

With all methods, as has been found for dilution plates, the type of fungi isolated can, to some degree, be altered by the use of different media, choice of bacteriostatic agent, and use of substances, such as rose bengal or sodium desoxycholate, to limit colony size. Use of these agents, however, must be considered in relation to the problem being studied. Rose bengal will limit fungal colony size and inhibit many bacteria and Actinomycetes, and thus may increase colony count on dilution plates considerably; however, it appears to prevent the growth of some hyphae isolated from soil or in residues, so it is of less value in these studies.

In studies on activity of fungi, it is my opinion that we can best proceed by a combination of microscopic and isolation techniques. Since no method appears entirely satisfactory as yet, a variety of methods with as much direct observation as possible will probably yield maximum information.

REFERENCES

AGNIHOTHRUDU, V. (1955). State in which fungi occur in the rhizosphere. *Sonderdruck aus die naturwissenschaften*, **18**, 515–16.

ANDERSON, E. J. (1951). A simple method for detecting the presence of *Phytophthora cinnamomi* Rands in soil. *Phytopath.*, **41**, 187–8.

BISBY, G. R., JAMES, N., & TIMONIN, M. I. (1933). Fungi isolated from Manitoba soils by the plate method. *Canad. J. Res.*, **8**, 253–75.

BRIERLEY, W. B., JEWSON, S. T., & BRIERLEY, M. (1927). The quantitative study of soil fungi. *Proc. 1st Internat. Congr. Soil Sci.*, **3**, 48–71.

BROWN, P. E. (1917). The importance of mould action in soils. *Science N.S.*, **46**, No. 1182.

CAMPBELL, W. A. (1949). A method of isolating *Phytophthora cinnamomi* directly from the soil. *Plant Dis. Rep.*, **33**, 134.

CHESTERS, C. G. C. (1940). A method of isolating soil fungi. *Trans. Brit. mycol. Soc.*, **24**, 352–5.

CHESTERS, C. G. C. (1948). A contribution to the study of fungi in the soil. *Trans. Brit. mycol. Soc.*, **30**, 100–17.

CHESTERS, C. G. C. (1949). Concerning fungi inhabiting soil. *Trans. Brit. mycol. Soc.*, **32**, 197–216.

CHESTERS, C. G. C., & THORNTON, R. H. (1956). A comparison of techniques for isolating soil fungi. *Trans. Brit. mycol. Soc.*, **39**, 301–13.

DAWSON, V. T., & DAWSON, R. C. (1947). Further observations on the use of rose bengal for the enumeration of soil fungi. *Proc. Soil Sci. Soc. Amer.*, **11**, 268–9.

DOBBS, C. G., & HINSON, W. H. (1953). A widespread fungistasis in soils. *Nature, Lond.*, **172**, 197–9.

DUDDINGTON, C. L. (1954). Nematode-destroying fungi in agricultural soil. *Nature, Lond.*, **173**, 500–1.

DULANEY, E. L., LARSEN, A. H., & STAPLEY, E. O. (1955). A note on the isolation of micro-organisms from natural sources. *Mycologia*, **47**, 420–2.

EASTWOOD, D. J. (1952). The fungus flora of composts. *Trans. Brit. mycol. Soc.*, **35**, 215–20.

EVANS, E. (1955). Survival and recolonization by fungi in a soil treated with formalin or carbon disulphide. *Trans. Brit. mycol. Soc.*, **38**, 335–46.

GARRETT, S. D. (1951). Ecological groups of soil fungi: a survey of substrate relationships. *New Phytol.*, **50**, 149–66.

GARRETT, S. D. (1952). The soil fungi as a microcosm for ecologists. *Sci. Progr.*, **40**, 436–50.

GARRETT, S. D. (1955). Microbial ecology of the soil. *Trans. Brit. mycol. Soc.*, **38**, 1–9.

HARLEY, J. L., & WAID, J. S. (1955). A method of studying active mycelia on living roots and other surfaces in the soil. *Trans. Brit. mycol. Soc.*, **38**, 104–18.

HAWKER, L. E. (1957). Ecological factors and survival of fungi. *Microbial Ecology, 7th Symposium Soc. Gen. Microbiol.*, Cambridge University Press, 238–58.

JAMES, N., & SUTHERLAND, M. (1939). The accuracy of the plating method for estimating the numbers of bacteria and fungi from one dilution and one aliquot of a laboratory sample of soil. *Canad. J. Res.*, C, **17**, 97–108.

JENSEN, H. L. (1931). The fungus flora of the soil. *Soil Sci.*, **31**, 123–58.

JENSEN, H. L. (1934). Contributions to the microbiology of Australian soils. II. *Proc. Linn. Soc. of N.S.W.*, **59**, 200–11.

JOHNSON, L. F. (1957). Effect of antibiotics on the numbers of bacteria and fungi isolated from soil by the dilution-plate method. *Phytopath.*, **47**, 630–1.

LA TOUCHE, C. J. (1948). Slide-traps for soil fungi. *Trans. Brit. mycol. Soc.*, **31**, 281–4.

LEDINGHAM, R. J., & CHINN, S. H. F. (1955). A flotation method for obtaining spores of *Helminthosporium sativum* from soil. *Canad. J. Bot.*, **33**, 298–303.

LEVISOHN, I. (1955). Isolation of ectotrophic mycorrhizal mycelia from rhizomorphs present in soil. *Nature, Lond.*, **176**, 519.

MCKEE, R. K., & BOYD A. E. W. (1952). Dry-rot disease of the potato. III. *Ann. appl. Biol.*, **39**, 44–53.

MCLENNAN, E. (1928). The growth of fungi in the soil. *Ann. appl. Biol.*, **15**, 95–109.

MARTIN, J. P. (1950). Use of acid rose bengal. and streptomycin in the plate method for estimating soil fungi. *Soil Sci.*, **69**, 215–32.

MILLER, J. H., GIDDENS. J. E., & FOSTER, A. A. (1957). A survey of the fungi of forest and cultivated soils of Georgia. *Mycologia*, **49**, 779–808.

MUELLER, K. E., & DURRELL, L. W. (1957). Sampling tubes for soil fungi. *Phytopath.*, **47**, 243.

PAHARIA, K. D., & KOMMEDAHL, T. (1954). A modified plating technique for the study of soil fungi. *Phytopath.*, **44**, 502.

PARK, D. (1954). An indirect method for the study of fungi in the soil. *Trans. Brit. mycol. Soc.*, **37**, 405–11.

SAITÔ, T. (1955). The significance of plate counts of soil fungi and the detection of their mycelia. *Ecol. Rev.*, **14**, 69–74.

SEWELL, G. W. F. (1956). A slide-trap method for the isolation of soil fungi. *Nature, Lond.*, **177**, 708.

SMITH, N. R., & DAWSON, V. T. (1944). The bacteriostatic action of rose bengal in media used for the plate counts of soil fungi. *Soil Sci.*, **58**, 467–71.

SPARROW, F. K. (1957). A further contribution to the phycomycete flora of Great Britain. *Trans. Brit. mycol. Soc.*, **40**, 523–35.

STOVER, R. H. (1953). Measurement of colonization and survival of soil *Fusaria* in detached plant tissue. *Nature, Lond.*, **172**, 465.

THORNTON, R. H. (1952). The screened immersion plate: a method of isolating soil micro-organisms. *Research*, **5**, 190–1.

THORNTON, R. H. (1956). *Rhizoctonia* in natural grassland soils. *Nature, Lond.*, **177**, 230–1.

WAID, J. S. (1956). Root dissection: a method of studying the distribution of active mycelia within root tissue. *Nature, Lond.*, **178**, 1477–8.

WAID, J. S. (1957). Distribution of fungi within the decomposing tissues of rye-grass roots. *Trans. Brit. mycol. Soc.*, **40**, 391–406.

WAKSMAN, S. A. (1916). Do fungi actually live in soil and produce mycelium? *Science N.S.*, **44**, 320–2.

WAKSMAN, S. A. (1922). A method of counting the number of fungi in the soil. *J. Bact.*, **7**, 339–41.

WAKSMAN, S. A. (1927). *Principles of Soil Microbiology*. Baltimore: Williams & Wilkins Co.

WAKSMAN, S. A. (1944). Three decades with soil fungi. *Soil Sci.*, **58**, 89–114.

WARCUP, J. H. (1950). The soil-plate method for isolation of fungi from soil. *Nature, Lond.*, **166**, 117.

WARCUP, J. H. (1951a). The ecology of soil fungi. *Trans. Brit. mycol. Soc.*, **34**, 376–99.

WARCUP, J. H. (1951b). Soil-steaming: a selective method for the isolation of Ascomycetes from soil. *Trans. Brit. mycol. Soc.*, **34**, 515–18.

WARCUP, J. H. (1952). Effect of partial sterilization by formalin on damping-off of Sitka spruce. *Trans. Brit. mycol. Soc.*, **35**, 248–62.

WARCUP, J. H. (1955a). Isolation of fungi from hyphae present in soil. *Nature, Lond.*, **175**, 953.

WARCUP, J. H. (1955b). On the origin of colonies of fungi developing on soil dilution plates. *Trans. Brit. mycol. Soc.*, **38**, 298–301.

WARCUP, J. H. (1957). Studies on the occurrence and activity of fungi in a wheat-field soil. *Trans. Brit. mycol. Soc.*, **40**, 237–62.

WARCUP, J. H. (1959). Studies on Basidiomycetes in soil. *Trans. Brit. mycol. Soc.*, **42**, 45–52.

WENSLEY, R. N. (1953). Microbiological studies of the action of some selected soil fumigants. *Canad. J. Bot.*, **31**, 277–308.

WILHELM, S. (1956). A sand-culture technique for the isolation of fungi associated with roots. *Phytopath.*, **46**, 293–5.

YARWOOD, C. E. (1946). Isolation of *Thielaviopsis basicola* from soil by means of carrot disks. *Mycologia*, **38**, 346–8.

INVESTIGATIONS OF SOIL
MICRO-HABITATS

D. PARKINSON AND W. B. KENDRICK

Department of Botany, University of Liverpool

Clear statements have been made by various workers (Chesters, 1949; Garrett, 1951) regarding the importance of the micro-habitat in the ecology of fungi in the soil. Despite these, there still appear in the literature reports of indiscriminate isolations of fungi from soil, reports which provide species lists, but which give little or no indication as to the substrates in the soil from which the species are isolated or whether they are present as spores or mycelium.

The soil micro-habitats which can be studied with the greatest facility are those associated with plant roots and with fragments of plant débris, as these are easily separated from the mineral soil. Of these types of micro-habitat only the root region has been widely studied.

Washing techniques have been used by many workers for the study of active mycelia, particularly with reference to the root surface (Kürbis, 1937; Simmonds & Ledingham, 1937; Robertson, 1954; Harley & Waid, 1955; Stenton, 1958). However, despite the work of Chesters (1948) and Harley & Waid (1955), such techniques have not been sufficiently applied to other micro-habitats. We have applied variations of the Harley & Waid washing technique in the study of various types of plant débris on and in soil. The results given here refer to two types of decomposing plant material, pine-leaf litter and decomposing couch-grass material (*Agropyron repens*. Beaur).

Pine-leaf litter

Successions of fungi on naturally occurring plant débris, decomposing on the surface of the soil, have been studied by Chesters (1950), Mangenot (1952), Webster (1956, 1957), Hudson & Webster (1958) and Pugh (1958). One of the principal forms of such débris is the leaf litter of forest trees. This litter is the material from which the greater part of the organic horizon of soil is derived, and certain of its properties play dominant roles in determining the nature of the organic horizon (Handley, 1954) and in the development of the soil profile (Joffe, 1932).

The leaf litter of a pure stand of *Pinus sylvestris* is a very convenient subject for study, as it has strong mor-humus-forming tendencies and the protracted breakdown process leads to a considerable accumulation of litter in progressive stages of decay which may be recognized as the 'litter', 'fermentation', and 'humification' sub-horizons (L, F, and H layers) as defined by Hesselman (1926). In the habitat chosen the accumulation is so great that a further sub-division of the 'fermentation' layer into F_1 and F_2 layers is clearly recognizable (Kubiena, 1953); F_1 needles being dark in colour and frequently still intact, and the F_2 needles greyish, fragmentary, and compressed together.

Most previous microbiological studies of podzols under pine species have either ignored the organic horizon altogether, or employed techniques such as the soil plate and the soil dilution plate, which are known to give an incomplete picture of the fungal population. Application of these techniques to the different layers of the organic horizon under consideration indicated a population almost entirely composed of heavily sporing moniliaceous forms such as *Trichoderma viride* and species of *Penicillium*. Microscopical examination of the H layer, however, showed the presence of large numbers of dematiaceous hyphal fragments, an observation previously made by Müller (1879) and Romell (1935). Many of these fragments were isolated directly by the method of Warcup (1955), but they invariably failed to grow.

This led to the belief that they were, at least in part, produced in the overlying layers of the organic horizon during the active decomposition of the litter, and persisted in the lower layers only because of their resistance to microbiological attack.

We have selected for active mycelia growing on or in the decomposing pine needles by applying a modification of the serial washing technique devised by Harley & Waid (1955) for the removal of detachable surface propagules. Batches of needles from each of the layers were shaken in 10 changes of a sterile 1% (v/v) aqueous solution of 'Teepol' detergent, followed by 10 changes of sterile water, prior to plating on 2% (w/v) malt agar. This technique was shown, by pouring dilution plates with samples of the washing water, to give satisfactory removal of spores from living needles and those of layer L, but was less effective for needles of the lower layers.

Mycelia growing in the interior of the pine needles were selectively isolated by surface sterilization of the needles with 0·1% (w/v) aqueous mercuric chloride solution before plating.

The results of a year's isolations obtained by the parallel application of these two techniques to the different layers of the organic horizon are shown in Fig. 1.

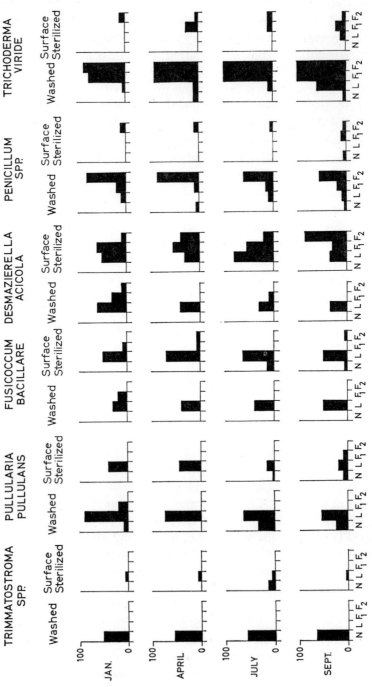

Fig. 1. Percentage occurence of frequently isolated fungi on washed and surface sterilized pine needles from the layers of the organic horizon (L,F$_1$ and F$_2$) and living needles from the trees (N).

Only the six most frequently isolated genera are represented. Of these, *Trimmatostroma*, *Pullularia*, *Fusicoccum*, and *Desmazierella* produce dark pigment. This is a very different picture from that obtained from dilution plates. *Desmazierella acicola*, perhaps the most important internal colonizer of the needles, was never isolated on dilution plates, and *Fusicoccum* was isolated only rarely by this method.

In addition to the cultural techniques, this particular micro-habitat lends itself admirably to direct microscopic observation, and this showed that at all stages of decomposition, even the specialized cultural techniques employed did not give a full picture of the active fungal population. Needles of the L layer were often seen to be colonized by the parasitic *Lophodermium pinastri*, which persists and fruits in the litter but does not grow in artificial culture (Jones, 1935). Numerous conidiophores of two hitherto undescribed dematiaceous hyphomycetes, *Helicoma monospora* and *Sympodiella acicola*, were seen on needles of the F_1 layer, and sterile dark hyphae and strands of Basidiomycete mycelium were observed in the F_2 layer. The two hyphomycetes and the sterile dark mycelium have been cultured by the direct plating of conidia or hyphae, but none of them was ever isolated by the normal cultural techniques described above. The Basidiomycete mycelia were not isolated on standard media.

These facts emphasize the importance of combining direct observation with cultural techniques if a fairly complete picture of the fungal population is to be gained.

Couch-grass debris

Here the soil under investigation was an acid sandy soil of low organic matter content. Samples of this soil were separated into two crude fractions—the mineral and the organic fractions. The organic matter consisted of fragments of dead plant material derived from couch grass.

The large organic fragments were subjected to serial washing with sterile water, after which pieces of organic matter (2 mm. long) were placed in nutrient agar. Throughout this group of experiments Czapek-Dox agar plus yeast extract and rose bengal adjusted to pH 5·0 was used as the medium for fungal isolations.

The crude mineral fraction was also washed serially, and fungi were isolated from the washed mineral material by the soil-plate technique (Warcup, 1950).

As well as the isolations from washed organic and inorganic matter, isolation of fungi from unwashed soil was accomplished by the normal application of the soil plate technique.

Table 1 gives data on the fungi isolated with the greatest frequency in these experiments. From this it can be seen that differences exist between the species complement of the washed mineral fraction, the washed organic fraction, and the unwashed soil. The main points may be summarized as follows:

(*a*) *Fusarium* spp. and *Cylindrocarpon* spp. are much more in evidence from plated organic fragments; in accordance with the results of other workers.

(*b*) Sterile mycelial forms are isolated with the greatest frequency from washed mineral material.

(*c*) Heavily sporing forms show a reduction in frequency of isolation from the washed fractions. This is particularly the case with the *Penicillia*.

(*d*) Certain members of the Mucorales (*Mucor hiemalis* and *Zygorrhyncus moelleri*) are isolated most frequently from washed mineral matter, but for the rest of the members of this order there is a decreased frequency of isolation from washed substrates.

(*e*) Isolates from washed organic fragments included several species not isolated from washed mineral material or from unwashed soil; for example, *Pythium* sp., *Cladosporium herbarum*, *Dicoccum asperum*, *Phoma* sp., *Microdiplodia* sp., and *Pyrenochaeta* sp. These occurred only rarely (with between 1 and 3% frequency), and have therefore not been shown in Table 1.

These results indicate that information regarding the distribution of fungi in soil will be given by the use of washing techniques; such information is not provided by many of the methods frequently used for the isolation of soil fungi. The results indicate that, for the most part, there is a decrease in the frequency of isolation of heavily sporing forms when washed material is plated. This may support the contention that many of the isolates are from mycelium present in the washed substrates.

This type of study is obviously only a preliminary step in soil micro-habitat studies. The organic and inorganic fractions used each represent groups of micro-habitats. The various plant parts from which the macroscopic organic matter of the soil is derived can often be easily recognized and separated, and dissection techniques on such material to allow more critical micro-habitat studies have been developed (Waid, 1956).

Separation of the mineral soil into fractions of known particle size can easily be achieved by sieving. This form of separation can easily be incorporated into a simple apparatus which will enable vigorous washing of the soil fractions. A modification of the apparatus described by Chesters (1948) has been used for this purpose. The sieving-washing technique provides a practicable method easily adapted for dealing with many replicate samples.

It would seem that the use of washing techniques of the types described provide a quick and efficient means for the study of the active fungal population of soil and the distribution of these fungi. The hyphal isolation technique (Warcup, 1955) appears ideal for the study of fungi present as hyphae in soil. However, the hyphal isolation technique has limitations which have been given (Warcup, 1959); added to these there is the fact that the time taken for the picking and plating of hyphal fragments is considerable, and therefore the type of study for which this method is applicable is limited.

TABLE 1

Major fungi isolated from unwashed soil, washed mineral material and washed organic material

(*Figures represent % frequency of isolation*)

Fungi isolated	Unwashed soil	Washed mineral soil	Washed organic matter
Trichoderma viride	81	65	13
Penicillium spp.	70	7	10
Mucor ramannianus	24	18	—
Mortierella spp.	23	10	3
Ascomycetes	10	—	—
Sterile white forms	16	60	3
Mucor hiemalis	24	55	7
Zygorrhynchus moelleri	25	40	—
Sterile dark forms	1	18	4
Fusarium spp.	4	20	50
Cylindrocarpon spp.	—	—	17
Stemphylium sp.	1	—	8

REFERENCES

CHESTERS, C. G. C. (1948). A contribution to the study of fungi in the soil. *Trans. Brit. mycol. Soc.*, **31**, 100–17.

CHESTERS, C. G. C. (1949). Presidential address: Concerning fungi inhabiting soil. *Trans. Brit. mycol. Soc.*, **32**, 197–216.

CHESTERS, C. G. C. (1950). On the succession of microfungi associated with the decay of logs and branches. *Trans. Lincs. Nat. Union.*, **12**, 129–35.

GARRETT, S. D. (1957). Ecological groups of soil fungi: a survey of substrate relationships. *New Phytol.*, **50**, 149–66.

HANDLEY, W. R. C. (1954). Mull and mor formation in relation to forest soils. *For. Comm. Bull.*, **23**.

HARLEY, J. L., & WAID, J. S. (1955). A method of studying active mycelia on living roots and other surfaces in the soil. *Trans. Brit. mycol. Soc.*, **38**, 104–18.

HESSELMAN, H. (1926). Studier över barrskogens humustäcke, dessegenskaper och beroende av skogsvarden. *Medd. Skogsförsöksanst Stockh.*, **22**, 169–552.

HUDSON, H. J., & WEBSTER, J. (1958). Succession of fungi on decaying stems of *Agropyron repens*. *Trans. Brit. mycol. Soc.*, **41**, 165–77.

JOFFE, J. S. (1932). Soil profile studies. IV. Morphological and chemical evidence of podzolization. *Soil Sci.*, **33**, 217–37.

JONES, S. G. (1935). The structure of *Lophodermium pinastri* (Schrad.) Chev. *Ann. Bot.*, **49**, 699–728.

KUBIENA, W. L. (1953). *Soils of Europe*. London: Thomas Murby & Co.

KÜRBIS, W. P. (1937). [Studies on the fungi associated with the roots of ash]. *Flora, Jena*, **131**, 129–75.

MANGENOT, F. (1952). Recherches methodiques sur les champignons de certaine bois en decompostion. *Rev. gén. Bot.*, **59**, *702*, 381–99; *704*, 77–9; *705*, 544–55.

MULLER, P. E. (1879). Studier over Skorjord, som Bidrag til Skoroykningens Theori. *Tidsskr. Skorbrug*. Berlin (cited by Handley, 1954).

PUGH, G. J. F. (1958). Leaf-litter fungi found on *Carex paniculata* L. *Trans. Brit. mycol. Soc.*, **41**, 185–95.

ROBERTSON, N. F. (1954). Studies on the mycorrhiza of *Pinus sylvestris*. *New Phytol.*, **53**, 253–83.

ROMELL, L. G. (1935). Ecological problems of the humus layer in the forest. *Cornell Univ. Agric. Exp. Sta. Memoir*, **170**.

SIMMONDS, P. M., & LEDINGHAM, R. J. (1937). A study of the fungus flora of wheat roots. *Sci. Agric.*, **18**, 59–69.

STENTON, H. (1958). Colonization of roots of *Pisum sativium* L. by fungi. *Trans. Brit. mycol. Soc.*, **41**, 74–80.

WAID, J. S. (1956). Root dissection: a method of studying the distribution of active mycelia within root tissue. *Nature, Lond.*, **178**, 1477–8.

WARCUP, J. H. (1950). The soil-plate method for isolation of fungi from soil. *Nature, Lond.*, **166**, 117–18.

WARCUP, J. H. (1955). On the origin of colonies of fungi developing on soil-dilution plates. *Trans. Brit. mycol. Soc.*, **38**, 298–301.

WARCUP, J. H. (1959). Methods for isolation and estimation of activity of fungi in soil. *Proc. Symposium Ecology of Soil Fungi*. Liverpool (1958).

WEBSTER, J. (1956). Succession of fungi on decaying cocksfoot culms. Part I. *J. Ecol.*, **44**, 517–44.

WEBSTER, J. (1957). Succession of fungi on decaying cocksfoot culms. Part II. *J. Ecol.*, **45**, 1–30.

THE OCCURRENCE OF SOME LOWER FUNGI (*CHYTRIDIALES*) IN LAKE MUDS AND SOIL

WITH SPECIAL REFERENCE TO A SITE AT ESTHWAITE

L. G. WILLOUGHBY

Freshwater Biological Association, Westmorland

This investigation is being carried out for several reasons. In the first place, the aquatic fungal flora of the small body of water at Esthwaite is becoming increasingly known, and it is hoped that eventually a considerable amount of data will be collected on this subject. It has therefore become of interest to know whether the same aquatic organisms are active in the surrounding pasture-land, or whether the latter has a different flora of water moulds. Again, and particularly with reference to the saprophytic chytrids, examination of the relevant literature shows that it is not always clear whether certain water moulds which have been studied should be regarded as essentially aquatic forms or as members of the soil microflora. To quote one species, *Asterophyctis sarcoptoides* is frequently encountered in the Lake District growing on floating insect exuviae, and hence might be regarded as an aquatic form, but the same organism is also reported from the U.S.A. as occurring 'rather commonly in soil as a saprophyte'.

Considering the role of chytrids in soil decomposition, the presumption is that they play a part in decomposing freshly added organic matter before this breaks down to humus; but there is little information on how active these forms are under natural conditions. Microscopic examination of mud or soil in order to find these fungi has so far yielded no information. However, although the parent thalli cannot themselves be observed, the zoospores can, in some cases, be obtained directly from mud by the following method.

Mud collections weighing 6 g. are covered with sterile water in a small beaker, and surface loopings are taken at intervals and examined immediately for chytrid zoospores. These mud collections are taken from the marginal zone of Esthwaite Water from which high water has recently receded, leaving this zone of soil twice as wet as the adjacent pasture-field, which has not been covered by the lake at high water. The method depends for its success on the fact that chytrid zoospores are aerotactic, and tend to rise to the surface meniscus of the water in the beaker, from where they can be looped off, and readily recognized under the low powers of the compound microscope. Zoospores are not recovered immediately, but appear after 30–210 min. if the sample is kept at 25°. At 5° there is a longer lag period before zoospores are recorded. These results suggest that mature sporangia are present in quantity in the mud collections, and dehiscence has been induced by adding water and raising the temperature. Possibly this method could be refined to give further information by plating out the zoospores on to solid agar media, since a certain amount of information is available on the nutritional requirements of some of the chytrids known to be present. Using soil from the pasture-field, zoospores have not been obtained by this method, even after heavy rain, and it is possible that in this case so few zoospores are released that the method is too crude to give a positive result.

An indirect method of investigation which has become standard practice in studies on the lower saprophytic fungi is to place 3–4 g. of mud or soil in a Petri dish, add sterile water and a suitable bait, and incubate for 2–3 weeks.

This indirect method is being used in studying the chytrid distribution at a site on Esthwaite in the English Lake District. Collections of mud and soil are made at intervals of approximately a fortnight. The collections are taken along a line transect at three levels; namely: (i) the *Littorella* zone at 2 m. depth; (ii) the marginal zone where the soil layer is a thin one overlying gravel, and which is periodically inundated when lake levels are high; and (iii) the adjacent pasture-field, where the collection is taken from the top 5 cm. of soil. The mud or soil from each zone is divided up and baited. The baits used are (i) cellulose materials ('Cellophane', grass leaves, and epidermal strippings); (ii) chitin materials (purified shrimp exo-skeleton and termites' wings); and (iii) keratin material (snake skin). For each zone two Petri dishes of each bait are prepared, i.e. two of 'Cellophane', two of grass leaves, two of epidermal strippings, etc. In this way a relatively large amount of substratum can be added and subsequently examined. Since it is common for individual species to be restricted to one type of bait, the pairs of dishes tend to have a different chytrid population. Each pair of dishes is regarded as representing a single sample, and individual species counted as present or absent. Due regard is also made of species which can grow on several of the different baits. The aim is to make the list of species recovered from any one sample as comprehensive as possible, rather than to attempt to assay actual numbers of organisms present. Indeed, the latter would be very difficult to accomplish, since it is quite common for one portion of a bait to be covered with one particular species, while the remainder is apparently devoid of it.

The Esthwaite samples indicate that it is possible, at this site at least, to distinguish forms which occur over and over again in collections from the same zone, and which are regarded as common, from those which occur only occasionally in different collections. Many of the 'occa-. sional' forms are incompletely known and have not yet been identified. Furthermore, it is possible to distinguish the typical soil forms from the aquatic ones. Considering the samples from the permanently submerged level first, the common chytrids are *Asterophlyctis sarcoptoides*, species of *Chytriomyces*, and species of *Nowakowskiella*. The common chytrids from the soil-level are species of *Rhizophlyctis* (including *Rhizophlyctis (Karlingia) rosea*) and multipored species of *Rhizophidium*. The marginal zone is remarkable in that both these sets of organisms occur together, with the single exception of *Asterophlyctis*, which to date has only been obtained from the permanently submerged zone samples. All the species mentioned so far are monocentric (unicellular), except the *Nowakow- skiella* sp., which form a rapidly spreading rhizomycelium. It appears that the polycentric species *Nowakowskiella elegans* and *Nowakowskiella profusa*, which are outstandingly active fungi and often form dense extramatrical growths on 'Cellophane' bait in a short time, are confined to the strictly aquatic environment, despite their capacity for potentially unlimited linear growth. To these two might well be added *Clado- chytrium replicatum*, which occurs rarely in the Esthwaite samples but is a common aquatic form in Windermere. If the results obtained so far are substantiated by further work, it will be interesting to speculate as to why the multicellular thallus should be a successful one in fresh water but not in the adjacent soil in this group of fungi. The three polycentric species mentioned grow on cellulose baits, while *Asterophlyctis sarcop- toides* and the *Chytriomyces* species are chitin-decomposers. Pure cul- ture work on *Chytriomyces aureus* has failed to demonstrate any capacity to decompose cellulose in this species.

Considering the soil microflora, perhaps the most interesting feature is the prolific growth which occurs on keratin baits. The organisms responsible for this intense activity are two multipored species of *Rhizo- phidium*, one of which is *Rhizophidium keratinophilum*, and a *Rhizo- phlyctis*-like form as yet unidentified. Although this activity on keratin is much less pronounced at the lower levels, two of these three chytrids have been obtained, always in small quantity, from the submerged mud collections. Since the field being investigated is used as sheep pasture, it is possible that the fragments of wool and horn which these animals undoubtedly contribute to the soil is the main substratum for these 'keratinophilic' forms. It may well be, however, that in nature these organisms occupy quite a different ecological niche, but the particular synthetic capacities which they possess enables them to use keratin sources when these are supplied in the laboratory. Clearly there is great scope for further work on these little-known fungi.

Turning to the other common soil chytrids at Esthwaite, none of these has so far been collected from the permanently submerged mud. The predominant chitin-decomposing form is a species of *Rhizophlyctis*, and on cellulose baits a multipored *Rhizophidium* and *Rhizophlyctis* (*Karlingia*) *rosea* are the common chytrids. The latter is perhaps the best known of all the soil chytrids, but the ease with which it can be recognized, due to its pigmentation and large size and also because it grows well on 'Cellophane' and hence is easily examined, has perhaps tended to over-emphasize its relative importance in comparison with other forms. Other smaller soil chytrids, particularly species of *Rhizophidium*, which can rarely be obtained on 'Cellophane' bait but appear on other cellulose substrata, are less well known, and it is especially difficult to give these *Rhizophidium* species a specific name. They occur frequently on grass-leaf baits, and work both in the Lake District and in the South of England tends to indicate that they are equally typical soil forms.

In conclusion, mention may be made of the parasitic chytrids which are obtained from soil from time to time. Two such forms which have been studied parasitized another chytrid species, and a soil *Mucor* respectively. They provide further evidence of the diversity of habitat and nutritional requirements of these lower fungi in soil.

SOME OBSERVATIONS ON FUNGAL
SPORES IN SOIL[1]

C. G. DOBBS AND W. H. HINSON[2]

University College of North Wales

Work on soil mycology at Bangor started with a special interest in the Mucorales and a realization of the fact that they are nearly all wet-spored (Dobbs, 1942). From this came a curiosity about how these moulds exist and behave in the soil. Visibility is the first problem in such an investigation, and this led to trials with cellulose film to see if this would provide a suitable surface for fungal extension and growth within the soil; but the results of burying cellulose films in the soil and lifting after a few days, insufficient for any obvious exploitation of the cellulose, were disappointing as compared even with plain glass.

When protected between two glass slides however (a simple development suggested by the slide traps of La Touche, 1948) the cellulose was found to wrinkle into hollows and folds, offering a convenient observation chamber for fungal growth and sporulation. Such slide traps were used by G. D. Holmes in 1947–8, and a number of mycelia isolated from them by means of 2-mm. blocks of malt agar placed upon the hyphal tips, gave cultures of common soil moulds, mainly *Penicillium* spp., *Trichoderma* and Mucorales. More interesting were the profusion of chlamydospores and sometimes stylospores of *Mortierella* spp. formed on the cellulose film, and the frequency of animal tracks, and sometimes of the animals themselves, on the protected surfaces of the traps.

A trial of Chesters' (1940) immersion tubes also drew our attention to the importance of animal movement in the soil, as mites and small insects in particular (rather than nematodes or other worms) were found to enter the tubes via the capillary holes. Were they carrying spores? Probably, but we could not see what was happening in the tube; though in the slide traps spores could sometimes be seen germinating on the protected surfaces.

Some slide traps were lifted from a forest soil in which they had been

[1] This paper incorporates material from a thesis by W. H. Hinson approved in 1954 for the Ph.D. degree of the University of Wales.

[2] Present address: Forestry Commission, Forest Research Station, Alice Holt Lodge, Wrecclesham, Farnham, Surrey.

buried for a period of more than 6 months. A mass of organic material, bodies and faeces of mites, nematodes and other animals, matted together with mycelium and bacteria, was found to have invaded them. The cellulose had almost disappeared. The two main impressions which we had gained up to this point were, therefore, the importance of chlamydospores in the soil, and the importance of soil animals as movers of spores and organic materials.

Realizing that the cellulose film was acting as a nutrient, we eliminated it and reduced the traps to the simplest possible devices for ensuring good visibility of whatever growth of fungi occurs on an inert, protected glass surface buried in the soil.

The all-glass slide trap

Fig. 1 shows the so-called 'gap trap' which resulted. This, simple as it is, embodies a good deal of preliminary work on the sporulation of moulds in bread and soil and in graded sands of varying pore size moistened with 2% (w/v) malt extract.

Except for the tall sporangia of *Mucor albo-ater*, sporulation of all the moulds tested occurred freely in coarse sand with cavities estimated to be of the order of 0·3 mm., but in fine sand with cavities about 0·15 mm. it was suppressed in some moulds (e.g. *Mucor hiemalis* and *M. varians*), but occurred in others (*M. albo-ater* 'Kurztrieben', *M. racemosus, Penicillium notatum*). *M. ramannianus* also failed to form sporangia in this fine sand, but its mycelium when recovered by flotation showed numerous chlamydospores. On the other hand, all the species tested were found to sporulate in autoclaved soil, and when pieces of bread, about 4 × 3 × 3 cm., were buried in the litter layer on a woodland site, 14 days later various moulds, including *Mucor ramannianus* and *Penicillium* spp., were found to be sporing freely in the soil within a zone of about 15-cm. radius from the bread.

Tests with the slide traps buried in soil and in sterilized sand, moistened with 2% (w/v) malt extract and inoculated with a mixture of these moulds, showed that a glass-fibre spacer, 0·7 mm. thick, inserted at one end gave a suitable range of gap size for sporulation, and a suitable compromise between capillary flooding of the gap and entry of soil. In natural soil these traps gave sporulation in the gap (e.g. of *Mortierella tuberosa* and *Penicillium* spp.) only when buried within the zone of influence of some source of nutrient, e.g. 10 cm. below buried pieces of bread. Without nutrient, though there was no sporing, sterile mycelia were almost invariably found upon the protected surfaces of the glass within 10–14 days.

The method of isolation with malt agar blocks (*m*) placed on hyphal tips was repeated, but with the addition of control blocks (*c*) placed clear of the mycelium. These soon confirmed the suspicion that after 1–2 weeks in the soil the protected glass surfaces were infected all over with 'spores'. A comparison of the number of isolates from the *m* and *c* blocks led to the conclusion that at least half the mycelia on which *m* blocks had been placed were dead or unculturable, and about a third of the *m* blocks were contaminated with spores. Infection during burying and lifting was found to be negligible, but a group of 40 slide traps,

A

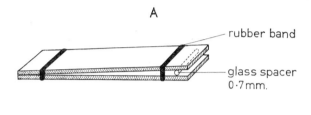

rubber band

glass spacer
0·7mm.

B

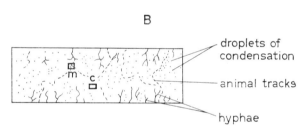

droplets of
condensation

animal tracks

hyphae

Fig. 1A. the 'gapped' Slide-Trap. B, diagram of protected side of one slide after lifting from soil. m, agar block placed on mycelium. c, agar block placed clear of mycelium.

buried together and lifted in groups of 5 at intervals up to 14 days and tested with *c* blocks, showed a progressive but erratic entry of spores. There could be little doubt about the origin of this infection, as the trails of soil animals were usually numerous and easily visible in the mist of condensation seen on the inner surfaces of the traps when lifted.

As for the isolates themselves, they were much the same set of soil moulds—species of *Penicillium, Cephalosporium, Trichoderma* and Mucorales, that were isolated from 'Cellophane' traps by Holmes.

All this led to a more careful examination of the origin of the mycelia in the traps. In many cases they originated on the slide surfaces, and closer inspection showed their spore origin. Some still seemed to be growing in from the edges, but when the ground edges of the slides were examined in immersion oil, the origin of many of these could also be traced to germinating spores, and those which could not be traced to their source presented the same general appearance and staining characters as the others. Moreover, when the slide traps were merely wiped along the edges with soil or fine soil suspension, and then kept in buried Petri dishes to exclude soil animals, the appearance of the growths on them was indistinguishable from that of the ordinary buried slide trap. Altogether, there was no evidence of any invasion of the traps by mycelia growing in the soil, though the possibility could not be disproved.

This showed that our method of isolating from glass surfaces had no validity as a method of studying the growth of mycelia existing in the soil, though it might have a strictly limited value as a way of studying the moving population of water-germinable spores; and it does have a bearing on the interpretation of other methods of isolating soil fungi which involve the use of glass, or other condensing surfaces, in the soil. Why should spores germinate in such numbers on the glass when they had not done so in the soil? The only difference that we could see was that the glass, when lifted, was covered with droplets of condensed water. Could this contain some special nutrient brought in by the soil animals? This seemed unlikely, as when allowed to dry it left no visible residue on the clean glass as did soil extract, even after Seitz filtering, and also tap water. All the species commonly isolated from the traps were tested and found to germinate readily in distilled water (except some strains of *Absidia cylindrospora*). We finally realized that the soil solution must in some way inhibit germination of these spores, and this inhibition is discussed later (p. 130). Meanwhile, it seemed advisable to examine the spores in the soil as closely as possible.

'Spores' in the soil

The surfaces of agar plates were covered with 'Cellophane' discs and flooded with soil suspension from an A_2 horizon under beech. After 24 hr. incubation the discs were stripped off the agar, stained and examined under high power. There were numerous 'germlings', some of which were obviously of spore origin. Others were similar, but developed from angular-looking particles which looked like mineral particles and stained only slightly or not at all with cotton blue. Even the recognizable spores, which stained more intensely, were often irregular and indented or with mineral particles attached to them; and these graded into angular objects quite unlike the usual conception of spores. It is impossible, by the nature of the problem, to distinguish these from mineral particles by photography or drawing, or even by sight; except that sometimes they have *curved* facets, they would not show interference effects with crossed Nicols, and would sometimes show a weak staining with gentian violet or erythrosin or a weak fluorescence when stained with acroflavine orange and examined in near U.V. light from a mercury vapour lamp.

By sedimentation and decanting a suspension of soil particles between 2–12μ diameter was prepared. Apart from a few fragments of plant material, nearly all of these looked like mineral fragments; yet plating out showed that 20% of these were viable units giving rise to fungal colonies.

Sedimentation of soil 'spores'

We come now to the behaviour of these queer-looking spores during sedimentation. In Fig. 2 the graph at the top shows the number of viable

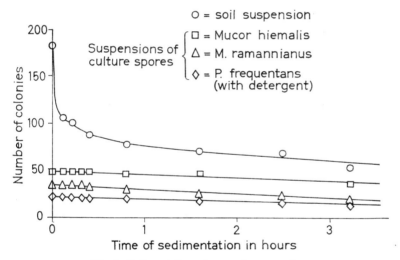

Fig. 2. Sedimentation of spores in suspension.

particles plated out from standard samples of the suspension at intervals of time during the sedimentation. Below it are similar curves for suspensions of the culture spores of two species of *Mucor* and a *Penicillium* (this last with detergent added). It will be seen that with the soil the number falls off heavily at the start, owing no doubt to the carrying down of spores with the heavier mineral particles; it then approaches the slow rate of reduction of the culture-spore suspensions. When the soil is ground up in water with a glass rod before sedimentation, the longer the grinding the less the initial fall in colonies, and the larger the proportion of spores which remain in suspension even after 2 hr.

Fig. 3 shows that the species composition of the colonies obtained by plating out did not change appreciably during the process of sedimentation. There was clearly no major sorting out of wet- and dry-spored species and, furthermore, the surface of the soil suspension, when decanted and plated out, did not show any accumulation of dry spores. In fact, it looks as if there are no xerospores in the soil, or at least in this soil (A_2 horizon under beech), despite the fact that in another experiment it was shown that the xerosporous conidia of *Penicillium nigricans* lost none of their non-wetting properties after 5 weeks of incubation, mixed with moist soil.

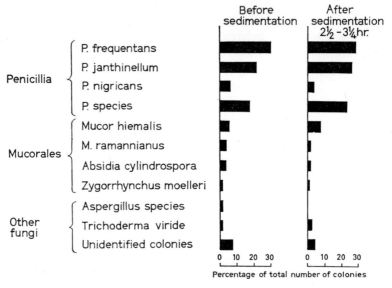

Fig. 3. Frequency of species in soil suspension before and after sedimentation.

To test this further, a simple variant was tried of Burges' experiment (1950) with the movement of spores through a sand column. A Buchner funnel packed with sand showed that wet spores (*M. hiemalis*) passed through it, but dry spores (*Penicillium frequentans*) were retained, forming a surface scum which reappeared with a rising water-level. When a *soil* suspension was passed through, no such differentiation occurred. Penicillia were numerous in the effluent, as tested by plating out, and if the colonies came from conidia, they must have lost their unwettable surface properties.

It has been shown (Burges and Hepple, 1954) that culture spores will not percolate through fine soil, as distinct from sand, and Hinson further showed that, with soil in the funnel, even under gentle suction

95% of the viable spores in a soil suspension are retained; so it did seem reasonable to suppose that, so far as the movement of water is concerned, the layers of the soil might retain most of the spores which fall on them or are formed in them, until they die or germinate. The next step, therefore, was to investigate the distribution of spores in undisturbed soil to see what record might be retained there of sporulation and survival of spores.

Distribution of spores in clods of soil

Clods of silty loam were carefully removed, with the top marked, from the A_2 horizon under beech which had been studied. In the labora-

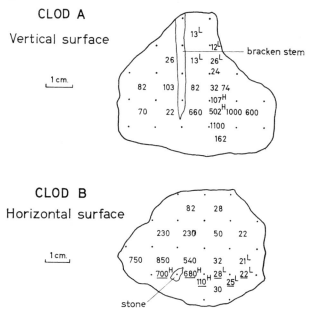

Fig. 4. Distribution of 'spore' population over surfaces of two adjacent clods of soil.

Diagrams are scale drawings of surfaces examined. Dots represent markers; figures represent colonies per mg. of soil referred to points of origin of samples; figures underlined were from samples taken 14 days later; plates from samples marked H or L were used to enumerate the species in areas of high and low 'spore' density respectively.

tory these were broken across to expose fresh surfaces, and these surfaces were marked out in 1-cm. squares with glass fibres as markers. From the centre of each square a minute sample was removed on the flattened end of a needle and weighed on a glass-fibre balance. These little crumbs varied in weight from 4 to 29 mg. Each was carefully ground up for 5 min. in a measured amount (1 ml. per mg.) of water, sedimented for 5 min., and a 0·5 ml. sample was plated out. In some cases further standard dilutions were necessary to get a count. Colonies were counted after 14 days, and a wide range of spore density (no. per mg. soil) was disclosed. These were recorded in the appropriate squares on a scale diagram of the clod surface (as shown in Fig. 4). In some cases a 'transect' of closer samples was taken across the clod surface to confirm the variation of high and low density. This intricate technique took a good deal of practice to make perfect, and was repeated on a number of clods. Fig. 4 shows two typical examples of the results from *adjacent* clods, broken vertically and horizontally, respectively. The variation in spore density within each clod is very marked, even within 1 or 2 cm.

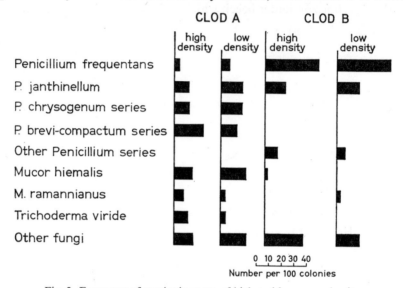

Fig. 5. Frequency of species in zones of high and low spore density.

Fig. 5 shows roughly the species composition on certain plates taken from zones of high and low density in these two neighbouring clods of soil. It seems that none of these few-milligram samples came from a point of sporulation of one species. The composition of the spore population was mixed, but substantially the same at all points—of high and low spore density—within the clods; but a few inches away in the other clod the composition had changed somewhat.

As a further test, broken clod surfaces were inoculated at marked points with spores of several moulds, some dry, some in water, some in malt extract. The two halves were carefully fitted together and incubated for 2–4 weeks; then separated again and examined at the marked points with a Leitz Ultropak. Where no nutrient had been added spores could be seen but no germination, but at the 'malt' points germlings were to be seen after 24 hr., and extensive mycelia after 2 weeks, with sporangia of *Mucor ramannianus* where that species had been inoculated.

The soil picture

From these observations added to those of many other workers, we are beginning to get the barest outline of a picture of the biology of these common ephemeral moulds in the soil. It seems reasonable to assume that at least in moist, well-aerated soil and at suitable temperatures, they are able to spore in the soil wherever there is sufficient nutrient and cavities of the order of 200μ. Some of them also form numerous chlamydospores, on the survival of which in soil Caldwell (1958) has recently thrown some light. But these local accumulations of spores must be very ephemeral, for they seem to be subjected to a continual local churning and mixing which gives every soil crumb an almost uniform species composition within a clod of a few centimetres, although it varies somewhat when we explore on a larger scale.

This mixing process would apply also to spores washed or carried down from the surface layer, although, except in freely draining soils, the washing down of spores in rain-water would mainly occur along vertical fissures in the soil. As for the agency which performs this mixing and churning, the continual invasion of the slide traps by soil animals and by spores leaves no doubt about it. The important paper of Hartmann (1944) revealed the enormous part played in forest soils by the fauna and their excreta, which indeed can make up a large proportion of the soil organic matter; but the extent to which the soil-spore pattern varies in mull and mor soils, dominated by different animals, and in soils which restrict animal movement, remains at present uninvestigated.

To what extent these points of high but mixed spore density and these queer angular shapes which spores take up in the soil, and their lack of non-wetting surfaces, are associated with passage through the animal's gut; and to what extent they are merely adaptations to soil surfaces and cavities, remains to be discovered, as also does the proportion of chlamydospores to conidia and sporangiospores. In addition to the 20% of soil particles in suspension between 2–12μ in size which germinate quickly to give mould colonies, how many of the others are not mineral particles but chlamydospores, basidiospores, or other spores with special germination requirements, not to mention cysts of algae, protozoa, or other organisms? We are still very far from getting a clear picture, but the shadowy outline is beginning to be very interesting.

REFERENCES

BURGES, A. (1950). The downward movement of fungal spores in sandy soil. *Trans. Brit. mycol. Soc.*, **33**, 142–7.

BURGES, A., & HEPPLE, S. (1954). Factors affecting the washing down of spores through soil. *Demonstration at Conversazione of Brit. mycol. Soc.*, London, 1954.

CALDWELL, R. (1958). Fate of spores of *Trichoderma viride* Pers. ex Fr. introduced into soil. *Nature, Lond.*, **181**, 1144–5.

CHESTERS, C. G. C. (1940). A method of isolating soil fungi. *Trans. Brit. mycol. Soc.* **24**, 352–5.

DOBBS, C. G. (1942). Spore dispersal in the Mucorales. *Trans. Brit. mycol. Soc.*, **25**, 441.

HARTMANN, F. (1944). Waldhumusformen. *Zeitschr. f. d. ges. Forstwesen.*, **76/70** (1/6 H.), 39–70.

HINSON, W. H. (1954). *A study in the biology of soil moulds.* Ph.D. Thesis, University of Wales.

LA TOUCHE, C. J. (1948). Slide traps for soil fungi. *Trans. Brit. mycol. Soc.*, **31**, 281–4,

VALUE OF THE DILUTION METHOD

J. MONTÉGUT

École Nationale d'Horticulture, France

The method entailing dilution, suggested by bacteriological procedures, has been used by us consistently for the analysis of soil fungi: with careful control of the dilutions, the separation, counting, and close correlation of the developing colonies with a 'unit soil' can be achieved.

Gradually, the need to simulate actual conditions progressively closer attracted workers to more or less direct methods of observation, giving results not always in agreement with those of the earlier procedure. On this ground the dilution method collected more critics than adopters; furthermore, the present tendency is to discard the concept of species and to be concerned only with systematic and biological groups, recognizing, even, only two types of mycelium.

Accordingly, before discussing the value of the dilution method it will be worth while to specify the objectives of the research.

Choice of method

For a global investigation aimed at the identification and calculation of the frequency of all the species in each sample involved, only a precise and standardized method can be applied. In this context, it is well known that more precise work on a particular species, on the localization and importance of the mycelial and sporulative stages and on the activity at the level of roots or in the vicinity of vegetable deposits living or in a state of decomposition, cannot be realized in the absence of appropriate methods; in other words, the direct inoculation method and dilution methods; for only these two methods, which provide results that can be related to a unit soil, are comparable from one sample to the other, from one locality to another.

In this paper we are considering only the choice of a method for studying microflora on a world-wide scale. There cannot be one standard method applicable to all the soils whose structure and fertility to fungi demand the use of the direct-inoculation or dilution methods: the first will be applicable to soils with a predominantly sandy structure containing up to 1000 micro-organisms per gram, the second to all the other cases.

Examples

(i) Sand, sandy soil with diffused humus, of uniform structure.

One can in all cases use direct inoculation, but when the frequency of micro-organisms is too high, delicate weighings of the milligram order are necessary.

(ii) Compact, clayey soils.

Their generally fine particle-size involves constant risk of agglomeration: the dilutions method alone is likely to ensure complete uniformity.

(iii) Humus (organic waste, forest horizon O, leaf-mould, peat, etc.).

The agglomeration of organic débris, interwoven with mycelial bonds, is eminently suited to sporulation and complicates the homogenizing of these substrates, no matter which method is used.

Technological and statistical value of the method

(i) Provision of samples: by direct-inoculation the soil sample cannot exceed 50 mg. per Petri dish, so that there is not more than 50 colonies per dish; the sample source is thus very defective.

With the dilution method that we use, the sample provides a total of 10–15 g. of soil taken from several sites for a given horizon in the field, and is thus adequate and always provides good reproducibility.

(ii) Homogenization: homogenization by agitation creates a problem in so far as it may cause heterogeneity (segregation of the micro-organisms and fragmentation of the hyphae proportional to intensity and duration of agitation). Experience has shown us that, by taking the precaution of allowing the soil to disperse for about half an hour, one minute's shaking by hand just before measuring-out gives results comparable from one test to another.

(iii) Limiting the development of bacteria: acidifying the culture medium and the use of antibiotics are not justified in ecological research. It is more logical to adjust the medium to the pH of the soil being examined. We avoid the rapid multiplication of bacteria, resulting from prolonged confinement of a compact and humid soil in the specimen holder, by performing in a single day, all the operations leading up to the preparation of the culture.

(iv) The culture medium: the choice of culture medium is by far the most exacting. We have adopted the one medium in order to make the counts statistically comparable: for our purposes this being the malt agar; but to this cause can be ascribed the low frequency, amongst the fungi collected by us, of species which are unable to find a nutritive substrate or compatible physical properties in this medium. The use of specific supplementary media for the detection of aquatic Phycomycetes and Basidiomycetes has not given any more satisfaction.

(v) Number of dishes: experience has shown us that the minimal number of dishes for a given horizon is from 15 to 20, spread over two dilutions and thus allowing the ideal threshold of counting to be obtained.

(vi) Unit soil: having made the counts, they should be related to a well-defined unit soil.

(a) Dry soil (dried at 105° for 4 hr.), assuming that, as a preliminary, the humidity of the sample has been calculated, which must be taken into account when the dilution is made.

(b) The dry weight provides an excellent relative measure for samples of the same physical structure; but soil density varies according to horizon, both within a given locality and between one locality and another (more particularly between the surface humus and the true soil). The only correct procedure would be to relate the results in the first place to a dry weight which can itself be related to a volume of given soil.

From the technical and statistical angle, the dilution method, properly standardized, is beyond criticism. We shall attempt to prove that if this is done the method has an undeniable absolute value for assessing the activity of fungi in the soil.

Absolute value

The most telling criticism of the dilutions method is that it gives an advantage to sporulating species compared with purely mycelial or weakly sporulating species.

(i) It is certainly true that the highest frequencies obtained are for species with high sporulative capacity, such as *Penicillium, Cephalosporium, Verticillium, Sphaeropsideae.*

(ii) We can immediately say that a large number of species do not exhibit in the soil a frequency proportional to their sporulative capacity in artificial media. Let us take, for example, the behaviour of *Trichoderma viride* (*sensu lato*), the ubiquitous species known for the rapidity and intensity of its mycelial growth and rich sporulation *in vitro*.

For our part we have found that for a wide range of soils this species appears in a noticeably unchanging degree but, compared with that of numerous other Moniliaceae, the number of colonies (less than five) in each Petri dish is restricted. If one admits for *Trichoderma* the liberation of conidia in quantities that authors attribute to the other sporulating fungi, and which the former does show *in vitro*, the examination from culture dishes of any soil containing such a common fungus would become impossible. Thus, one should accept that isolated *Trichoderma* colonies arise mainly from hyphae and that this species shows poor sporulation in the soil. This can be applied, to a lesser extent, to species of *Fusarium* such as *F. lateritium, F. bulbigenum, F. culmorum, F. avenaceum, F. solani*, of *Cylindrocarpon* spp., all good soil species for which the number of colonies isolatable is not at all proportional to their sporulative capacity *in vitro*.

There is no reason to suppose that that which is valid for *Trichoderma*, and these latter species in particular, is not so for the majority of sporulating species.

(iii) Conversely, species such as certain *Monotospora* in which the aleuriospores are not readily detached have frequencies comparable to many Moniliaceae.

(iv) Granted even that the soil contains a large number of so-called 'inert' conidia, we can still say that all sporulation is the result of a previous mycelial activity. It is normally asserted that the uppermost horizons, which receive the best aeration, give the most abundant sporulation and thus the highest frequencies. As the aeration diminishes with depth, the sporulative capacity of the species, in theory, decreases also; but at these levels certain species, present also at the surface, show

TABLE 1

Distribution of four typical species of the pine-land according to proportion of humus

horizons / species		A0 (0 cm.)	A1 (5 cm.)	A2 (washed soil 50 cm.)	B1 (humic acids 100 cm.)	C (washed soil more than 1 m.)
Penicillium restrictum	I	600 (1)	200	70	10,900	60
	II	750	90	13	640	1
Oidiodendrum sp.	I	0	100	50	1,800	0
	II	0	225	47	9,600	45
Spicaria sp. MO128	I	0	0	10	1,300	0
	II	0	24	4	100	1
Spicaria sp. MO129	I	0	0	120	1,600	0
	II	0	7	4	1,100	1

Key: I and II: Coastal pine-land, September 1956.
(1): Number of colonies per 100 mg. of soil.

their maximum frequency; for example, *Penicillium, Gliomastix convoluta* in the Grignon soils. Similarly we note that in the sandy soils of Landes (see Table 1) the frequency of the *Oidiondendrum* spp., *Spicaria* spp., *Penicillium restrictum* shows a sharp increase at the B1 horizon level, situated 1 m. deep. Of course, with sandy soils access to air extends deeper and is improved in this case by the localization at this level of a pine-root system. We think, however, that such an improvement in frequency, peculiar to certain species which find at this level ideal conditions of nutrition and humidity, signifies intense fungal activity expressing itself in a corresponding mycelial activity. One should also point out that, at this depth, the degree of competition is reduced owing to a drop in the number of other species.

To sum up, the sporulation of species is not distributed equally at all levels in the soil.

(v) A final example will lend further support to our assessment of fungal life in the soil. Variations in frequency for two species of *Penicillium* relative to depth, fertilizer, and weather, determined over two years, are shown in Table 2. The observed modifications have invariably conformed to the pattern of frequency interrelation between the two species, the depth-change curve is similar in all localities for each of them. Each of their sensitivities to fertilizer is practically constant and allows one to attribute to each an individual physiological activity. They both show similar response to variations in climatic factors.

Such flexibility, speed, and reproducibility of response in a certain case can only correspond to the reaction of a living organism and certainly not to a latent state.

In conclusion, the theory of sporulation always allows one to interpret the rise in the number of colonies isolated in terms of a previous rise in the amount of mycelial activity. But if one witnesses a sudden dimunition in the number of micro-organisms, the accompanying diminution of sporulative capacity in the soil will be masked by the 'inert' stock of the conidia already formed. It would then be necessary to assume that the majority of these micro-organisms had been destroyed; very little is known about the conservation of germinating capacity of spores in the soil. The relative sensitivity of spores compared with the mycelium to drops in the temperature or humidity is still a matter under discussion. However, it seems more reasonable to believe that the mycelial hyphae of sporulating species (more particularly the Moniliaceae) are more easily destroyed than their true conidia. To explain the reduction in micro-organisms, only the theory of preponderance of the mycelial state in the soil is valid.

TABLE 2

Distribution of two species of Penicillium *according to fertilizer, depth, and time of year*

Nature of the specimens / Species		NPK	Organic fertilizer	Without fertilizer since 1902	Without fertilizer since 1875
P. Lilacinum	1	164 (1)	78	119	86
	2	101	29	91	98
	3	53	34	30	24
	4	116	70	182	117
P. canescens	1	84	75	35	28
	2	33	57	13	8
	3	43	31	19	10
	4	250	210	48	34
Depth / Species		5 cm.	10 cm.	20 cm.	40 cm.
P. Lilacinum	1	40	44	92	271
	2	29	21	57	214
	3	29	28	28	56
	4	64	60	120	215
P. canescens	1	107	72	43	0
	2	33	40	36	2
	3	52	41	10	0
	4	108	96	70	0

Key 1: Betterave, June 1955.   3: Betterave, September 1955.
2: Bte, September 1955.   4: Bte, November 1955.
(1): Number of colonies per 20 mg. of soil.

Conclusion

One must adapt to each type of study of the fungi of the soil one particular method which is likely to become standard. For the world-wide analysis of microflora in different horizons of a given soil, for the determination of the frequency and its variations to ecological factors, for all comparative study, only the dilution method (and in some cases the direct-inoculation method) can give coherent results. It is known that some soils are not susceptible, on account of their structure, to the use of this method, but as far as we have been able to ascertain, it seems thoroughly justified in the case of cultivated soils. Thus, far from being in competition, the different methods are complementary and await one apt method which permits the coupling of the more general observations of the one to the more precise observations of the other.

DISCUSSION

Dr. J. L. Harley. With reference to Dr. Warcup's observations on the fragmentation of roots in a blender before the isolation of fungi from living roots. A reduction of fungal species and numbers may be observed growing from root fragments blended before plating on agar. It is possible that there is a release of phenolic oxidation products during the blending of the roots. Dr. M. Moser (Innsbruck, Austria), working at Oxford, had this experience working with beech roots.

Dr. G. W. F. Sewell. I should like to draw attention to the fact that there is the possibility that rapidly growing fungi in the extreme surface layers of a soil may be isolated selectively by the immersion-tube method. In studies of Calluna-heathland soil fungi by the soil-plate method (Warcup), *Trichoderma viride* was isolated very frequently from the surface inch of soil, but with greatly reduced frequency from lower levels. *T. viride* was also very commonly isolated from surface soils using immersion tubes—frequently to the exclusion of other fungi. One-sided immersion tubes (in which three capillary inlets were in line with the longitudinal axis of the tube) were prepared and buried horizontally in the soil profile, thus enabling the soil to be sampled at definite depths. By this method *T. viride* was isolated from soils of 0–1 in. depth, but infrequently at 2–3 in. depth. It seems possible, therefore, that, with normal immersion tubes, rapidly growing fungi on the soil surface may enter tubes through the uppermost capillary inlets and rapidly colonize the agar medium, so excluding the isolation of more slowly growing fungi penetrating at deeper levels.

In comparisons of methods of isolation of soil fungi, the effect of season on the species isolated is frequently overlooked. Methods designed to isolate actively growing mycelia (e.g. Chesters' immersion tube, Sewell's slide trap) reflect seasonal changes in the fungal flora, particularly in the isolation of *T. viride* in acid heathland soils. This fungus may be isolated almost exclusively during the summer months, but may be absent in the winter. This seasonal variation in the isolation of *T. viride* which markedly affects the isolation of other fungi, is not demonstrated by standard plating techniques. Any comparison of plating and 'active' isolation techniques may, therefore, be valid only if the results are based on isolations carried out throughout a complete seasonal cycle.

Prof. J. Ziemiecka. The estimation of numbers of active fungi in the soil may be greatly helped by a proper technique for differentiation between the numbers of their spores. In evaluating the numbers of active bacteria, we use pasteurization methods to kill the active cells in order to obtain the numbers of their spores. Has anyone tried to apply pasteurization methods for the evaluation of active and inactive fungi?

Dr. J. C. Brown. A modified impression-slide technique has been used for comparing the total amount of fungal mycelium in the various stages of the development of sand-dune soils. The method is a development of the Rossi-Cholodny contact-slide technique. A slide smeared with a strong adhesive (nitrocellulose) is pressed against the soil profile so that a thin film is obtained which is examined using a metallurgical objective with a long working distance. In the Rossi-Cholodny method the coarser particles are removed, here they are retained. This retention is important when dune soils are being studied, as most of the mycelium in immature dune soils is closely

wrapped round sand grains. The method is quick and the slides are simple to prepare. Comparisons between soils can be made on a soil-volume instead of a soil-
weight basis. Unfortunately most of the fungi cannot be identified unless the hyphae
are removed by micro-manipulation methods, and can be induced to grow and
sporulate in pure culture. The method showed that there was 2–4 times as much
mycelium in the fixed acid dunes as in the alkaline dunes. The fact that fungi are
more abundant in acid soils than in alkaline is well known, but it has normally been
deduced from counts of fungal colonies. An increase in mycelium with dune development and decrease down the soil profile has also been shown.

Dr. M. Witkamp. I have used a technique based on the microscopic examination of
a known volume of soil suspension (aqueous) dried on a known area of glass slide.
The total length of mycelium observed on a certain area of the slide times a conversion factor gives the length or volume of mycelium in the original sample.

Lengths obtained correlate well with organic matter and moisture content, and
rather well with the number of colonies developing on dilution plates from the
various depths in the soil profile; but there was no accordance between numbers of
colonies and mycelial lengths from various types of soil. Another technique is based
on placing soil crumbs on sterile cover slips on to agar plates. Active mycelium
spreading from the crumbs will colonize the agar and can be isolated. This technique favours fast-growing species, mainly Phycomycetes.

Mrs. M. Turner. Has anyone tried the 'most probably number' method?

Dr. D. Park. This method has been used for some plant pathogenic spores in soil
(MALOY, O. C., & ALEXANDER, M. (1958). *Phytopath*, **48**, 126–8).

Prof. A. Burges. Dr. Y. T. Tchan (Sydney) used this method successfully for soil
algae, but no success was achieved for soil fungi.

Dr. H. Katznelson. The dilution extinction procedure for the enumeration of soil
fungi suffers from the same difficulty as the plating procedures, as spores will be
disturbed in both cases and counted to the exclusion of hyphal forms.

A clarification of the term 'activity' of soil fungi seems to be necessary. Need one
expect a relationship between activity and numbers unless by the term a distinction
is implied between dormant and actively growing hyphae? Many types of fungi or
bacteria may be isolated from soil, but their activity in the physiological sense, is
markedly different.

Mr. J. S. Waid. In order to make an estimate of the amount of mycelium being
formed in a soil over a given period of time, the nylon-mesh technique was developed
by myself and Mr. M. Woodman. Nylon is biologically inert, and probably does
not provide any nutrient for soil fungi. Squares of the mesh (12 mesh per cm.) are
buried in soil for varying periods. On recovery, hyphae are counted in the gaps or
the length of mycelium per mesh is measured, these measurements are used as a
measure of hyphal production. The limitation of the technique is that there may be
an upset of the local environment when the mesh is inserted but this probably
diminishes with time of exposure. The advantage of the technique over the Rossi-
Cholodny slide method is that there is no continuous water-film over the sampling
material, and the growth of hyphae and roots through the mesh is allowed. There is
also little interference to the passage of soil animals, water, and gases in the region
of the buried material.

Dr. C. G. Dobbs. We observed the entry of soil animals into the capillaries of
immersion tubes; mainly mites and insects, not nematodes.

Dr. E. Grossbard. A method is being developed at Hurley which might help to
elucidate the question of determining the amount of mycelial development in soil.
We hope to achieve this by the use of radio-isotope labelling.

When burying a radioactive inoculum in the soil, its location can be detected (by
methods already evolved). If the outgrowing hyphae would become labelled as well,

it should be possible to follow the progress of the fungus in the soil directly, at least over a limited distance. This technique depends on the ability of the fungus to translocate the radio-isotope from the radioactive inoculum to fresh hyphae. We were unfortunate in our first attempt to do this, the fungus seemed unable to do this even in agar culture. However, recently we were able to demonstrate translocation of Cobalt[40] and Caesium[137] by some fungi. We thus hope that the technique will eventually develop into a useful research tool to study the problem of a fungus existing in the soil as mycelium.

Dr. J. L. Harley. Some kinds of mycelium in soil can be identified by direct inspection, e.g. certain Basidiomycetes. Is it not possible that Mr. Waid's nylon-mesh method could be used for the identification of actual quantities of certain chosen species in certain situations.

Mr. J. S. Waid. When nylon grids were left for 410 days in a moder-humus type of woodland soil, we were struck by the almost universal occurrence of clamp-bearing and pigmented hyphae on the nylon meshwork. However, in one area the fruit bodies of an Ascomycete truffle fungus, *Elaphomyces granulatus*, were very abundant in the organic-soil horizons; also we could only find septate and pigmented hyphae resembling those of the Ascomycete on the nylon mesh buried in the same area. This seemed strong evidence that *E. granulatus* had been the most active producer of mycelium during the latter part, at least, of the sampling period.

Prof. J. Guillemat. La question relative a le mycoflore de débris deviant etre consideree dans un ces plus general par exemple celui de le rhizospere. Il est possible de faire une suspension homogene et un calcul de frequence de le mycoflore avec un sol renfermant un minimum de débris organiques. Au niveau O ou plutot a le surface du sol cela deviant impossible les divers ensemencements etant heterogene. Il en est de meme avec l'analyse de la mycoflore de le surface des racines et de le rhizosphere. Il faudrait une méthode permettant d'appresier le quantite de terre fumant le gaine de le racine et de determiner une frequence de champignons par rapport a un poids doone de terre.

Dr. D. Parkinson. In our work, fungi growing from washed and unwashed soil were recorded as advocated by Warcup (1951), that is on a presence or absence basis on the group of plates prepared from each soil sample. When dealing with segments of organic débris, the figures we provided represent the percentage of segments yielding each fungus. We have tried to represent the relative frequency of occurrence of the major fungal species isolated.

Dr. J. L. Harley. It seems to me that there are two objectives in the study of soil fungi which are being confused. We may compare these with the methods of study of woodland ecology. These are the estimate of absolute numbers of different species per unit area and the estimate of the relative frequency of different species. Methods suitable for one are not suitable for the other. The two kinds of methods are complementary and together give a more complete picture than each applied alone.

I was impressed by Professor Montegut's defence of the soil-dilution plate method. It is time that people ceased sneering at this method, which in appropriate studies can be useful.

Dr. J. Webster. The decomposition of humus is a late phase of the overall decomposition process, and studies on decomposition of organic material should begin with the decay of plant remains before they come into the soil. At Sheffield we have been following the microbial colonization of grasses above the soil surface, mainly by direct examination of the grass internodes. The point made by Drs. Parkinson and Kendrick that micro-habitats can be demonstrated in soil is also true of habitats above the ground; one finds great differences between fungi colonizing different parts of grass tissue, e.g. lower internodes compared with upper internodes.

Do Drs. Parkinson and Kendrick feel that the species isolated from the organic substrates are common soil organisms (in Dr. Pugh's work he claims many of his isolates from *Carex* are common soil organisms)? Dr. Hudson and myself have come to the opposite viewpoint. Many isolates from *Agropyron* are not fungi which one commonly regards as soil organisms. Are there differences between the types of tissues, e.g. those of *Carex* being more water-logged or more acid? (The published accounts of the investigations of Dr. J. Webster, Dr. H. J. Hudson and Dr. G. J. E. Pugh are cited by Dr. D. Parkinson and Dr. W. B. Kendrick.)

Dr. D. Parkinson. The fungi which we have isolated from organic débris do not appear to be common 'soil' fungi. *Cylindrocarpon*, for example, has been isolated in our experiments exclusively from organic débris. Similarly many of the pine-needle isolates have not been isolated from the soil.

Dr. G. J. E. Pugh. There are differences between the relative numbers of species isolated from surface sterilized leaf portions and from washed-leaf portions which may be compared with the unwashed and washed soil particles described by Parkinson and Kendrick; namely, *Penicillium* spp. are more numerous than *Mucor* spp. in surface sterilized leaf portions. In washed-leaf portions the opposite is found. This may be explained by assuming that the *Mucor* spp. grow mainly superficially, so they can grow only from the washed-leaf portions. Their rapid growth may then swamp the species within the leaf tissues, and prevent them from appearing.

It would be advantageous in this study of leaf-litter fungi and soil fungi to investigate the species present in leaf litter and in the soil beneath the litter.

THE GROWTH OF FUNGI IN SOIL

THE GROWTH OF FUNGI IN SOIL

J. S. WAID

Levington Research Station, Suffolk

Introduction

Saprophytic fungi and other heterotrophs which are active in the litter, humus, and mineral horizons of the soil exploit the energy-containing materials in decomposable organic matter, and bring about the release of nutrients locked up in the decaying substances. A significant proportion of these nutrients are taken up by photosynthetic plants, which utilize them in the production of the organic materials with which the energy intake of the community is maintained (Macfadyen, 1957). The efficiency of fungi in their utilization of available carbon substrates in the soil complex was appreciated by Foster (1949), who points out that soil fungi probably account for the bulk of the cell material that is formed by soil microbes. However, despite the ecological importance of the activities of filamentous soil fungi, we know little about the biology of the production and depletion of mycelium in the soil environment.

The characterization of soil-inhabiting fungi

Our knowledge of the events which occur in the soil is limited, like all other branches of ecological science, by the scope and the limits of accuracy of available techniques (Garrett, 1955). The amount of research which has been devoted to the study of soil fungi has been prodigious; in 1916, Waksman was able to refer to 125 publications, and Thom, in 1927, mentioned that the subject was expanding rapidly. Until recently it was mainly various groups of sporing fungi, in particular members of the Mucorales and the Fungi Imperfecti which grow well in artificial media, that had received detailed study (Chesters, 1949; Warcup, 1957). As investigators could not be sure that the sampled fungi were in a vegetatively active state or were taking part in soil processes, generalizations about the behaviour of single species of fungi in the soil environment could not be made (Harley & Waid, 1955a; Thornton, 1956; Warcup, 1955a, b).

Many important developments in the study of the fungus flora of the soil have evolved from attempts to classify the behaviour of soil-inhabiting as well as mycorrhizal and parasitic root-infecting fungi (Garrett, 1944, 1950, 1951, 1952, 1956a; Harley, 1948, 1950, 1952; Waksman, 1916, 1917, 1944). The grouping of fungi on the basis of their ability to utilize chemical substrates such as lignin and cellulose has been developed as a system of ecological classification by various authors (Thom & Morrow, 1937; Burges, 1939; Chesters, 1948; Garrett, 1951). Such 'substrate groups' have been characterized by Garrett (1956a) as possessing 'some special physiological or biochemical attribute conferring a competitive advantage for colonization of a particular substrate'. Similarly, Stanier (1953) emphasized that the many kinds of substrate present in the soil are each colonized by a characteristic and limited range of organisms, each with its individual nutritional requirements. He also stressed that the environments of free-living microorganisms are micro-environments, and such micro-environments occur everywhere, for example cellulose fibres.

The distribution of fungi in the soil has been graphically described by Garrett (1955) as 'a three-dimensional pattern of substrates'. Each substrate 'passes in its turn through the successive phases of colonization, exploitation, and exhaustion'. When the capacity of the micro-habitat to support further life is reduced to zero, only those surviving resting cells, or mycelia growing outwards through the soil, mark the sites of former substrates.

The examination of the behaviour of fungi in the soil environment in the presence of organisms which are antagonistic towards them has been the basis of many recent studies. 'Competitive saprophytic ability' has been defined by Garrett (1956a) as the 'summation of physiological characteristics that make for success in competitive colonization of dead organic substrates'. Park (1958) has pointed out that the various kinds of antagonism which occur between associated pairs of species include antibiosis, parasitism and predation as well as competition for the same object in the environment.

Various criteria that have been employed to designate a fungus as a soil inhabitant have been resolved by Park, who defines such a fungus as 'an ecological saprophyte . . . able to continue its existence and activities in the soil, colonizing and utilizing decomposable dead substrata, and maintaining itself alongside other members of the soil population, without the necessity of an interposed parasitic phase'. The last phrase in Park's definition could be modified to read 'without the necessity of an obligate association between a fungus and a living host organism'.

Other fungi occurring in the soil: Other fungi which occur in the soil and contribute to the ultimate breakdown of organic materials, but which do not qualify as soil inhabitants, are called *soil invaders* (Waksman, 1917). They are also called *allochthonous* fungi by Saitô (1955*a*) and *exochthonous* fungi by Park (1957*b*). Soil invaders do not possess the ability to develop or maintain themselves in an active condition in the soil environment. They are, in general, unable to colonize dead organic materials in the soil, although their propagules will ensure their survival in an inactive state. Even so, their hyphae can survive in dead organic materials provided they do not succumb to the antagonistic activities of other members of the soil population.

Soil invaders can be subdivided into two groups on the basis of the habitats in which they grow. The first group is formed by fungi which utilize substrates not developed within the soil. An example is the fungus *Pullularia pullulans*, which colonizes deciduous leaves as an epiphyte, but which ceases to be active soon after the leaves fall (Smit & Wieringa, 1953). The second group is made up of two kinds of *root-inhabiting fungi*, namely specialized root parasites and mycorrhizal fungi. Of the latter, only the ectotrophic and not the endotrophic forms will be considered here.

The growth and survival of the root-inhabiting fungi is mainly confined to the surfaces and the tissues of the root of their host plants. The association with their hosts is manifest only when such factors as soil conditions, host physiology, competition from other organisms, the state of the fungal inoculum, etc., are suitable. Many root-inhabiting fungi are capable of ectotrophic growth over the surfaces of the host root without penetrating the host tissues and so can co-exist with other rhizosphere and root-surface organisms inhabiting the root region. Thus a parasitic or a symbiotic association with the higher plant is not necessarily the eventual outcome of the presence of root-inhabiting fungi on the root surfaces of a host. But their low competitive saprophytic ability imposes a restriction upon the spread of such fungi from host to host *via* the soil.

Root-inhabiting fungi can colonize new hosts by two methods. The first is by root contact between neighbouring pairs of plants, and the second by the spread of hyphae or mycelial aggregates, for example rhizomorphs, from the tissues of infected host plants, which are utilized as a food base. The success of the latter method of root infection is limited by the size, number and nutritional status of the infecting units. It has been shown that the maximal radius for spread of mycelium from a food base is greater than the maximal radius for successful infection (Garrett, 1956*a*).

Studies of the growth of fungi in the soil environment

Some recent studies on the growth of fungi in non-sterile soil are discussed in the remaining three sections. The first describes some of the attributes which enable fungi to grow in the soil. The material under review relates to the reactions of fungal isolates to certain factors in the soil environment, and is derived mainly from experimental observations made under controlled conditions. The growth of soil fungi in pure culture experiments is not discussed as several excellent accounts exist (Foster, 1949; Hawker, 1950, 1957; Lilly & Barnett, 1951; Wolf & Wolf, 1947).

The second section is devoted to conclusions obtained from field surveys of the growth of mixed populations of fungi. The situations which are described were generally complex, and the effects of the many animate and inanimate components of the ecological environment were not resolved.

The third section is concerned with various factors which influence the production and depletion of mycelium in soils.

1. OBSERVATIONS ON THE PATTERN OF GROWTH OF SOIL-INHABITING FUNGI

Germination. Dobbs & Hinson (1953) and other authors (Chinn, 1953; Hessayson, 1953; Jackson, 1958; Jefferys & Hemming, 1953; Molin, 1957; Stover, 1955) have described a fungistatic factor in the organic horizons of the majority of the temperate and tropical soils studied. This factor, which is diffusible in the soil solution, inhibits the germination of fungal spores buried in the soil, although such spores germinate when placed in distilled water or in nutrient solutions. The chemical nature of this factor is unknown. Its effects can be temporarily nullified by the addition of a critical concentration of glucose or easily decomposable organic materials to the soil. Although it appears to be of biological origin, the evidence indicates that it acts not as an antibiotic (Dobbs & Hinson, 1953) but as a competitive inhibitor to the enzymes concerned in carbohydrate metabolism. It is possible that the reaction of the fungus spores to this factor brings about a reduction in the wastage which would follow germination of fungal propagules in the absence of organic matter suitable for supporting growth.

Broadbent & Norman (1947) demonstrated that the addition of fresh organic material to soil accelerates the rate of decomposition of materials already present in the soil. Burges (pers. com.) suggests that this pheno-menon could be partially explained by a local and temporary reduction of the fungistatic effect sufficient to permit microbial attack on organic matter. Such a reduction in the fungistatic effect may accompany the increase in fungal activity which follows soil cultivation (Guillemaut & Montégut, 1956, 1957; King, Hope, & Eaton, 1934; Warcup, 1957).

Buxton (1957a) and Kerr (1956) have demonstrated variation in the behaviour of root-disease fungi during the pre-penetration stages of the infection of their host plants. It is of interest that Jackson (1957) has shown that spores of five species of soil fungi will germinate in rhizo-sphere soils, and that their germ tubes, with the exception of one of the species studied, show a tropic response to plant roots. It is conceivable that dextrose, fructose, or other energy sources are liberated in sufficient quantity in the root region to eliminate the fungistatic factor present in the surrounding soil.

Colonization of soil substrates. Once fungal propagules or mycelia start or renew growth, then the duration and the nature of the response to stimuli may determine the success of such fungi in exploiting chemical substrates suitable for growth. In general, the rapidity of the response of a soil-substrate colonist seems to depend upon its potential enzyme complement and the availability of nutrients for the generation of active protoplasm. Park (1954) found that the duration of such responses or 'induction' phases depends upon the size of the fungal inoculum and the nature and quantities of the food materials which are available. Waid & Woodman (unpublished) have observed that the duration of the period between the insertion of inert materials into soils and their initial colonization by hyphae can be shortened by increasing the temperature.

Colonization by fungi developing from spores. Few mucoraceous Phyco-mycetes can utilize carbon sources more complex than simple sugars (Jefferys *et al*, 1953). The typical response of their spores to the addition of fresh organic matter to soil is rapid germination and colonization of the material in precedence over other soil fungi. Their duration as active mycelia is probably very short, but their high metabolic rate enables them to exploit the available materials successfully.

The remaining fungi that develop from spores in soil colonize decom-posable materials less rapidly than the Phycomycetes. These fungi are mainly cellulose-decomposing Ascomycetes and Fungi Imperfecti (Gar-rett, 1951), and it is the production of suitable cellulases that probably delays their colonization of substrates containing cellulose (Siu, 1957).

Chinn (1953) and Park (1954, 1955, 1956) demonstrated that even after the addition of decomposable organic materials to soil, most of the fungal spores decomposed rapidly, and that those which germinated

were either destroyed by the activities of other soil organisms or produced chlamydospores in response to the adverse environment. The
survival in soil of the spores of soil-inhabiting and soil-invading species
of fungi in a variety of ecological conditions has been studied by Park
(1955, 1957a, b), who showed that the soil-invaders were incapable of
colonizing organic materials buried in soil in the presence of antagonists.

Tribe (1957) has recorded that when a cellulose film is buried in soil,
it is first of all colonized and exploited by cellulose-decomposing fungi.
He observed no evidence of antagonism between fungal colonies exploiting the cellulose, and also that bacteria and soil mites were mainly
responsible for the decomposition and disappearance of fungal hyphae.
He never observed the reappearance of saprophytic fungi as colonizers
of the cellulose residues. The inability of fungi to recolonize organic
matter in soil may account for the difficulty of demonstrating the
presence of active hyphae in humified organic matter.

Colonization by fungi equipped with relatively large food reserves. An
interesting correlation between the size and the potential resistance of a
host plant and the degree of specialization of the structures employed
during colonization by root-infecting fungi has been described by
Garrett (1956a). The concept implies that a fungus which colonizes
materials containing chemical substances resistant to decomposition,
such as lignin and cellulose, has severe difficulties to overcome. The
development by an induced or inherent biochemical synthesis (Sussman,
1957) of enzymes capable of utilizing the available substrates necessitates
a supply of suitable nutrients and energy-containing materials (Brown
& Wood, 1953; Norkrans, 1950). As such fungi generally colonize
materials previously occupied by species with high growth rates, nutrients are in short supply. The late arrivals have therefore to resort to
translocating nutrients from a suitable food base. They also have to
combat antagonism from other organisms, and it is conceivable that
some part of their nutrient supplies are utilized to develop protoplasm
and structures resistant to the effects of antibiosis, fungistasis, and
parasitism.

Blair (1943) showed that the establishment of *Rhizoctonia solani* was
dependent on the size and nature of the available food base. His results
do not prove that this fungus relied upon a translocatory system, but
that the food base was necessary to enable establishment in the soil
environment.

Lignin decomposition is brought about mainly by Basidiomycetes,
which form either mycelial strands or rhizomorphs. Factors which affect
the success or failure of such fungi to colonize a fresh substrate have

been shown conclusively to be the quantity of nutrients available at the food base, the length and efficiency of the translocatory system, and the resistance of the organic materials to mechanical penetration and to enzyme attack (Garrett, 1956a, b).

Exploitation and exhaustion of soil substrates—mycelial growth. The rate of fungus growth in a uniform soil environment has been found to be independent of its inoculum potential during the colonization phase (Blair, 1943; Park, 1954). However, the time taken to exhaust a substrate depends upon the number of active hyphae capable of penetrating and decomposing the material under attack. Waid & Woodman (1957) found that soon after growth had begun upon nylon gauze buried in soil, a maximum rate of branching was attained, and shortly afterward most meshes (that is, sites available for colonization) became occupied. The relatively high surface to volume ratio of individual hyphae in the three-dimensional system of branching developed by filamentous fungi presents a large interface accessible to changes in outside conditions and for rapid exchange of materials between hyphae and soil. This system enables the production of sufficient quantities of enzymes, for example carbohydrases, in loci situated on the cell surfaces for conversion of extracellular substances to a form which can be assimilated by the cell if conditions are favourable (Hawker, 1957; Rothstein, 1954; Sussman, 1957).

Heterokaryosis. Heterokaryosis—the multiplication side by side of two or more genomes in a common cytoplasm—is a genetic mechanism unique to fungi which may be of importance during the exploitation phase of soil substrates (Stanier, 1953; Shepherd, 1957). The proportions of the various nuclear strains may be adjusted by their differential multiplication, thus conferring considerable plasticity on the genotype of the growing mycelium in relation to adaption to external conditions (Jinks, 1952; Pontecorvo, 1949). There is evidence that nuclei conferring pathogenic properties may develop incorporated in a mycelium containing nuclei of a type allowing a fungus to survive as a soil saprophyte (Buxton, 1954; Park, 1958; Rishbeth, 1955). Heterokaryosis may be a mechanism whereby the mycelia of Ascomycetes and Fungi Imperfecti, by adjustment of the nuclear population within their hyphae, can remain active for considerable periods in a changing ecological environment such as decomposing organic materials. In theory, species which do not possess a mechanism permitting variation of the genotype are at a disadvantage when exploiting a changing substrate in competition with a heterokaryotic species.

Translocation. The experimental studies of Schütte (1956) on the translocation of various substances within fungal colonies are of interest. The hyphae of *Aspergillus* and *Penicillium* were found to be incapable of translocation, and no streaming of their protoplasm was observed. The contrary was recorded for Phycomycetes and Basidiomycetes (cf. Melin, 1953), where the translocated materials accumulated in the apical regions of growing hyphae and streaming of their protoplasm was observed.

Soil-inhabiting fungi have been recorded as exhibiting a variety of types of growth habit (Chesters, 1948, 1949). This variation may be related to the degree to which the fungi can translocate nutrient materials. For example, soil fungi such as the Penicillia have short periods of vegetative growth followed by sporulation with the production of great numbers of spores. On the other hand, soil Basidiomycetes exist mainly in a mycelial state with the elaboration of complex translocatory structures formed by mycelial aggregation (Garrett, 1956a, b; Warcup, 1957).

Survival of soil fungi. Variation in behaviour of soil fungi appears to be related to the manner in which individual species survive to colonize fresh soil environments. The two methods of survival adopted by soil fungi can be either passive or active, and their development depends qualitatively and quantitatively upon the nutritional status of the mycelium. Passive methods of survival, such as by sclerotia or spore formation, are employed when the level of nutrition is adequate and antagonism is not excessive (Hack, 1957). When food supplies are depleted or other growth conditions are adverse, the existing protoplasm and nutrients within the hyphae are modified as chlamydospores, resting hyphae, or oidia. For example, mycelia colonizing nylon gauze buried in soil have been observed to start to form chalmydospores soon after the surfaces of their hyphae have become colonized by soil bacteria (Waid & Woodman 1957, cf. Ram, 1952). Similarly, active methods of survival involve the development of translocatory structures such as rhizomorphs and mycelial strands when nutrition is adequate, but 'starvation growth' often entails linear spread by infrequently branching and rapidly growing hyphae (Hawker, 1957). An indication that the active survival of soil fungi depends on the presence of a substrate which will support growth is afforded by the fact the hyphal filaments traversing soil pores generally lack protoplasmic contents (Jones & Mollison, 1948) and are non-viable, whereas a high proportion of hyphae isolated from organic materials will grow in culture (Warcup, 1951, 1957). The survival of soil-invading fungi in decomposing substrates depends in part upon the environmental conditions being adverse for the development of antagonistic organisms (Dimbleby, 1953; Downie, 1943; Fellows, 1941; Rishbeth, 1951).

2. OBSERVATIONS ON THE GROWTH OF MYCELIUM IN VARIOUS SOIL ENVIRONMENTS

Macro-habitats for fungal growth. The surface vegetation has a considerable influence on the soil mycoflora. When a virgin soil habitat such as the fore-dune of a sand-dune system becomes colonized by higher plants, there is a parallel development of a fungal flora (Brown, 1958; Saitô, 1955b; Webley *et al.*, 1952). Changes in the composition of the surface vegetation, such as forest cover (Saksena, 1955; Tresner *et al.*, 1954), or an agricultural crop (Guillemat & Montégut, 1956, 1957) are also accompanied by changes in the composition of the soil flora. The effect is due partly to the accumulation of organic residues from the developing association of plants and animals, and partly to the development of a rhizosphere and root-inhabiting flora associated with the species of higher plants. The influence of a single species is illustrated by the development of a rich flora of soil-borne parasites when badly managed monocultural systems of agriculture are employed.

In general, fungi abound in well-aerated organic horizons of the soil (Warcup, 1951a), but it is not yet certain which species are most active in exploiting the different types of decomposable material which occur in the soil.

Micro-habitats for fungal growth. Chesters (1949) considering existing information on micro-habitats for fungal growth, mainly obtained by Kubiena (1938), suggested that attention should be paid to the growth of fungi such as *Pythium*, *Rhizoctonia*, the larger Ascomycetes, Basidiomycetes, and the darker-coloured Hyphomycetes associated with organic debris in the soil. Saitô (1956), Stenton (1953), and Warcup (1951a, b, 1955b, 1957) have each provided evidence that Basidiomycetes and sterile mycelia are active in certain horizons of undisturbed and cultivated soils. Thornton (1956) observed that *Rhizoctonia* occurs in a mycelial state in natural grassland soils, and formed 49 % of his isolates on screened-immersion plates. Warcup (1955a, 1957b), by analysis of the origin of individual isolations from soil, found that Basidiomycetes, Rhizoctonias, and sterile fungi, especially those with dark-coloured hyphae, form the main component (70%) of the population of viable hyphae in a wheat-field soil.

On the other hand, the species of the Mucorales and the Fungi Imperfecti, which are recorded as predominant in soil (Gilman, 1957) and which belong to such genera as *Mucor, Absidia, Mortierella, Aspergillus, Cladosporium, Fusarium, Penicillium* and *Trichoderma*, were generally isolated by Warcup from passive survival structures. On the few occasions when species of the above-mentioned genera were isolated from hyphae they were present either upon plant débris or on decomposing residues which had been ploughed in. Such observations on the active compoents of the soil population correlate well with those of Tribe (1957) who, when following the fate of cellulose in soil, found few of the above-mentioned genera, but noted a restricted flora of species not generally considered (Siu, 1951) to be abundant on decomposing cellulose.

Substrates in soil exert a selective effect on their associated microflora, an extreme example being the complete dominance of ectotrophic mycorrhizal fungi on the surfaces of infected tree roots (Harley, 1948). Various techniques have been used to study the microflora colonizing soil substrates, and a selection of roughly comparable results of surveys of active mycelia on root surfaces is given in Table 1.

A general observation derived from the table is that sterile fungi and occasionally Basidiomycetes are very abundant on lateral roots; that is, small inocula which bear few antagonists. Sporing fungi increase in abundance as the roots age, and are so numerous on tap roots that it may be that they are involved in minor ecological successions on senescent cortical tissues. For example, such fungi as *Cylindrocarpon, Mortierella*, and *Mucor rammanianus* are particularly abundant on the surfaces of roots with secondary thickening. Fusaria, on the other hand, abound on the roots of pasture plants with decomposing cortical tissues.

Harley & Waid (1955*a, b*) have shown that the fungal population of root surfaces varies with the distance from the root apex, the age of the plant, the soil, and the conditions for growth (for example, light intensity).

The composition of root surface populations can vary considerably over very short distances. The course of the fungal invasion of two layers of plant tissue, the inner and outer cortex of decomposing roots of rye-grass, has been studied by Waid (1956, 1957). Sterile species of fungi were the dominant initial colonists, and they were gradually replaced by *Fusarium culmorum* and other succeeding groups of fungi which grew into the cortex.

It is frequently found in surveys of this nature that a single fungus species grows from adjacent fragments of root, especially on the older portions of root systems (Harley & Waid, 1955*a*). If it were known whether such growth represented one or several separate mycelial colonies a significant contribution would be made to the knowledge of the growth and development of fungi in soil habitats. A possible approach might be by a combined study of the distribution of mycelia and of fungal mating-type factors as employed by Burnett & Partington (1956) for the higher fungi.

TABLE 1

The most abundant fungi isolated from the surfaces of living roots of several species of plants.

Host and Roots Sampled	Most Abundant Fungi	Author
Pinus sylvestris —lateral	*Mycelium radicis atrovirens* *Pyrenochaeta terrestris*	Robertson (1954)
Fagus sylvatica —lateral —tap	Sterile mycelia including *Mycelium radicis atrovirens* *Cylindrocarpon* sp.	Harley & Waid (1955a)
Fraxinus excelsior —tap	*Cylindrocarpon* sp. *Rhizoctonia* (?)	Kürbis (1937)
Pisum sativum —tap	*Fusarium* sp. Mucorales	Buxton (1957b)
Pisum sativum —tap	*Cylindrocarpon* sp. *Fusarium* sp.	Stenton (1958)
Trifolium repens —tap	Sterile mycelia *Fusarium* sp. *Cylindrocarpon* sp.	Waid*
Dactylis glomerata —fibrous	*Fusarium* sp.	Waid*
Lolium perenne —fibrous	*Fusarium* sp. Mucorales	Waid (1957)

* Unpublished work.

3. MYCELIUM PRODUCTION AND DEPLETION
IN SOIL

Consumption of nutrient supplies. Several attempts have been made to estimate the relative importance of micro-organisms and fauna in the breakdown of organic matter in soil. The estimates agree in that fungi and heterotrophic bacteria, together with nematodes and protozoa, form the major part of the living material in soil. Because the respiratory rates of soil fungi are higher than that of soil animals and because they require external substrates for growth, the general conclusion has been that soil fungi are among the main primary consumers of decomposable material in soil (Birch & Clark, 1953; Macfadyen, 1957; Russell, 1950).

The energy-containing materials which support the growth of soil fungi become available to them in two ways. One is where the communal consumption of energy is balanced by a continuous inflow of energy-containing materials. Such a state occurs, for example, in the root region of plants. Here organic materials are being continuously released from the plant roots in sufficient quantity to maintain the growth of root-surface and rhizosphere fungi. The second way is where the flow of energy is not maintained and where the activity of the heterotrophs is limited by the energy content of the habitat; for example, an annual leaf fall. In a given soil locality it is not yet possible to estimate the rate at which energy-containing materials are utilized, either in the synthesis of mycelia or in fungal respiration. Such estimates would be important in terms of the effect of the soil microflora on the growth and nutrition of higher plants. Apart from the beneficial activities of the soil microflora in making plant nutrients available to higher plants, there are also competing activities. One is the drain on nutrients required for the maintenance of the cell mass of the soil microflora (Nilsson, 1957). Another is the conversion of plant nutrients to forms which are unavailable to the higher plants; for example, the nitrogen in the glucosamine units of fungal chitin. The activities of higher plants and soil flora are interdependent and, perhaps their influence upon one another is mainly through the rhizosphere.

The few estimates which have been made of the efficiency of higher fungi as consumers of simple substances show that under pure culture conditions a variety of Ascomycetes and Basidiomycetes, especially those inhabiting forest litter, have considerable biosynthetic potentialities, and that a large proportion (as much as 65%) of their substrate can be converted to mycelium (Gray & Bushnell, 1955; Mikola, 1956).

Influence of non-biological factors

Temperature. The maximum temperature for growth of mesophilic fungi lies between 35° and 40° (Brown & Wood, 1953), so it would be expected that the rate of fungal growth would fall off sharply in summer months in the surface layers of British soils where temperatures can exceed 35° (Russell, 1950). Various reports that fungi can cause damage to snow-covered plants (Lebeau & Cormack, 1956) are indirect evidence that certain species of fungi can flourish in soil at low temperatures. Waid & Woodman have observed that the rate at which nylon gauze buried in organic soils at various altitudes (300–900 m.) is colonized by fungal mycelium decreases with an increase in altitude. These results were not thought to be due entirely to the influence of soil temperature, but an experiment carried out during July 1957 in moist humus shaded by a yew tree and repeated at the same site in December showed that activity fell off in the colder season. As this decreased activity was only 43% of that observed in summer, it was concluded that fungi are still active in the humus layers of forest soils during winter months. Laboratory investigations showed that mycelium would steadily accumulate on gauze buried in soil at temperatures from 13°–25° over a period of 8 days, but at 30° there was no accumulation after 2 days' incubation and none at 2°. The apparent lack of hyphal activity over the period from 2–8 days in the soil held at 30° may have been due to two processes which are accelerated by an increase in temperature. The first of these is the exhaustion of available substrates for growth with perhaps the accumulation of staling products. Secondly, breakdown of senescent and dead hyphae by other soil organisms giving the false impression that active hyphal growth has ceased or decreased in rate. The results agree with Fellows' (1941) observations that soil conditions which support growth of an organism are not necessarily optimal for survival from antagonists.

Moisture. When the water content of a soil either falls below the wilting percentage (Mitchell, Adams & Thom, 1941) or becomes sufficiently great to impede soil aeration there is a great reduction in the active growth of fungal hyphae (Waid & Woodman, unpublished). Warcup (1957) found negligible activity in an Australian wheat-field soil during the dry season. He observed a relatively high rate of survival among fungi isolated from humus particles which probably afforded a certain degree of protection against desiccation, but he could not determine whether fungi survived in the humus particles in an active or passive state. With rain, fungi became very active, and after a few days there was a large increase in the proportion of viable hyphae which could be isolated from the soil, and at the same time several species of mould fungi had sporulated abundantly.

Stover (1953) reports a reduction in the ability of Fusaria to survive in soils held at high moisture contents, where the multiplication of soil bacteria is favoured at the expense of the nutrient and oxygen supplies of soil fungi. Reduction in soil aeration would influence the growth of strongly aerobic fungi, but Kubiena (1938), Boswell & Sheldon (1951), and Stover have noted the abundance of *Hyalopus, Cephalosporium,* and various other species of fungi in water-logged soils. Blair (1943) noted a reduction in the growth of *Rhizoctonia solani* in soils held at high-moisture contents. The growth of the fungus at these high-moisture contents was least in soils with small-sized particles, where presumably the reduction in soil aeration was most marked.

Soil reaction. Soil pH affects the availability of nutrients in the soil. It is possible that it also influences the physiological functioning of the fungal thallus, possibly through its effect on the reactions occurring on the cell surfaces rather than through a direct influence on the internal processes of the cell.

The optimum pH for the growth of *Rhizoctonia solani* in soil was found by Blair (1943) to be at about 7·0. Warcup (1951) recorded that more species of fungi abound in neutral than in acid or alkaline grass-land soils. He observed that a few species had a high-sporing capacity in the acid soils, which may account for the records of large numbers of mould fungi in acid soils obtained by the dilution-plate technique. Bacterial decomposition of senescent and dead hyphae may proceed more rapidly in alkaline soils than in acid soils, and may thus keep the quantity of mycelium at a low level in alkaline soils.

Carbon dioxide and oxygen concentration. Burges & Fenton (1953) studied the effect of carbon dioxide and oxygen on the growth in culture of a variety of mould fungi isolated from various horizons of a soil profile. Their results show that fungi abundant in surface horizons were intolerant of carbon dioxide, but those abundant in subsurface horizons, where carbon dioxide can accumulate in the field (Russell, 1950), could tolerate carbon-dioxide concentrations as great as 10% by volume. These authors found no differential effect of oxygen on the growth of their various isolates.

Size of soil-pore spaces. Kubiena (1938) made some interesting obser-vations on the comparative morphology of fungi inhabiting soil spaces where he found that in general there was a reduction in the size of the fruiting structures of sporing fungi with decrease in pore size. The dimensions of these fruiting structures were much smaller than those recorded for specimens grown in culture.

Durability of fungal mycelium. The hyphae of Phycomycetes do not appear to be very resistant to decay, and soon disappear in the soil. At the other extreme, the hyphae of Basidiomycetes seem to be highly resistant, especially to adverse conditions such as drought (Warcup, 1957). They are more resistant than Phycomycetes to bacterial or actino-mycete attack, and the dark-coloured hyphae of certain species appear to endure for a long time in the soil (Tracey, 1956). In forest soils mycelial wefts, rhizomorphs, and mycorrhizal roots are visible evidence of the abundance of Basidiomycetes, yet little is known about the rates of production and decomposition of their mycelia. Waid & Woodman (unpublished data) have noted that the proportion of dark-coloured mycelia, hyphae with clamp connexions and rhizomorphs, colonizing nylon gauze buried in woodland soils increased with the duration of the exposure period. After a year such mycelia formed from 80–100% of the mycelial populations on the gauze, but the viable proportion was not determined.

Interactions between soil fungi and soil fauna. The interactions between saprophytic soil fungi and the soil fauna is a neglected field of study due perhaps to the difficulties of sampling methods, the identification of species and the development of suitable techniques for the measurement and comparison of their relative activities (Waid, 1959). A few aspects of this topic in so far as they affect the growth of fungi in soil will be very briefly considered here.

The mixing of plant remains from the litter layer of the soil with lower soil horizons is mainly brought about by soil animals. Such activity probably increases the rate of breakdown of decomposable materials because in the litter layer environmental conditions such as moisture régime, humidity, light intensity, and diurnal fluctuations in temperature are less favourable for microbial growth than in the other biological horizons of the soil, especially in dry seasons (Macfadyen, 1957). Comminution of plant remains by litter-feeding animals almost certainly facilitates decomposition by breaking down the hard tissues and making the organic matter more readily available to the soil microflora (Birch & Clark, 1953; Winston, 1956). The activities of soil animals and fungi must initiate a multiplicity of linked processes and biological successions on fragments of organic materials (Murphy, 1956), which cannot be satisfactorily studied by present methods. Many food chains of soil animals seem to depend upon an initial attack on plant remains by soil fungi; in fact, fungi form the main constituent of the diet of many members of the soil fauna, especially of species of mites and nematodes (Birch & Clark, 1953; Park & Auerbach, 1954). It is possible that the estimation of the consumption of fungal mycelium cropped by and supporting the growth of a population of soil animals may be one way of estimating part of the mycelium produced in the soil.

Jacot (1939) and Winston (1956) have both shown that the succession of animals in decaying plant tissues is influenced by the nature of the decay and the palatability of the fungal mycelia. Twinn & Waid have gathered together information shown in Table 2 concerning the biology of the invasion of decomposing oak-leaf litter obtained from a series of experiments concerned with the breakdown of forest litter (Capstick, 1956; Gilbert, 1957). The results show that the relative quantities of mycelia and nematodes do not remain constant but vary with season. It is possible that an accumulation of hyphae on the leaves was prevented by the activities of other organisms including nematodes, the majority of which were found to be fungal feeders. Winston (1953) recorded that soil animals were agents in the dispersal of fungi in decaying plant materials in soil, and that established fungal mycelium grew actively and was repeatedly cropped by successive populations of soil animals.

TABLE 2

The invasion of decomposing oak leaves by fungi and nematodes. Leaves collected during leaf fall 1956 and laid down in November

	Length hyphae/ microscopic field in mm. Mean 20 fields sample size = 6 leaves	Number of field with hyphae Total 20	Number of nematodes/g. dry weight of leaf. Sample size = 12 leaves
November, 1956	0	0	0·3
December, 1956	1·4	3	1·8
January, 1957	4·0	7	5·4
February, 1957	3·5	9	9·9
March, 1957	2·6	8	9·4
April, 1957	2·0	8	1·7
May, 1957	1·8	8	15·5
June, 1957	4·0	9	10·3
July, 1957	5·4	10	37·1
August, 1957	4·0	10	43·5
September, 1957	13·3	10	—*
October, 1957	8·8	14	—*
January, 1958	2·6	7	—*

* Not sampled.

Acknowledgements

The author would like to acknowledge the encouragement and help he received during investigations mentioned in this article, which were carried out whilst he was employed by the Nature Conservancy and the Grassland Research Institute, and also during the tenure of a training grant from the Agricultural Research Council. The paper was prepared at Levington Research Station.

REFERENCES

BIRCH, L. C., & CLARK, D. P. (1953). Forest soil as an ecological community Quart. Rev. Biol., **28**, 13–36.
BLAIR, I. D. (1943). Behaviour of the fungus *Rhizoctonia solani* Kühn. in the soil. Ann. Appl. Biol., **30**, 118–27.

BOSWELL, J. G., & SHELDON, J. (1951). The microbiology of acid soils. II. Ringing-low Bog near Sheffield. *New Phytol.*, **50**, 172–8

BROADBENT, F. E., & NORMAN, A. G. (1947). Some factors affecting the availability of the organic nitrogen in soil; a preliminary report. *Proc. Soil Sci. Soc. Amer.* (1946), **11**, 264–7.

BROWN, J. C. (1958). Fungal mycelium in dune soils estimated by a modified impression-slide technique. *Trans. Brit. mycol. Soc.*, **41**, 81–8.

BROWN, W., & WOOD, R. K. S. (1953). Ecological adaptions in fungi. *Adaptions in Micro-organisms. Third Symposium Soc. gen. Microbiol.*, Cambridge University Press, 326–39.

BURGES, A. (1939). Soil fungi and root infection. *Broteria*, **8**, 64–81.

BURGES, A., & FENTON, E. (1953). The effect of carbon dioxide on the growth of certain soil fungi. *Trans. Brit. mycol. Soc.*, **36**, 104–8.

BURNETT, J. H., & PARTINGON, M. (1957). Spatial distribution of fungal mating-type factors. *Proc. roy. Phys. Soc. Edin.*, **26**, 61–8.

BUXTON, E. W. (1954). Heterocaryosis and variability in *Fusarium oxysporum* f. *gladioli* (Snyder and Hansen). *J. gen. Microbiol.*, **10**, 71–84.

BUXTON, E. W. (1957a). Some effects of pea-root exudates on physiologic races of *Fusarium oxysporum* Fr. f. *pisi* (Linf.) (Snyder & Hansen). *Trans. Brit. mycol. Soc.*, **40**, 145–54.

BUXTON, E. W. (1957b). Differential rhizosphere effects of three pea cultivars on physiologic races of *Fusarium oxysporum* f. *pisi*. *Trans. Brit. mycol. Soc.*, **40**, 305–16.

CAPSTICK, C. K. (1956). Soil fauna. *Rep. Nature Conservancy*, 10–11, 1956

CHESTERS, C. G. C. (1948). A contribution to the study of fungi in the soil. *Trans. Brit. mycol. Soc.*, **30**, 100–17.

CHESTERS, C. G. C. (1949). Concerning fungi inhabiting soil. *Trans. Brit. mycol. Soc.*, **32**, 197–216.

CHINN, S. H. F. (1953). A slide technique for the study of fungi and actinomycetes in soil with special reference to *Helminthosporium sativum*. *Canad. J. Bot.*, **31**, 718–24.

DIMBLEBY, G. W. (1953). Natural regeneration of pine and birch on the heather moors of North-east Yorkshire. *Forestry*, **26**, 41–52.

DOBBS, C. G., & HINSON, W. H. (1953). A widespread fungistasis in soils. *Nature, Lond.*, **172**, 197.

DOWNIE, D. G. (1943). Source of the symbiont of *Goodyera repens*. *Trans. bot. Soc. Edin.*, **33**, 383–90.

FELLOWS, H. (1941). Effects of certain environmental conditions on the prevalence of *Ophiobolus graminis* in the soil. *J. agric. Res.*, **63**, 715–26.

FOSTER, J. W. (1949). *Chemical activities of fungi*. New York: Academic Press Inc.

GARRETT, S. D. (1944). *Root disease fungi*. Waltham, Mass.: Chronica Botanica.

GARRETT, S. D. (1950). Ecology of the root-inhabiting fungi. *Biol. Rev.*, **25**, 220–54.

GARRETT, S. D. (1951). Ecological groups of soil fungi: a survey of substrate relationships. *New. phytol.*, **50**, 149–66.

GARRETT, S. D. (1952). The soil fungi as a microcosm for ecologists. *Science Progress*, **159**, 436–50.

GARRETT, S. D. (1955). Microbial ecology of the soil *Trans. Brit. mycol. Soc.*, **38**, 1–9.

GARRETT, S. D. (1956a). *Biology of root-infecting fungi*. Cambridge University Press.

GARRETT, S. D. (1956b). Rhizomorph behaviour in *Armillaria mellea* (Vahl). Quel. II. Logistics of infection. *Ann. Bot. Lond.*, N.S., **20**, 193–209.

GILBERT, O. (1957). Successional changes in litter breakdown. *Rep. Nature Conservancy*, 12–13, 1957.

GILMAN, J. C. (1957). *A manual of soil fungi.* Iowa: State College Press.

GRAY, W. D., & BUSHNELL, W. R. (1955). Biosynthetic potentialities of higher fungi. *Mycologia,* **47,** 646–63.

GUILLEMAT, J., & MONTEGUT, J. (1956). Contribution à l'étude de la microflore fongique des sols cultivés. *Ann. Épiphyt.,* **7,** 472–540.

GUILLEMAT, J., & MONTEGUT, J. (1957). Deuxième contribution à l'étude de la microflore fongique des sols cultivés. *Ann. Épiphyt.,* **8,** 185–207.

HACK, J. E. (1957). The effect of spore germination and development on plate counts of fungi in soil. *J. gen. Microbiol.,* **17,** 625–30.

HARLEY, J. L. (1948). Mycorrhiza and soil ecology. *Biol. Rev.,* **23,** 127–58.

HARLEY, J. L. (1950). Recent progress in the study of endotrophic mycorrhiza. *New. Phytol.,* **49,** 213–47.

HARLEY, J. L. (1952). Associations between micro-organisms and higher plants (mycorrhiza). *Ann. Rev. Microbiol.,* **6,** 367–86.

HARLEY, J. L., & WAID, J. S. (1955a). A method of studying active mycelia on living roots and other surfaces in the soil. *Trans. Brit. mycol. Soc.,* **38,** 104–18.

HARLEY, J. L., & WAID, J. S. (1955b). The effect of light upon the roots of beech and its surface population. *Plant and Soil,* **7,** 96–112.

HAWKER, L. E. (1950). *Physiology of fungi.* University of London Press.

HAWKER, L. E. (1957). Ecological factors and the survival of fungi. *Microbial Ecology. Seventh Symposium Soc. gen. Microbiol.,* Cambridge University Press, 238–58.

HESSAYSON, D. G. (1953). Fungitoxins in the soil. II. Trichothecin, its production and inactivation in unsterilized soil. *Soil Sci.,* **75,** 395–404.

JACKSON, R. M. (1957). Fungistasis as a factor in the rhizosphere phenomenon. *Nature, Lond.,* **180,** 96.

JACKSON, R. M. (1958). An investigation of fungistasis in Nigerian soils. *J. gen. Microbiol.,* **18,** 248–58.

JACOT, A. P. (1939). Reduction of spruce and fir litter by minute animals. *J. For.,* **37,** 858–60.

JEFFERYS, E. G., BRIAN, P. W., HEMMING, H. G., & LOWE, D. (1953). Antibiotic production by the microfungi of acid heath soils. *J. gen. Microbiol.,* **9,** 314–41.

JEFFERYS, E. G., & HEMMING, H. G. (1953). Fungistasis in soils. *Nature, Lond.,* **172,** 872.

JINKS, J. L. (1952). Heterokaryosis—a system of adaption in wild fungi. *Proc. roy. Soc.,* B, **140,** 83–99.

JONES, P. C. T., & MOLLISON, J. E. (1948). A technique for the quantatitive estimation of soil micro-organisms. *J. gen. Microbiol.,* **2,** 54–69.

KERR, A. (1956). Some interactions between plant roots and pathogenic soil fungi. *Aust. J. Biol. Sci.,* **9,** 45–52.

KING, C. J., HOPE, C., & EATON, E. D. (1934). Some microbiological activities affected in manurial control of cotton-root rot. *J. agric. Res.,* **49,** 1093–1107.

KUBIENA, W. L. (1938). *Micropedology.* Iowa: Collegiate Press Inc.

KÜRBIS, W. P. (1937). Mykologische Untersuchungen über den Wurzelbereich der Ersche (*Fraxinus excelsior*). *Flora, Jena,* **131,** 129–75.

LEBEAU, J. B., & CORMACK, M. W. (1956). A simple method for identifying snow mould damage on turf grasses. *Phytopath.,* **46,** 298.

LILLY, V. G., & BARNETT, H. L. (1951). *Physiology of the fungi.* London: McGraw Hill & Co.

MACFADYEN, A. (1957). *Animal ecology—aims and methods.* London: Pitman.

MELIN, E. (1953). Physiology of mycorrhizal relations in plants. *Ann. Rev. Plant. Physiol.,* **4,** 325–46.

MIKOLA, P. (1956). Studies on the decomposition of forest litter by basidiomycetes. *Comm. Inst. Forest. Fenn.*, **48**, 2.

MITCHELL, R. B., ADAMS, J. E., & THOM, C. (1941). Microbial responses to organic amendments in Houston black clay. *J. agric Res.*, **63**, 527–34.

MOLIN, N. (1957). (A study of the infection biology of *Fomes annosus.*) *Medd. fr. Stat. Skogsf. inst.*, **47**, (3), 1–36.

MURPHY, P. W. (1956). Soil faunal investigations. *Rep. For. Res., Lond.*, (1954–5), 83–4.

NILSSON, P. E. (1957). Influence of crop on biological activities in soil. *Ann. Royal Agric. College Sweden*, **23**, 175–218.

NORKRANS, B. (1950). Studies in growth and cellulolytic enzymes of *Tricholoma* with special reference to mycorrhiza formation. *Symb. bot. Upsaliens*, **11**, 1–126.

PARK, D. (1954). An indirect method for the study of fungi in the soil. *Trans. Brit. mycol. Soc.*, **37**, 405–11.

PARK, D. (1955). Experimental studies on the ecology of fungi in soil. *Trans. Brit. mycol. Soc.*, **38**, 130–42.

PARK, D. (1956). On the role of amendments in the biology of fungi in soil. *Proc. 6th Congr. Int. Soc. Soil Sci.*, **3**, 25.

PARK, D. (1957a). Behaviour of soil fungi in the presence of fungal antagonists *Trans. Brit. mycol. Soc.*, **40**, 358–64.

PARK, D. (1957b). Behaviour of soil fungi in the presence of bacterial antagonists. *Trans. Brit. mycol. Soc.*, **40**, 283–91.

PARK, D. (1958). The saprophytic status of *Fusarium oxysporum* Schl. causing vascular wilt of oil palm. *Ann. Bot. Lond. N.S.*, **22**, 19–35.

PARK, O., & AUERBACH, S. (1954). Further study on the tree-hole complex with emphasis on quantitative aspects of the fauna. *Ecology*, **35**, 208–22.

PONTECORVO, G. (1949). The origin of virulent strains as recombinants from non-virulent strains and the kinetics of epidemics. *Proc. 4th Int. Congr. Microbiol., Copenhagen*, (1947), 376.

RAM, C. S. V. (1952). Soil bacteria and chlamydospore formation in *Fusarium solani. Nature, Lond.*, **170**, 889.

RISHBETH, J. (1951). Observations on the biology of *Fomes annosus*, with particular reference to East Anglian pine plantations. III. Natural and experimental infections of pines, and some factors affecting severity of the disease. *Ann. Bot. Lond. N.S.*, **15**, 221–46.

RISHBETH, J. (1955). *Fusarium* wilt of bananas in Jamaica. I. Some observations on the epidemiology of the disease. *Ann. Bot. Lond. N.S.*, **19**, 293–328.

ROBERTSON, N. F. (1954). Studies on the mycorrhiza of *Pinus sylvestris. New Phytol.*, **53**, 253–83.

ROTHSTEIN, A. (1954). The enzymology of the cell surface. *Protoplasmatologica. Handbuch der Protoplasmaforschung.* Vienna: Springer-Verlag.

RUSSELL, E. W. (1950). *Soil conditions and plant growth.* London: Longmans, Green & Co.

SAITÔ, TOSHI (1955a). The significance of plate counts of soil fungi and the detection of their mycelia. *Ecological Review*, **14**, 69–74.

SAITÔ, TOSHI (1955b). Soil microflora of a coastal dune. I. Relationships between vegetational features of the habitat and the soil population. *Sci. Reports. Tohoku University, 4th Series. Biology*, **21**, 145–57.

SAITÔ, TOSHI (1956). Microbiological decomposition of beech litter. *Ecological Review*, **14**, 141–47.

SAKSENA, S. B. (1955). Ecological factors governing the distribution of soil micro-fungi in some forest soils of Sagar. *J. Ind. Bot. Soc.*, **34**, 262–98.

SCHÜTTE, K. H. (1956). Translocation in the fungi. *New Phytol.*, **55**, 164–82.

SHEPHERD, C. J. (1957). The genome as a component of the ecosystem. *Microbial Ecology. Seventh Symposium Soc. gen. Microbiol,* Cambridge University Press, 1–21.

SIU, R. G. H. (1951). *Microbial decomposition of cellulose.* New York: Reinhold Publishing Corpn.

SMIT, J., & WIERINGA, K. T. (1953). Microbiological decomposition of litter. *Nature, Lond.,* **171,** 794.

STANIER, R. Y. (1953). Adaption, evolutionary and physiological: or Darwinism among the micro-organisms. *Adaption in Micro-organisms. Third Symposium Soc. gen. Microbiol.,* Cambridge University Press, 1–20.

STENTON, H. (1953). The soil fungi of Wicken Fen. *Trans. Brit. mycol. Soc.,* **36,** 304–14.

STENTON, H. (1958). Colonization of roots of *Pisum sativum* L. by fungi. *Trans. Brit. mycol. Soc.,* **41,** 74–80.

STOVER, R. H. (1953). The effect of soil moisture on *Fusarium culmorum. Canad. J. Bot.,* **31,** 693–7.

STOVER, R. H. (1955). Flood fallowing for eradication of *Fusarium oxysporum f. cubense.* III. Effect of oxygen on fungus survival. *Soil Sci.,* **80,** 397–412.

SUSSMAN, A. S. (1957). Physiological and genetic adaptability in the fungi. *Mycologia,* **49,** 29–43.

THOM, C. (1927). Present and future studies of soil fungi. *Proc. 1st Int. Cong. Soc. Soil Sci.,* **3,** 39–47.

THOM, C., & MORROW, M. B. (1937). Fungus mycelia in the soil. *J. Bact.,* **33,** 77–8.

THORNTON, R. H. (1956). *Rhizoctonia* in natural grassland soil. *Nature, Lond.,* **177,** 230–1.

TRACEY, M. V. (1956). The properties of resistant parts of fungal mycelium which might accumulate in soils. *Rep. Rothamsted. Exp. Sta.,* 1955, 87–8.

TRESNER, H. D., BACKUS, M. P., & CURTIS, J. T. (1954). Soil microfungi in relation to the hardwood forest continuum in Southern Wisconsin. *Mycologia,* **3,** 314–33.

TRIBE, H. T. (1957). Ecology of micro-organisms in soils as observed during their development upon buried cellulose film. *Microbial Ecology. Seventh Symposium Soc. gen. Microbiol.,* Cambridge University Press, 287–98.

WAID, J. S. (1956). Root dissection: a method of studying the distribution of active mycelia within root tissue. *Nature, Lond.,* **178,** 1477–8.

WAID, J. S. (1957). Distribution of fungi within the decomposing tissues of ryegrass roots. *Trans. Brit. mycol. Soc.,* **40,** 391–406.

WAID, J. S. (1959). Soil microbiology in relation to soil zoology. Colloquium on *Research Methods in Soil Zoology.* (In the Press.)

WAID, J. S., & WOODMAN, M. J. (1957). A method of estimating hyphal activity in soil. Symposium on *Methodes d'Études Microbiologiques du Sol.,* **3,** 1–6.

WAKSMAN, S. A. (1916). Soil fungi and their activities. *Soil Sci.,* **2,** 103–55.

WAKSMAN, S. A. (1917). Is there any fungus flora of the soil? *Soil Sci.,* **3,** 565–89.

WAKSMAN, S. A. (1944). Three decades with soil fungi. *Soil Sci.,* **58,** 89–116.

WARCUP, J. H. (1951a). The ecology of soil fungi. *Trans. Brit. mycol. Soc.,* **34,** 376–99.

WARCUP, J. H. (1951b). Studies on the growth of basidiomycetes in soil. *Ann. Bot. Lond. N.S.,* **15,** 305–17.

WARCUP, J. H. (1955a). Isolation of fungi from hyphae present in soil. *Nature, Lond.,* **175,** 953.

WARCUP, J. H. (1955b). On the origin of colonies of fungi developing on soil-dilution plates. *Trans. Brit. mycol. Soc.,* **38,** 298–301.

WARCUP, J. H. (1957). Studies on the occurrence and activity of fungi in a wheat-field soil. *Trans. Brit. mycol. Soc.*, **40**, 237–62.

WEBLEY, D. M., EASTWOOD, D. J., & GIMINGHAM, C. H. (1952). Development of a soil microflora in relation to plant succession on sand-dunes including the 'rhizosphere' flora associated with colonizing species. *J. Ecol.*, **40**, 168–78.

WINSTON, P. W. (1956). The acorn microsere, with special reference to arthropods. *Ecology*, **37**, 120–32.

WOLF, F. A., & WOLF, F. T. (1947). *The Fungi*. New York: John Wiley.

THE INFLUENCE OF BIOTIC FACTORS
ON THE DEVELOPMENT OF SOIL FUNGI

A. G. WINTER, HELGE PEUSS,
AND F. SCHÖNBECK

Botanische Abt. Madaus, Köln-Merheim, Germany

For a long time there has been discussion on whether substances of biotic origin might affect the development of micro-organisms in the soil as do other environmental factors, e.g. nutrient supply, pH, physical properties. Such biotic substances include the metabolic products of micro-organisms, excretions of living plant roots, substances originating from old and decomposing higher plants, and sloughed-off root hairs and cells of the root cortex. The counter-argument has been that such substances could not possibly accumulate to any effective concentration in natural soil because they would be continually decomposed by microbial action. No one has ever succeeded in extracting a chemically defined substance of biotic origin in an effective quantity from natural soil. Winter (1942, 1949, 1950a) has repeatedly pointed out that, except in pure cultures, this is not unexpected because of the heterogeneous composition of the soil, which varies from one millimetre to another as do the living conditions of the microflora and their metabolic products. However, this does not exclude the fact that substances of biotic origin may be effective in the soil (Winter, 1942). Knowledge of all these factors can be gained only from studying the co-existence of the micro-organisms within a minimum of space.

As observations on any glass slide will show, the environment of a plant root, bits of decaying forest litter or root particles, etc., provide a variety of special micro-environments for fungi which differs considerably from the surrounding soil in the species present and in the quantity of its microflora. Here local pure cultures of micro-organisms produce, within a minimum of space, substances of uniform biotic origin, which then influence the biocoenosis in the immediate neighbourhood. Their decomposition by microbial action does not *a priori* prevent their activity, for normally they are continuously regenerated. The concentration of the active substance depends upon the respective rates of formation and decomposition.

If, therefore, one wishes to discover whether antagonistic substances are effective in soil, the immediate neighbourhood of the fungal hyphae must be investigated for the presence of microbes of different species, which might account for the occurrence of antagonistic or antibiotic phenomena.

Soil fungi can be influenced by other soil microbes in different ways. A single species of microbe can become locally abundant in the neighbourhood of certain nutrients, parts of plants, etc. There would then be the possibility of a localized inhibiting or stimulating effect similar to the conditions in pure culture. Or else, one soil fungus can develop extremely well throughout the test soil owing to particular conditions within the soil, such as partial sterilization. In this case, there may be an excessive growth of other fungi around its hyphae or even parasitizing it.

Thorough research, by means of the inoculation-plate method, on the co-existence of soil microbes revealed close associations of microorganisms, especially fungi, to occur frequently. The hyphae showed all transitory stages from a temporary paralleling of the hyphae to the typical forms of symbiosis as shown by the lichens.

From all these investigations it was found that the fungal hyphae create around themselves an environment *sui generis*, which in every respect is similar to the rhizosphere and which we have called the 'hyphosphere'. Within it certain fungi and bacteria grow in vast numbers, so that in such close proximity there occur all the conditions necessary for metabolic products to exert an effective influence. The physiological attraction of the hyphosphere can be so strong that certain fungi are associated entirely with and adhere to the hyphae of their 'host'. In the end the influence may go so far as to make the associate adapt itself completely to the growth 'habit' or 'pattern' of the host hyphae as regards the development of lateral branches. This applies to fungi as well as to the Actinomycetes.

Having demonstrated this strong mutual influence of micro-organisms in the soil, it is therefore not surprising that out of 25 soil fungi examined by Winter (1947, 1949, 1951a) by the inoculation-plate method in natural soil, there were 23 for which the factor limiting their development was the proportion of inhibitors in the natural soil. Only in two cases (both sterile mycelia) could it be established that, even in quite different soils, the limiting factor was always the proportion of nutrients. The correlation between addition of nutrients and development of these fungi was shown to be comparable to that obtained in pure culture.

On the other hand, there were fungi incapable of any development in several natural soils, and on the addition of any concentration of nutrients never showed increased growth. With the majority of fungi tested, however, the addition of nutrients either intensified or decreased the inhibiting conditions in the soil, but never came near to eliminating them. This is evidence of microbes causing the inhibiting condition which varies when the microbiological balance is altered by adding nutrients, but which never changes drastically or ceases to exist.

We should like to apologize for reporting results of research carried out more than ten years ago, but this convincing evidence of the existence in soil of inhibiting conditions of biotic origin has caused us to investigate whether there are other parts of the edaphon that have a decisive influence on the development of soil fungi, as well as the micro-organisms themselves.

It is not only the metabolic products of lower organisms, such as bacteria and fungi, that may be of importance for the development of certain fungi in the soil, but also substances produced by higher plants, either owing to the particular conditions within the rhizosphere of the plant, or through root excretions, or inhibitors, etc. We first investigated whether the microflora of the rhizosphere is capable of influencing soil fungi. The virulence of *Ophiobolus graminis* has been found to vary considerably in different types of soil. Wheat requires, for immunity against infection, a relatively specific edaphon (in this case a black soil). Muller-Kogler's observation (1938) that *O. graminis* penetrates into the roots of many flowering plants grown in sterilized soil which under natural conditions are immune from infection, appears to prove that the host plant-parasite relationship can be shifted in favour of the host plant by the microflora.

Its influence on the course of infection was conclusively proved by Winter & von Rumker (1949, 1950) as far as *Ascochyta pinodella* was concerned. Peas were infected to the same degree in both sterilized and unsterilized soil, thus showing that the rhizosphere microflora has no effect. On the other hand, the root cortex of wheat, resistant to *A. pinodella* in natural soil, is thoroughly penetrated by the fungus in sterilized soil. If growth and infection are conducted on Zinzade agar under sterile conditions, the fungus will grow like a dense coat of mycelium on the surface of the roots, forming a so-called pseudomycorrhiza. Similarly the resistance of maize and wheat to a *Fusarium*, which is highly pathogenic on peas, depends upon the presence of the rhizosphere microflora.

Naturally, it is just possible for the particular conditions in the rhizosphere to permit a better development of the fungi without causing any infection. Thus von Rumker (1951) demonstrated that species of *Fusarium* develop better within the rhizosphere of resistant plants than in the surrounding soil. In particular, maize, as a resistant plant, accumulates *A. pinodella* in its rhizosphere to a high degree. From this it is evident that the resistant maize favours contamination of the soil much more than do the susceptible peas, and that this contamination is brought about by specific properties of the rhizosphere.

What then causes these fungi to behave so differently within the rhizosphere? Either the fungus itself may be influenced by microbes living in the rhizosphere, or else the plant, if susceptible to disease, may be affected by absorbing antibiotic substances produced by the rhizosphere microflora. The fungus would then find within the plant the same inhibitors as in the rhizosphere, since it has been shown that relatively complex molecules like streptomycin and penicillin are absorbed by plants and are traceable in an active condition within the plants (Winter & Willeke, 1951; Winter, 1952; Brian *et al.*, 1951; Blanchard & Dillard, 1951). It can therefore be assumed that inhibitors produced in the rhizosphere are actually absorbed by plants and are effective in their tissues.

Not only the rhizosphere but also substances produced and passed into the soil by plant roots (i.e. root excretions in a wider sense) may influence the growth of fungi. Thus Schönbeck (1958) found that oat roots excrete substances that inhibit the growth of certain soil fungi e.g. *Byssochlamys nivea* and *Trichoderma koningi*. The inhibiting substance was identified, by paper chromatography, as a glycoside from the root rip of oats.

The importance of the micro-biocoenosis appears in quite a different light if we look at single cultures. Here biotic substances of the same origin get into the soil in larger quantities. According to Winter & Willeke (1952) and Winter (1953, 1954) decaying leaves quite often contain substances capable of altering the microbiological balance in soil. Admixture of certain plant materials to the soil may even lead to a complete alteration of the bacterial population which no doubt affects the development of certain soil fungi. Schönbeck (1953, 1956) also showed that phytotoxic substances get into the soil and remain active there for an extended period. Borner (1956) identified these substances as ferulic acid, *p*-oxybenzoic acid, vanillic acid, etc. Knösel (1958) tested the effect of these substances on the growth of a large variety of soil fungal species, and nearly always found that they stimulated growth.

The soil water from raw humus under spruce also contains antibacterial substances in effective concentrations (Winter & Bublitz, 1953).

A compost suspension with added spruce litter extract brings about a complete bacteriostasis. After 7 days, however, fungi grew very well on the same plates on which the bacteria had been inhibited. From these experiments we may be justified in concluding that these substances hamper the normal process of humification because of the strong inhibition of bacteria and the more vigorous development of fungi; and also that by inhibiting germination they prevent the natural regeneration of the pine and fir stands.

Detritus of higher plants—e.g. withered roots and decaying leaves—were thus shown to be capable of influencing the biocoenosis. They do so by means of substances which could be identified in some cases.

But the roots of living plants, too, can decisively influence the wholesale change of fungi with a parasitic life-phase. This applies particularly to fungi in which the saprophytic phase as a harmless root fungus is considerably reduced, such as *Rhizoctonia solani* and the endotrophic mycorrhiza.

According to Winter (1951a), *R. solani* was never found growing in bare soil without a nutrient base. When the nutrient base was exhausted the fungus ceased to grow, and even by adding organic nutrients (glucose, malt, peptone, etc.) to the soil, the mycelium could not be made to grow on again. If, however, the fungus came upon new roots, it surrounded them and grew vigorously in all directions from the new nutrient base. Bosch (1948) had already observed that the rate of spread of *R. solani* depends upon the density of susceptible plants. Obviously *R. solani* cannot extract all the substances necessary for its growth from the soil alone, but depends upon substances produced by the living root, if perhaps only as supplementary ones.

This was confirmed to a certain extent by Boyle (1956), who failed to isolate *R. solani* from bare soil to which he had added soya-bean hay, even though the organic material was interspersed with it. He, too, came to the conclusion that the spread of the fungus in soil depends on the availability of organic substances. Sanford (1952) also noticed that the fungus developed better in soil bearing vegetation than in bare soil. According to Stuckenbrucker (unpublished data) the conditions in the rhizosphere would suffice to allow the fungus to develop.

The endotrophic mycorrhiza occupy a particular position among the soil fungi. They require living roots for their development, and they cannot, as yet, be isolated and cultivated in artificial nutrient medium. These fungi can therefore only be classified approximately; they probably belong to the Endogeonaceae. The mycorrhizal fungi are of particular interest since about 80% of the herbaceous plants in Central

Europe are associated with them, and in several plants the mycorrhizal fungus can be shown to have a stimulating influence on the development of the host plants. Thus Mosse (1957) found that the presence of mycorrhiza caused better growth of apple shoots than when the mycorrhiza were absent. A stimulating effect of mycorrhiza on tobacco was observed by Peuss (1957, 1958) and on maize by Winter & Meloh (1958). The stimulating influence of the fungus becomes all the more obvious as the environmental conditions for the plant get worse. Peuss, for instance, found that tobacco plants growing in water culture at different pH were stimulated most when the hydrogen-ion concentration was highest. At all pH levels the plants infected with mycorrhiza developed better than those without infection. At pH 4·0 the plants grew least, but even so the plants with mycorrhiza had 30 % more dry weight than those devoid of fungi had at pH 7·0, the optimum pH for growth of tobacco.

Although growth and spread of the fungus depend on the living root, there must be a saprophytic phase which enables the fungus to survive the period devoid of vegetation and to infect plants anew. Experiments showed that tobacco plants were infected, either by mycelium growing out from root remains or by germinating vesicles. Under natural conditions infection by vesicles is likely to be the more important and frequent one, since the vesicles, by their structure, are better protected against environmental influences than the mycelium. Thus the fungus may grow in the soil as well, but perhaps only close to the plant root. Its growth in the soil, as has been demonstrated, is subject to influences either through the root or else through the soil.

It has been shown that, where the assimilation of plants was disturbed by reduction of the light-intensity or of the assimilating surface, infection occurred later and the spreading of the fungus inside the plant was also retarded. One may conclude that the inferior assimilative capacity of the plant had effect, not only on the parasitic phase but also on that outside the plant.

However, the saprophytic phase of the mycorrhizal fungus may be influenced by biotic soil factors in yet another way. If infected soil is mixed with peat, the delay in infection is proportional to the amount of peat added. Similar results were obtained by adding, instead, aqueous peat extracts. In this case active water-soluble substances from peat prevent the development of the fungus outside the plant, i.e. the saprophytic phase. If spruce-needle litter were mixed with soil in various quantities, it had a restrictive influence on the amount of fungal growth, but never delayed its beginning. In certain conditions the development of mycorrhiza was stimulated, particularly if spruce litter extract had been added to soil. Whether the fungus was also affected outside the plant, however, we could not verify.

REFERENCES

BLANCHARD, F. A., & DILLER, V. M. (1951). Uptake of aureomycin through the roots of *Phaseolus lunatus*. *Amer. J. Bot.*, **38**, 111–12.

BÖRNER, H. (1956). Die Abgabe organischer Verbindungen aus den Karyopsen, Wurzeln and Ernterückständen von Roggen (*Secale cereale* L.) Weizen (*Triticum astivum* L.) und Gerste (*Hordeum vulgare* L.) und ihre Bedeutung bei der gegenseitigen Beeinflussung der höheren Pflanzen. *Beitr. Biol. d. Pfl.*, **13**, 33–83.

BOSCH, E. (1948). Untersuchungen über die Biologie und Bekämpfung der Vermehrungspilze *Moniliopsis Aderhaldi* und *Rhizoctonia Solani Landw. Jahrb. Schweiz.*

BRIAN, P. W., WRIGHT, J. M., STUBBS, J., & WAY, A. M. (1951). Uptake of Antibiotic metabolites of soil micro-organisms by plants. *Nature, Lond.*, **167**, 347.

KNÖSEL, D. (1958) Über die Wirkung aus Pflanzenresten freiwerdender phenolischer Substanzen auf Mikroorganismen des Bodens. *Ztschr. f. Pflanzenernährg., Düngg. und Bodenkde.*, **80**, 225–37.

MOSSE, BARBARA (1956). Fructifications of an *Endogone* species causing endotrophic mycorrhiza in fruit plants. *Ann. Bot.*, **20**, 349.

MÜLLER-KÖGLER, E. (1938). Untersuchungen über die Schwarzbeinigkeit des Getreides und den Wirtspflanzenkreis ihres Erregers. *Arb. Biol. R.A.*, **22**, 271.

PEUSS, HELGE (1958). Untersuchungen zur Oekologie und Bedeutung der Tabakmycorrhiza. *Archiv f. Mikrobiol.*, **29**, 112–42.

RÜMKER, ROSEMARIE VON (1951). Über die Ökologie von *Ascochyta pinodella* und *Fusarium culmorum* in der Rhizoshäre anfälliger und nicht anfälliger Pflanzen. *Phytopath. Z.*, **18**, 55–100.

SANFORD, G. B. (1952). Persistence of *Rhizoctonia solani* Kühn in soil. *Can. J. Bot.*, **30**, 652–64.

SCHÖNBECK, F. (1953). Die Bedeutung von Hemmstoffen in der Landwirtschaft. *Madaus Jahresbericht*, S. **81**.

SCHÖNBECK, F. (1956). Untersuchungen über Vorkommen und Bedeutung von Hemmstoffen in Getreiderückständen innerhalb der Fruchtfolge. *Z. Pflanzenkrankh.*, **63**, 513–45.

SCHÖNBECK, F. (1958). Untersuchungen über den Einfluss von Wurzelausscheidungen auf die Entwicklung von Bodenpilzen. *Naturwiss.*, **45**, 63–4.

WINTER, A. G. (1942). Der Einfluss partieller Sterilisation des Bodens auf die Entwicklung der Laufhyphen von *Ophiobolus graminis*. *Phytopath. Z.*, **14**, 204–302.

WINTER, A. G. (1947). Eine Methode zur quatitativen Bestimmung des Wachstums parasitischer oder saprophytischer Pilze im natürlichen Boden. *Festschrift Appel, Biol. Zentralanst.*, 12–15.

WINTER, A. G. (1949). Untersuchungen über die Beziehungen zwischen *Ophiobolus graminis* und anderen Organismen mit Hilfe der Aufwuchsplatten-methode. *Arch. Mikrobiol.*, **14**, 240–70.

WINTER, A. G. (1950a). Untersuchungen über die Ökologie und den Massenwechsel bodenbewohnender mikroskopischer Pilze. I. *Arch. Mikrobiol.*, **15**, 42–71.

WINTER, A. G. (1950b). Neue Gesichtspunkte in der Bodenmikrobiologie. *Zbl. Bakt. I. Abt.*, **155**, 342.

WINTER, A. G. (1950c). Uhtersuchungen über die Verbreitung und Bedeutung der

Mycorrhiza bei kultivierten Gramineen und einigen anderen landwirtschaftlichen Nutzpflanzen. *Phytopath. Z.*, **17**, 421–32.

WINTER, A. G. (1951). Untersuchungen über die Ökologie und den Massenwechsel bodenbewohnender mikroskopischer Pilze. II. *Arch. Mikrobiol.*, **16**, 136–62.

WINTER, A. G. (1952). Untersuchungen über die Aufnahme von Penicillin und Streptomycin durch die Wurzeln von *Lepidium sativum* L. und ihre Beständigkeit in natürlichen Böden. *Z. f. Botanik.*, **40**, 153.

WINTER, A. G. (1953). Grundsätzliches zur Hemmstoff-Forschung in der Land- und Forstwirtschaft. *Madaus Jahresber.*, S. **74**.

WINTER, A. G. (1954). Antibiotische, in vivo aktive Wirkstoffe aus Blütenpflanzen und ihre therapeutische Bedeutung. *Vort. Int. Botan. Kongress Paris.*

WINTER, A. G. (1955). Untersuchungen über Vorkommen und Bedeutung von Antimikrobiellen und antiphytotischen Substanzen in natürlichen Böden. *Ztschr. Planzenernährg., Düngg. u. Bodenk.*, **69**, 224–237.

WINTER, A. G. (1957). Beziehungen zwischen Edaphon und Pflanze im Lichte neuerer Biocönoseforschung. *Z. Pflanzenkrkh.*, **64**, 407.

WINTER, A. G., & BUBLITZ, W. (1953). Untersuchungen über antibakterielle Wirkungen im Bodenwasser der Fichtenstreu. *Naturwiss.*, **40**, 345.

WINTER, A. G., & MELOH, K. A. (1958). Untersuchungen über den Einfluss der endotrophen Mycorrhiza aufdie Entwicklung von *Zea mays* L. *Naturwiss.*, **45**, 319.

WINTER, A. G., & VON RÜMKER, R. (1949). Die Bedeutung der Mikroflora der wurzelnahen Zone für die Resistenz von Wurzeln gegen Pilzkrankheiten. *Naturwiss.*, **36**, 30.

WINTER, A. G., & VON RÜMKER, R. (1950). Die Mikroflora der Rhizospäre als resistenzbestimmender Faktor. *Arch. für Mikrobiol.*, **15**, 72–84.

WINTER, A. G., & SCHÖNBECK, F. (1953). Untersuchungen über den Einfluss von Kaltwasserextrakten aus Getreidestroh und anderer Blattstreu auf Wurzelbildung un-Wachstum. *Naturwiss.*, **40**, 168–9.

WINTER, A. G., & SCHÖNBECK, F. (1954). Untersuchungen über wasserlösliche Hemmstoffe aus Getreideböden. *Naturwiss.*, **41**, 145, 146.

WINTER, A. G., & WILLEKE, L. (1951*a*). Untersuchungen über Antibiotika aus höher en Pflanzen und ihre Bedeutung für die Bodenmikrobiologie und Pflanzensoziologie. *Naturwiss.*, **38**, 262–4.

WINTER, A. G., & WILLEKE, L. (1951*b*). Untersuchungen über Antibiotika aus höheren Pflanzen. *Naturwiss.*, **38**, 354.

WINTER, A. G., & WILLEKE, L. (1952*a*). Hemmstoffe im herbstlichen Laub. *Naturwiss.*, **39**, 45.

WINTER, A. G., & WILLEKE, L. (1952*b*). Hemmstoffe in Blättern und Blattstreu der Gramineen. *Naturwiss.*, **39**, 190.

WINTER, A. G., & WILLEKE, L. (1952*c*). Gasförmige Hemmstoffe aus *Tropaeolum majus* und ihr Verhalten im menschlichen Körper bei Aufnahme von Tropaeolum-Salat per os. *Naturwiss.*, **39**, 236–7.

GROWTH OF FUNGI IN SOME FOREST AND GRASSLAND SOILS

R. H. THORNTON

Soil Bureau, Department of Scientific and Industrial Research,
Wellington, New Zealand

SOIL BUREAU PUBLICATION No. 158

Fungi active in a number of different English and New Zealand soils under various types of higher plant cover have been examined at various seasons by the screened immersion-plate technique (Thornton, 1952; Chesters & Thornton, 1956). Isolation of mycelia from soil by this method depends upon the growth of hyphae from soil through apertures (about 3 mm. diam.) in the lid of a thin 'Perspex' box on to a layer of distilled-water agar (2% w/v) inside. These screened immersion plates are buried in mineral soil layers for 4–7 days. As the method has been standard throughout the various investigations the results provide, within the limits of the method, a comparison of the growth and distribution of fungi within several soils.

Although many species have been isolated, a great number of the mycelia isolated belong only to a few species. 'Soil fungal patterns' were employed (Thornton, 1956) to demonstrate this point. These patterns express the percentage frequency of occurrence of species isolated by screened immersion plates, arranged in decreasing order. Soil fungal patterns of those species contributing 2% or more of total isolations from any one soil are shown for several soils in Table 1. This by no means constitutes a full list of the species isolated from these soils. Several species, present in some soils at the 2% level, were also isolated from other soils shown in the table, but at a lower frequency of occurrence. The presence of these fungi in those soils is indicated in the table by a dash (—). Table 1 is divided by vertical lines into four divisions. The first two deal with results from forest soils, and the other two with results from grassland soils. The soils in each division were examined as a parallel series of investigations. Although the table is largely self-explanatory, a brief description of the relationships of the soils and the higher plant cover may be helpful.

In the first division of the table dealing with forest soil fungi, results

TABLE 1

Frequency of occurrence of common fungi isolated by screened immersion plates in some forest and grassland soils expressed as the percentage of total isolations from the particular soils. (—) signifies occurrence at a frequency less than 2% of total isolations

Columns 1–6: **Forest soil fungi with change of vegetation**
Columns 7–11: **Low tussock grassland soil fungi** (7–9 Naturally occurring; 10–11 with Change of vegetation)

Fungi / Site	1	2	3	4	5	6	7	8	9	10	11
	Mixed oakwood forest	Pinus forest	Calluna heath	Tawa forest	Pasture	Pasture	Tussock	Tussock	Tussock	Tussock	Pasture
PHYCOMYCETES											
Mucor hiemalis	—	—	22	—	5	4	—	—	—	3	2
M. ramannianus	—	—	—	—	—	—	—	—	4	—	2
Absidia glauca	2	—	—	—	—	—	—	—	—	3	3
Zygorrhynchus moelleri	—	—	3	—	4	—	—	—	—	—	—
Mortierella alpina	—	8	—	—	2	5	—	4	—	—	—
M. elongata	4	4	14	—	—	—	—	4	—	—	—
M. gracilis	10	11	—	—	—	—	—	—	—	—	—
M. humilis	6	—	—	—	—	—	—	—	—	—	—
M. nana	5	—	—	—	—	—	—	—	—	—	—
M. stylospora	—	—	—	2	—	—	—	—	—	—	—
M. spinosa	—	14	—	—	—	—	—	—	—	—	—
M. vinacea	—	—	—	—	—	—	—	—	—	—	—
ASCOMYCETES											
Pseudogymnoascus roseus	—	3	—	—	—	—	—	—	—	—	—
FUNGI IMPERFECTI											
Trichoderma viride	33	4	23	4	10	24	—	4	—	—	5
Penicillium frequentans	6	—	17	—	—	—	—	—	—	—	—
P. janthinellum	—	4	—	—	—	—	—	2	3	—	—
P. melinii	—	—	—	—	—	—	—	—	—	—	—
P. stoloniferum	—	7	—	—	—	—	—	2	—	—	—
Humicola grisea	—	7	—	32	7	—	—	7	—	—	—
Cylindrocarpon radicicola	—	—	—	5	—	—	20	—	—	12	17
C. olidum	—	—	—	—	—	—	—	—	—	—	—
Fusarium culmorum	—	—	—	—	16	4	3	—	4	5	7
F. oxysporum	—	—	—	—	25	22	—	—	—	—	—
F. sambucinum var. coeruleum	—	—	—	—	—	—	—	—	—	—	—
MYCELIA STERILIA											
Papulaspora spp.	—	—	—	9	4	7	3	5	—	16	28
Rhizoctonia sp.	—	—	—	12	2	4	41	37	56	26	25
Fungus S.B.235	—	—	—	3	—	—	5	11	—	20	3
Other non-sporing mycelia	9	15	—	20	13	15	4	7	9	—	—
Total no. of isolations	151	158	485	161	285	272	586	521	562	117	126
Total no. of apertures exposed	750	300	1000	300	300	300	900	900	900	150	150
Av. no. of isolations per 10 apertures, i.e. per plate	2·0	5·3	4·8	5·4	9·5	9·1	6·5	5·8	6·2	7·8	8·4

from three sites, on soils derived from Bunter sandstone in north Nottinghamshire, England, are given. Originally the three sites were covered by mixed oakwood, the natural vegetation of this area.

The first site was a remnant of the oakwood cover. At the second, the oakwood had been removed, and, after an unknown period of agricultural use, a plantation of mixed *Pinus sylvestris* and *P. nigra* var. *calabrica* had been established 18 years before this investigation. These soils would be classed as brown earths. At the third site *Calluna vulgaris* had become dominant after removal of the oakwood about 30 years previous to this investigation, and the soil would be classed as a podzol. The results thus provide a comparison of the effects of change of higher plant cover on the basic fungal flora of an oakwood soil. Some of the changes are quite marked, particularly the development of *Mucor ramannianus* under *Calluna*, of *Mortierella vinacea* under *Pinus* spp., and the absence of *Mortierella humilis* from beneath *Calluna*. Details of much of this work have already been presented (Thornton, 1956).

Results in the remaining divisions of the table refer to investigations carried out in New Zealand soils which, in general, occur under mild to cool, humid, climates, in temperate latitudes. The main zonal soils are yellow-brown earths which correspond to brown earths in England (N.Z. Soil Bureau, 1954, p. 275).

In the second division of Table 1 dealing with fungi of forest soils, results are shown from studies at two sites, (4 and 5) only 200 yards apart, on a yellow-brown earth derived from alluvium, from greywacke sandstone and rhyolitic volcanic ash. Site 4 is a remnant area of native evergreen mixed podocarp forest, now dominated by tawa (*Beilschmiedia tawa* (Lauraceae)), which is maintained as a forest reserve. Site 5 was cleared of a similar type of forest 100 years ago and, after a fern-scrub stage, has been under permanent grass-clover pasture for approximately 60 years. The tawa forest soil has several species of fungi in common with the English oakwood soil, although the relative frequency of occurrence varies. In the tawa forest soil, however, a number of non-sporing fungi, notably *Papulaspora* sp., *Rhizoctonia* sp., and fungus S.B.235 (hyaline hyphae, 2–3μ diam., off-white, sclerotia 1–3 mm. diam.) form a relatively large proportion of the population. The change of higher plant cover from forest to pasture has brought about a sharp change in the relative occurrence of some species, e.g. *Cylindrocarpon radicicola*, *Papulaspora* sp., together with the appearance and strong dominance of *Fusarium* spp. in the pasture soil. Results from another site, 6, on a yellow-brown earth derived from greywacke sandstone, 100 miles distant from sites 4 and 5, on which permanent grass-clover pasture replaced forest approximately 90 years ago, are also given to show the close parallel of the fungal patterns in the two pasture soils. This similarity suggests that a uniform soil environment is being developed at sites 5 and 6 as the result of the establishment of the same higher plant cover, together with the raising of the soil-nutrient status by the use of lime and phosphatic fertilizers, and by the use of sheep as the grazing animal. More recent work, not reported here, has shown that the replacement of coastal forest with permanent grass-clover pasture over 50 years ago, brings about a similar dominance by *Fusarium* spp. in the pasture soil, whilst the remnant areas of the forest are devoid of these fungi. The appearance and dominance of *Fusarium* spp. in these permanent pasture soils, while they are absent from the natural forest soils, and their occurrence also in natural grassland soils but not in such high proportions, suggests that these fungi may be favoured by graminaceous plants, particularly where grass-clover pastures are established. Meyer (1954) has also found differences in the fungal populations under pasture and under tree saplings.

The third and fourth divisions of Table 1 concern soil fungi of some modified remnants of natural grasslands, the 'low tussock grasslands' of New Zealand (Cockayne, 1928), which are characterized by 'bunch' grasses, dominated by small (1–2 ft. high) plants of *Festuca* and *Poa* species.

From the third division of Table 1, it will be seen that the soil fungal populations of three tussock grassland soils, sites 7, 8, and 9, are dominated by non-sporing mycelia, and particularly by *Rhizoctonia* sp. This occurs irrespective of the widely differing soils, i.e. a yellow-brown pumice soil derived from rhyolitic volcanic ash (7); a yellow-brown earth from greywacke sandstone (8), and a brown-grey earth (of semi-arid areas) from mica schist (9), and irrespective of the distance between the sites, approximately 200 miles in each case. The very close relationship between the fungal population at site 7 and at site 8 is paralleled by close similarity of the vegetation at the two sites and by the similar climate influencing soil development. Details of these investigations are in the course of publication (Thornton, 1958). A study of the soil fungi under prairie grasslands in America by Orpurt and Curtis (1957) also showed a strong relationship between the fungal flora and the higher plant cover. The influence that the higher plant cover has on soil fungi is further indicated by the fact that the soil at site 8 had originally developed under beech forest (*Nothofagus cliffortioides*), which was burnt and replaced by tussock grassland about 100 years ago.

In the fourth division of Table 1, it can be seen that the change of plant cover from tussock to permanent grass-clover pasture (sites 10 and 11, 20 yds. apart) had, after 18 years, produced little change of fungal population. These sites were 3–4 miles from site 7, on the same soil type. This lack of marked change may have been due to the recent alteration of plant cover. On the other hand, it is possible that it is due more to the fact that a change from one type of permanent grassland, tussock, to another, pasture, may not greatly alter the type and supply of food material available to fungi, and thus little change in population would be expected. A change from forest cover to grass-clover cover, however, would probably involve a marked change in type and supply of organic materials, and this could possibly account for the changes in fungal populations recorded in these soil, *Fusarium* spp. being particularly favoured by a grass cover. The establishment of pasture on former tussock grassland resulted in a slight increase in incidence of *Fusarium* spp. and a decline in occurrence of *Papulaspora* sp. This result has been confirmed in another site in the other island, South Island, not reported here. Mycelia of *Papulaspora* sp. showed the same trend when forest cover had been replaced by pasture. Thus it would appear that whereas *Fusarium* spp. are favoured by the establishment of pasture, *Papulaspora* spp. are adversely affected.

It can be seen that, in general, higher plant cover and the associated soil conditions have a marked influence on the soil fungal pattern as determined by the screened immersion-plate technique.

Recently attempts have been made to characterize fungal associations in soils. Peyronel (1956) proposed to group the different communities on the basis of the frequency with which different groups of species, conveniently chosen, are represented. A compass diagram method of expressing the communities was also proposed. Sappa (1956) suggested that soil fungal communities may be characterized by species combinations. From the results of the investigations shown in Table 1, the soil fungal communities may be characterized on the basis of one or more dominant or characteristic species, as is shown in Table 2.

The fungi listed for each soil in Table 1 contributed 75% or more of the total isolations from each soil. As most of these are strongly growing species, this may indicate that the method is selective for these fungi. Because of this strong growing habit, however, mycelium of these fungi may well dominate these soils. The total number of isolations from each soil are given in the table, together with the number of apertures (10 per plate) exposed in each soil. By calculating the average number of isolations per 10 apertures, i.e. per plate, in each soil, a comparison of the distribution of mycelia in each soil is able to be made. It can be seen

TABLE 2

Dominant or characteristic fungi of some forest and grassland soils

Site	Vegetation	Fungi
1	Mixed oakwood forest	*Trichoderma viride*
2	*Pinus* spp., formerly mixed oakwood	*Mortierella vinacea*—non-sporing mycelia
3	*Calluna* heath, formerly mixed oakwood	*Trichoderma viride—Mucor ramannianus*
4	Tawa forest	*Cylindrocarpon radicicola*—non-sporing mycelia
5	Grass-clover permanent pasture, formerly forest	*Fusarium oxysporum*
6	Grass-clover permanent pasture, formerly forest	*Fusarium oxysporum—Trichoderma viride*
7	Tussock grassland	*Rhizoctonia* sp.—*Cylindrocarpon radicicola*
8	Tussock grassland	*Rhizoctonia* sp.
9	Tussock grassland	*Rhizoctonia* sp.
10	Tussock grassland	*Rhizoctonia* sp.—fungus S.B.235
11	Grass-clover permanent pasture, formerly tussock grassland	*Rhizoctonia* sp.—fungus S.B.235

that a change of the natural plant cover of an area results in an increase in the number of mycelia isolated, e.g. oakwood to *Pinus* spp. or *Calluna*, and tawa forest to pasture. Fertile, permanent, grass-clover pasture soils had the highest number of mycelia.

In general, the numbers of mycelia isolated decreased with depth. However, in the podzol soil under *Calluna* the numbers of mycelia were highest at a depth of 12–14 in., i.e. the B_1 horizon, due to the accumulation of organic matter in this layer.

In all the New Zealand soils examined, a significant proportion of isolations was contributed by non-sporing mycelia, particularly *Rhizoctonia* sp., fungus S.B.235, and *Papulaspora* spp. Warcup (1957) found that the greatest proportion of fungi isolated from a wheat-field soil by a hyphal isolation method were non-sporing forms, which included *Rhizoctonia* spp. The relative incidence of *Rhizoctonia* sp. and *Trichoderma viride* in the English and New Zealand soils is interesting in view of the antagonistic effects *T. viride* has on other *Rhizoctonia* species (Weindling, 1938).

There is a difference in fungal patterns between pasture soils on former tussock grasslands and those on former forest soils. The latter were dominated by *Fusarium* spp. and the former by *Rhizoctonia* sp. It has already been suggested here that this may be related to the history of past vegetation and the extent of the alteration of the type and supply of organic material available to fungi consequent upon the alteration of the higher plant cover. This difference may also be related to the different levels of fertility in these soils; the pasture soils formerly under forest have a higher fertility than pasture soils formerly under tussock.

In all soils the greatest numbers of isolations were obtained in summer, i.e. conditions of warmer and relatively drier soils. There was little qualitative change between spring, summer, and autumn seasons, indicating a degree of stability in composition of the fungal population.

Several fungi were well distributed among the various soils examined, e.g. *Trichoderma viride*, *Cylindrocarpon radicicola*, *Mucor hiemalis*, *Mortierella alpina*, and in New Zealand soils, *Rhizoctonia* sp. and fungus S.B.235. Species of *Penicillium* were more frequently isolated from the cooler soils. *Fusarium* spp. occurred only in grassland soils.

There is a similarity between the more frequently isolated fungi from tussock and pasture soils and those shown by Waid (1957) to be concerned in the succession of fungi decomposing rye-grass roots, and it is possible that the fungi isolated by screened immersion plates were concerned in the decomposition of root materials.

At least 10 screened plates, buried at 5–10-yd. intervals, are employed in sampling a particular soil at any one time because it has been found that mycelia are not homogeneously distributed throughout the soil fabric. Mycelia are found, few in some plates and abundant in others, and often these aggregations are of one or two species only. This variable distribution of mycelia is likely to be related to the distribution of substrates.

The factors determining the dominance of one species in one soil and its low frequency in another are not fully known. In an attempt to contribute to the elucidation of aspects of this problem, studies on the nutrition and physiology of strains of several species of fungi isolated from different soils have been initiated in these laboratories. The yeast, bacterial, and protozoan populations of some of these soils are also being studied in these laboratories and results may provide interesting information regarding microbial relationships in soils, and may indicate the principal factors influencing the occurrence and distribution of micro-organisms in soils. Details of these investigations will be given at later dates.

REFERENCES

CHESTERS, C. G. C., & THORNTON, R. H. (1956). A comparison of techniques for isolating soil fungi. *Trans. Brit. mycol. Soc.*, **39**, 301–13.

COCKAYNE, L. (1928). The Vegetation of New Zealand. *Die Vegetation der Erde* Engler and Drude, 14, Leipzig.

MEYER, J. (1954). Écologie des moisissures du sol et leur relations avec la végétation. *Trans. 5th Intern. Congr. Soil Sci., Leopoldville*, **3**, 71–5.

N.Z. SOIL BUREAU (1954). General survey of the soils of North Island, New Zealand. *N.Z. Soil Bur. Bull.*, **5**, 286 pp.

ORPUT, P. A., & CURTIS, J. P. (1957). Soil microfungi in relation to the prairie continuum in Wisconsin. *Ecology*, **38**, 628–37.

PEYRONEL, B. (1956). Caracterisation des mycocenoses de climats et de milieux divers, et nouvelle methode pur les represente graphiquement. *Rept. 6th Intern. Cong. Soil Sci., Paris*, C. 45–9.

SAPPA, F. (1956). La mycoflore du sol comme element structurel des communautes vegetales. *Rept. 6th Intern. Cong. Soil Sci., Paris*, C, 57–61.

THORNTON, R. H. (1952). The screened immersion plate. A method of isolating soil micro-organisms. *Research*, **5**, 190–1.

THORNTON, R. H. (1956). Fungi occurring in mixed oakwood and heath soil profiles. *Trans. Brit. mycol. Soc.*, **39**, 485–94.

THORNTON, R. H. (1958). Biological studies of some tussock grassland soils. II. Fungi. *N. Z. J. agric. Res.*, **1**, 922–38.

WAID, J. S. (1957). Distribution of fungi within decomposing tissues of rye-grass roots. *Trans. Brit. mycol. Soc.*, **40**, 391–406.

WARCUP, J. H. (1957). Studies on the occurrence and activity of fungi in a wheat-field soil. *Trans. Brit. mycol. Soc.*, **40**, 237–62.

WEINDLING, R. (1938). Association effects of fungi. *Bot. Rev.*, **4**, 475–96.

DIRECT OBSERVATIONS OF
VERTICILLIUM ALBO-ATRUM REINKE AND BERTH. IN SOIL

G. W. F. SEWELL

East Malling Research Station

Tomato plants were grown in non-sterile John Innes potting compost contained in rectangular glass boxes, so constructed that any face could be swung open as a door. These plants were inoculated by pressing into the soil, at the observation face, small fragments of hop bine infected with *Verticillium albo-atrum*, or by applications of conidial suspensions. The subsequent behaviour of *Verticillium* on inocula, roots, and soil particles was then observed by the use of a wide-field binocular microscope.

V. albo-atrum* sporulated on all inoculum fragments in the soil, but mycelial extension from inocula was observed rarely and then was limited and transient. Sporulation continued for 2–7 weeks, and was not affected by the proximity or presence of host-plant roots, although sparse sporulation did occur, infrequently, on root surfaces where these were in contact with inocula. Where such direct contact occurred, dark mycelium also occasionally developed on the root surface. Generally, however (and never after applications of conidia), there was no visible sign of infection, although it could be demonstrated to have occurred by stem-base isolations made 6–8 weeks after inoculation.

The first external evidence of wide-spread root colonization by *V. albo-atrum* occurred only after death of the host at the end of its normal growing season or when deliberately killed. Shortly after the onset of visible degeneration of the root tissues sporulation of *Verticillium* commenced. Conidiophores developed firstly on fine roots, but not always on those in contact with inoculum fragments; conidiophores were also early to appear on the vascular tissues of roots which had been decorticated by sciarid larvae. Sporulation on fine roots was followed rapidly by sporulation on main lateral roots and finally the tap-root,

---

[1] A detailed account of this investigation will be published in the transactions of the British Mycological Society.

and in the larger roots was often accompanied by blackening of the cortical tissues caused by the presence within them of dark resting mycelium.

The duration of sporulation varied with the size and rapidity of degeneration of the root tissues. Sporulation on large roots was observed to extend over periods of up to 10 weeks, but was always most vigorous immediately following the first signs of collapse of the cortical tissues. During the initial 'flush' of sporulation a sparse mycelium, on rare occasions, extended into the soil surrounding the large roots, but this seldom exceeded 2 mm. in extent and was always ephemeral.

These observations suggest that the spread of *V. albo-atrum* through the soil from host to host is accomplished by the dispersal of conidia in soil water, rather than by mycelial extension, and provide some direct evidence to confirm the pattern of behaviour suggested by Garrett (1944) in the following words: 'A root does not become infectious to other roots in contact with it as soon as it becomes infected, because the fungus does not leave the vascular cylinder until the disease reaches its penultimate phase in the plant. . . . No means of active spread through the soil except from plant to plant by root contact has been demonstrated for any fungus belonging to this group' (i.e. the vascular wilt fungi). While, however, no means of active spread through the soil has been demonstrated, a volume of soil far larger than that occupied by the host-plant roots may be rendered infective as long as sporulation continues. With decline of sporulation, the infective soil volume will also reduce—finally to the size of the plant residues, when root contact may then become a necessary prerequisite of infection.

REFERENCE

GARRETT, S. D. (1944). *Root disease fungi*. Waltham, Mass.: Chronica Botanica Co.

SOME CHARACTERISTICS OF THE
MICROFLORA IN DESERT SANDS

MME J. NICOT

Laboratoire de Cryptogamie du Museum, Paris

Most of the work published up to the present on the telluric fungi relates to natural or cultivated soils in temperate regions or, in tropical regions, exclusively to intensively cultivated soils. For these various types of habitat, with basic knowledge of the floristic order and systematics, it is possible to extend the investigations farther and in greater detail into the compartments of ecology, physiology, and biochemistry.

The position is different for the biologist, who is dealing with environments as yet little explored or less accessible. The techniques of collection and study must then be adapted to the particular nature of the material; different perspectives shape the analysis and interpretation of the results. A certain number of research programmes have already dealt with such habitats: coastal sands, salt flats, organic débris. But the field of desert sands has been the subject of very few investigations, the preliminary work of Ch. Killian (1939) in the Algeria-Morocco area reflect the lack of precision and inadequacy of the accepted fundamentals of systematics. In fact, it is necessary to define at the outset the principal characteristics of the fungal population in such localities, to know and, if possible, to identify the dominant species or groups of species, to distinguish the unvarying and widely scattered features from those of purely accidental or local value. It is these physiognomical characters that we have tried to establish from many samples collected since 1952 in the various parts of the French Sahara, especially on the fringe of the Grande Erg Occidental in the region of Beni-Abbès; evidence derived from samples obtained in the desert zone of Kizil Koum in Turkestan endorses these observations.

Though the flora of pure sands (Grande Erg dunes) is very sparse and represented mainly by species of *Penicillium*, a wide range of species are found together in the uppermost layer of the 'dayas' soil. In these shallow basins, packed with a boggy sand of fine-particle size, is the strictly localized phanerogamic vegetation of the hamada: perennial species, generally thorny and, depending on the rainfall, quickly developing and short-lived therophytes.

Analysis of the micromycetes present in these soils alone raises difficulties of classification. A good number of species belong in effect to known genera widely represented in the saprophytic flora of soils in all the regions, but many of them cannot be identified with any species for which descriptions are available, and even the genera of some of them cannot be determined. Finally it is frequently almost impossible to identify, simply from their features in culture, Sphaeropsidales or Ascomycetes usually considered in relation to a natural host or base.

However, an original physiognomical and biological grouping appears from the numerous surveys made in the desert sands of dayas. The most characteristic and frequently obtained pattern in the isolations is the net predominance of strongly pigmented species: Phragmo- and dictyo-spored Demateae (*Helminthosporium, Curvularia, Alternaria, Stemphy-lium*), Sphaeropsidales with carbonaceous linings, dark, sterile mycelium with chlamydospores or bulbils. One finds both Ascomycetes (Plecto-scales and Pyrenomycetes) and, more closely linked with the vegetation and climatic features, some Mucorineae, and a small number of species of *Fusarium*.

This type of cryptogamic vegetation is found localized in the mobile surface layer of the basin soil and rapidly disappears with depth. Between 5 and 10 cm. below surface-level there is a sharp attenuation of the flora; about 10 cm. down there is an almost exclusive pre-dominance of *Aspergillus fumigatus*, which seems to find, at this level, suitable conditions for its growth: finally *Penicillium* and *Aspergillus* are the sole genera represented to the same degree at all depths. This very marked stratification of floral habitats is always upset in periods of rain. *Aspergillus* and *Penicillium* spread far beyond their usual zone of vegetation when the surface spores, swept down by the rain, germinate at lower levels; one thus finds in the isolations from the top 10 or 20 cm. of soil a mixture of species according to depth and surface position.

In mainly dry periods Micromycetes thus localized in the surface layers of a mobile soil are easily shifted by the wind. Groupings similar to those of the dayas are found in all the 'microsoils' formed by the accumulation of sand and of dust in the shelter of the slightest obstacles: tufts of desert Anabasis, clefts in the rock shelf, rock hollows, and in trails of dust built-up on the slopes of dunes after a fall of rain. The governing role of wind dispersion accounts for the relatively uniform distribution of the surface microflora in widely varying habitats, some-times remote from the place of origin.

At these points unconducive to their development, the species of fungi are liable to retain their vitality for long periods, which is confirmed by laboratory tests: the essential characteristics of the microflora are perpetuated for several years in samples of small volume, even subjected intermittently to desiccation at temperatures in the region of 60° C. The microfungal population of superficial sands and soils subject to desert conditions manifest in effect, like the phanerogamic flora, remarkable adaptive characteristics expressed simultaneously by morphological make-up and structures which protect them against the unfavourable edaphic conditions and by an increased fruitfulness of the species.

Amongst the mechanisms of protection against desiccation and strong light, we have already noted the brown pigmentation characteristic of most of the organisms isolated; in general, all the vegetative and reproductive apparatus of the fungus—mycelium, spores, lining of the pycnidia and of the perithecia—is strongly coloured. For the rest the membranes are thick and much variegated; their structure is complicated by scattered protuberances and coloured thickenings, the cross walls being embellished with rings and ridges. Finally the spores of most of the Dematiaceæ are multicellular, several septated transversely (*Curvularia, Helminthosporium*) and sometimes also longitudinally (*Alternaria, Stemphylium, Sporidesmium*); the chlamydospores of the mycelia, whether sterile or not, are often aligned or concentrated in bulbils. Each of the elements of reproduction or conservation of the species is thus found compartmented, and the protective structures are correspondingly multiplied. From this point of view we can emphasize here the analogy in structure of the divisions of the spores with those of the mycelium, both seeming equally fitted to assure the survival and dispersion of the fungi.

Another steady characteristic of the Micromycetes isolated from the desert sands is their rapid development and vast reproductive capacity. This abundant sporulation is particularly noticeable in the cultures of Sphaeropsidales, where the pycnidiospores are differentiated very rapidly in the interior of early formed pycnidia and, with most Demateae which produce their spores in long chains on conidiophores of indefinite growth. It is not rare to find a piece of mycelium fruiting directly on the grain of sand to which it is joined, or better, with certain species, false chains of spores which result in an accelerated fructification, each spore germinating directly at the conidiophore stage without passing through the vegetating mycelium stage.

The Sphaeropsidales of the genus *Peyronellaea*, found in the desert soils of the Beni-Abbès region and there represented by several species, well illustrate this double mechanism of adaptation: the linings of the hyphae and pycnidia are heavily pigmented and, furthermore, long chains of septate chlamydospores of the *Alternaria* type emerge in the passage of the mycelium; finally, the fruitfulness of the fungus observed in culture is perpetuated in the field, since we have frequently tested it in practice by introducing into the soil-perforated tubes containing diverse types of nutritional media.

Thus the surface microflora of desert sands offer in the wide range of genera represented a remarkable physionomic unit. An intense zone of sporulation and centre of effective dispersion, it shows a community of adaptive characteristics which makes it a clearly defined 'biological group'. It would be interesting to compare this micro-fungal population with that of other specialized habitats such as periodically submerged littoral sands, where structures of the same anatomical type have been met.

THE EFFECT OF MINERAL FERTILIZERS ON SOME SOIL FUNGI

J. GUILLEMAT

École Nationale d'Agriculture de Grignon

AND

J. MONTÉGUT

École Nationale d'Horticulture, France

The purpose of this note is to outline the effect of mineral fertilizers on the soil microflora. The research was carried out in 1957 on the 'Deherain plots' at L'École Nationale d'Agriculture de Grignon, as part of the general programme of study on microflora in cultivated soils. Unbalanced plots PK, NK, and NP, the first lacking N, the second P, and the third K, were investigated and the results compared with those for plots 'without the addition of fertilizer since 1902' (SE) and those for plots which had received a balanced mineral fertilizer 'NPK'. Dressings of fertilizer, given in the spring, were as follows (per 100 sq. m.):

Nitrogen: 1·5 kg. of nitrate of soda, and 3 kg. of ammonium sulphate.
Phosphorus: 5 kg. of superphosphate (18% of P_2O_5).
Potassium: 1·5 kg. of silvinite or its equivalent of potassium chloride.

The samples were collected on May 22, 1957, from the five sample plots at the following levels: 0, 5, 10, 20, and 40 cm. As in the preceding investigations, the method of dilutions was used. Only one medium was employed, malt at 1% (w/v) (Maltea Moser) plus 2 gr. of streptomycin per litre. For each level 15 Petri dishes were inoculated and, according to depth, the dilutions used ranged from 1/1000 to 1/5000. Invariably, two dilutions were used for each depth to allow the determination of the 'threshold dilution'; that is, the threshold beyond which all the micro-organisms contained in the sample of soil can show free development without risk of competitive action.

General observations

A comprehensive analysis of frequency distribution 'species by species' will not be given: full details of the results of this trial will be published in the *Annales des Epiphyties*.

TABLE 1

Distribution of species according to systematic position

	Total colonies isolated for each plot (comprising 5 depths: 0, 5, 10, 20 and 40 cm.)												Total colonies isolated at each depth (comprises 4 plots)										
	SE		PK		NK		NP		NPK		Total	0		5		10		20		40	
	(a)	(b)	(a)	(b)	(a)	(b)	(a)	(b)	(a)	(b)		(a)	(b)	(a)	(b)	(a)	(b)	(a)	(b)	(a)	(b)
6 Phycomycetes	80	3	91	2	96	4	108	2	97	2	472	33	1	117	4	141	3	141	4	40	3
6 Ascomycetes	—		10	1	8	2	64	4	8	2	90	4	2	18	2	4	1	28	2	36	2
27 Mucedineae	235	19	482	21	467	17	606	16	660	17	2,450	260	17	731	18	853	15	507	16	99	13
19 Penicillium	281	11	474	7	357	11	576	9	627	8	2,315	78	7	506	10	535	14	535	13	635	6
3 Aspergillus	2	1	8	3	10	3	8	1	5	1	33	—		5	1	13	3	13	2	2	1
16 Dematiae	300	11	286	11	253	12	276	11	400	10	1,515	344	13	492	10	451	12	165	10	63	6
4 Stilbaceae	27	1	7	3	98	2	46	2	113	2	291	26	1	66	1	110	3	85	2	4	2
2 Tuberculariaceae	13	1	15	1	20	2	—		27	1	75	14	2	18	1	32	1	11	1	—	
10 Fusarium-Cylindrocarpon	78	5	96	6	50	5	73	8	87	6	384	46	7	133	7	103	7	94	8	8	2
3 Melanconieae	86	3	51	2	19	2	91	3	63	3	310	33	3	103	3	102	3	57	3	15	1
8 Sphaeropsideae	119	4	150	3	165	5	180	3	223	4	837	119	5	230	4	338	4	148	2	2	1
2 Sterile Mycelium	5	2	6	1	6	1	5	1	5	1	27	2	1	11	2	4	1	10	1	—	
106 species: Total	1,226	61	1,676	61	1,549	66	2,033	60	2,315	57	8,799	959	59	2,430	63	2,712	67	1,794	64	904	37

(a) Number of colonies corresponding to 50 mg. of soil.
(b) Number of species corresponding to 50 mg. of soil.

Table 1 shows the behaviour according to systematic position of the 106 species isolated

Plots NPK and NP are the richest in number of colonies, but not in the number of individual species. The frequency of the number of colonies progressively increases from specimen SE to twice its value in specimen NPK. The value for specimen NP closely approaches that of NPK. Those of specimens NK and PK are virtually the same and intermediate to those of SE and NPK.

Based on the value for SE, the increase of frequency of colonies is as follows:

$$NK = 27\%$$
$$PK = 36\%$$
$$NP = 66\%$$
$$NPK = 88\%$$

Distribution according to systematic position

In Table 2 are given the frequency distribution of colonies according to plot treatment and systematic group. *Aspergillus*, sterile mycelia, and Tuberculariaceae have a low frequency and show little response to the mineral fertilizer. We have distinguished four groups of fungi on their behaviour with mineral fertilizer:

(i) *Unresponsive groups:* Their frequency is almost unaffected. The number of colonies decreases in the enriched plots. The group comprises Melanconiales, *Fusarium*, Phycomycetes, and Dematiaceae, the last is the most significant.

(ii) *Favoured groups: Penicillium* and in general the Moniliaccae.

(iii) *Indifferent groups:* Sphaeropsidales.

(iv) *Special groups:* In these groups some species exhibit an anomalous behaviour which distorts the general picture of the group. For example, Stilbaceae reach their maximum in plot NK, but this is due to the presence of *Tilachlidium racemosum*.

Ascomycetes are absent in the non-fertilized plots. They are, generally speaking, infrequent in all the plots. Their optimum is in plot NP, but this is mainly due to *Penicillium asperum*. This leads us to emphasize once again that two types of Ascomycetes should be distinguished: Ascomycetes fimicoles, favoured by mineral fertilizer, and Ascomycetes, more typical of the soil, which are encountered farther down: perithecial *Penicillium*, *Gymnoascus* spp., *Pleospora herbarum*, etc.

In general terms, the Dematiaceae of the soil represent a group of cellular species almost unaffected by mineral fertilizer, while the Moni-

TABLE 2

Distribution of species according to systematic position
(expressed as total number of colonies in each plot)

	SE	PK	NK	NP	NPK
MO = *Moniliaceae*	235	482	467	606	660
PN = *Penicillium*	281	474	357	576	627
DM = *Dematiaceae*	300	286	253	276	400
SP = *Sphaeropsidales*	119	150	165	180	223
ST = *Stilbaceae*	27	7	98	46	113
PH — *Phycomycetes*	80	91	96	108	97
FU-CY = *Fusarium-Cylin*	78	96	50	73	87
ML = *Melanconiales*	86	51	19	91	63
TU = *Tuberculariaceae*	13	15	20	—	27
AS = *Ascomycetes*	—	10	8	64	8
AL = *Aspergillus*	2	8	10	8	5
MY = Sterile Mycelium	5	6	6	5	5
Number of colonies per 50 mg.	1,226	1,676	1,549	2,033	2,315

TABLE 3

Types of behaviour
(Mean frequency, in the plots, of species in same behaviour group)

	SE	PK	NK	NP	NPK
Type 'A'	62*	73	63	66	83
Type 'B'	50	31	14	8	14
Type 'C'	5	23	19	19	28
Type 'D'	14	40	41	81	52
Type 'E'	23	27	39	85	108
Type 'F'	8	39	7	15	13

* Number of colonies per 50 mg. of soil

TABLE 4

More-or-less inert species
Type A

	Stock number	SE	PK	NK	NP	NPK
Stachybotrys alternans	DM 1	35*	28	40	35	42
Mortierella alpina	PH 11	74	90	76	89	92
Phoma sp.	SP 9	77	101	72	83	116

* Number of colonies per 50 mg. of soil

liaceae have a contrary physiology, reacting favourably to mineral fertilizer, especially nitrogen.

Behaviour-grouping of species

We have distinguished 6 types of behaviour. The distribution is indicated in Table 3.

Type 'A' embraces the more or less inert (Table 4). This includes *Stachybotrys alternans*, *Mortierella alpina*, and *Phoma* sp. SP9.

In type 'B', species of diminishing frequency with the richness of the mineral fertilizer, we place *Rhinotricum* DM50, *Monotospora* DM32, *Fusarium sambucinum*, *Sporotricum* MO12, *Colletotrichum graminicolum* (Table 5). Optimum frequency is in plot SE, decreasing through plots PK, NK, NP, to NPK.

Type 'C' comprises species with frequencies increased by the fertilizer in general, such as *Trichoderma lignorum* sclerotial *Cephalosporium* MO16, *Cephalosporium* MO45, *Gliocladium rosem* (Table 6).

Type 'D' behaviour emphasizes the effect of mineral fertilizer, in particular that of the unbalanced fertilizer NP, which clearly promotes the growth of some species. Table 7 shows the behaviour of selected species such as *Verticillium* sp. MO7, *Gloesporium* ML3, *Penicillium asperum*, *Fusarium bulbigenum*, and *Mucor adventitius*.

Type 'E' behaviour characterises a progressive effect of the mineral fertilizer with optimum at NPK. This applies to *Gliomastix convoluta*, *Cephalosporium* sp. MO57, *Pyrenochoeta* sp. SP20, *Cephalosporiopsis imperfecta*, and Dematiaceae DM85 (Table 8). It should be noted that nitrogen has a more pronounced effect than phosphorus.

Finally, type 'F' registers its optimum in the PK plots, showing the preponderant effect of P. In this group we find *Gliobotrys* MO35, *Penicillium* PN21, *Cylindrocarpon* TU12, *Monotospora* DM31, *Penicillium restrictum*, and *Trichoderma album* (Table 9).

Evolution of Penicillium species

The wide range of *Penicillium* species merit separate examination (Table 10). The number of species isolated decreases in proportion to the mineral range of the fertilizer, but the number of colonies observed follows an inverse curve. By contrast, the number of *Penicillium* colonies, as a proportion of the total number of colonies observed, remains without appreciable variation in the region of 25%. Two species are worth further consideration: *P. lilacinum* and *P. canescens*. *Penicillium lilacinum* (Table 11), reacted favourably to the nitrogenous fertilizer especially to NK and NPK. We have noticed in earlier work that

TABLE 5

Species of diminishing frequency relative to increase in the proportion of nitrogen

Type B

	Stock number	SE	PK	NK	NP	NPK
Rhinotrichum sp.	DM 50	100*	72	33	15	35
Monotospora sp.	DM 32	91	58	26	13	28
Fusarium sambucinum	FU 18	15	24	4	4	—
Colletotrichum graminicolum	ML 4	32	—	—	5	4
Sporotrichum sp.	MO 12	13	3	7	4	5

* Number of colonies per 50 mg. of soil

TABLE 6

Species uniformly improved by mineral fertilizer

Type C

	Stock number	SE	PK	NK	NP	NPK
Trichoderma lignorum	MO 20	4*	13	21	11	13
Cephalosporium a sclerotes sp.	MO 16	4	22	18	23	30
Cephalosporium rose sp.	MO 45	7	22	18	10	35
Gliocladium roseum	MO 3	5	37	20	30	34

* Number of colonies per 50 mg. of soil

TABLE 7

Species with selective response to the nature and amount of fertilizer: optimum in plot NP

Type D

	Stock number	SE	PK	NK	NP	NPK
Verticillium sp.	MO 7	53*	176	176	265	216
Gloeosporium sp.	ML 3	19	14	10	49	18
Penicillium asperum	PN 16	—	—	4	51	4
Fusarium bulbigenum	FU 10	—	9	12	21	15
Mucor adventitius	MO 3	—	—	4	19	5

* Number of colonies per 50 mg. of soil

TABLE 8

Species of increasing frequency depending on mineral composition of fertilizer: preference in the order N > P > K

Type E

	Stock number	SE	PK	NK	NP	NPK
Gliomastix convoluta	DM 20	7*	17	11	21	59
Cephalosporium sp.	MO 57	—	6	33	78	94
Pyrenochaeta sp.	SP 20	36	43	73	94	97
Cephalosporiopsis imperfecta	MO 18	72	62	75	105	117
Dematiee sp.	DM 85	2	7	5	125	171

* Number of colonies per 50 mg. of soil

TABLE 9

Species with optimal frequencies in plot PK

Type F

	Stock number	SE	PK	NK	NP	NPK
Gliobotrys sp.	MO 35	1*	10	—	—	—
Penicillium sp.	PN 21[bis]	15	41	12	25	25
Cylindrocarpon sp.	TU 12	2	32	4	5	4
Monotospora sp.	DM 31	28	43	21	34	21
Penicillium restrictum	PN 6	5	35	—	20	15
Trichoderma album	MO 23	—	71	2	7	5

* Number of colonies per 50 mg. of soil

TABLE 10

Behaviour of Penicillium species in general

Sequence of influence:	SE	NK	PK	NP	EPK
Number of species	11	11	7	9	8
Number of colonies	281	357	474	576	627
Number of colonies as a percentage of total colonies present	23	23	28	28.5	27
Increase, as percentage of SE value	—	26	67	103	121

TABLE 11

Sequence of influence, in ascending order:	Penicillium lilacinum						Penicillium canescens				
	SE	PK	NK	NP	NPK		SE	NK	NPK	PK	NP
Number of colonies	156	173	218	236	378		44	85	187	200	276
Number of colonies as percentage of total for the genus	55	36	61	42	60		15	24	31	43	47
Percentage increase of *P. lilacinum* or *P. canescens* based on value for SE	—	10	40	51	142		—	94	32	358	533
Percentage increase of all microflora based on SE value	—	36	26	65	88		—	26	88	36	65

P. lilacinum was depressed by the presence of farmyard manure (rich in P.), *P. lilacinum* is thus a species encouraged by nitrogen and impeded by phosphorus.

Penicillium canescens (Table 11) is promoted by mineral fertilizers, showing an optimum in PK and NP. In another connexion we saw that this species was ameliorated by manure. *P. canescens* is very sensitive to fertilizer in general and to phosphorus in particular. The other species of Penicillium show a mixed behaviour towards mineral fertilizers.

Summary

Soil fungi are clearly affected by mineral fertilizer. First, an appreciable growth in the total number of colonies is apparent compared with that of plots without fertilizer. This increase varies from 26% (plot NK) to 80% (plot NPK). The response curve, SE, NK, PK, NP, NPK shows a similarity of behaviour between the soil microflora as a whole and the yields of cultivated plants.

Moniliaceae are the most sensitive to mineral fertilizer. *Penicillium* come next: *P. canescens* react preferentially to nitrogen and phosphorus; *P. lilacinum* is less responsive to mineral variations.

Dematiaceae reflect the contribution of organic rather than inorganic fertilizer. Sphaeropsidales are inert to all fertilizers.

DISCUSSION

Dr. E. Grossbard. Which technique did Mr. Waid use to count the number of bacteria present on the hyphae on the nylon mesh?

Mr. J. S. Waid. Bacteria observed as clumps of cells on the surfaces of the fungal hyphae were recorded as the 'percentage of meshes with bacteria observed on hyphae'.

Mr. D. M. Hall. Did Mr. Waid find any pre-treatment of the nylon mesh necessary, i.e. to remove any additives which may have been added to facilitate the weaving, and which might have influenced favourably or adversely the growth of fungi?

Mr. J. S. Waid. Nylon was washed in tap water and rinsed in distilled water. We made tests which failed to confirm the presence of any additive which affects the counts of fungi on the nylon mesh.

Mr. R. Barton. Did you see any conidial heads in the nylon mesh?

Mr. J. S. Waid. Yes. The fruiting structures of species of *Mortierella*, *Hyalopus/ Cephalosporium*, and *Stysanus* were seen several times on 12 mesh per cm. gauze, but none were seen when meshes with 30 mesh per cm. were employed. It is possible that the smaller pore size had set a physical limitation to the development of sporing structures.

Dr. W. B. Kendrick. Were mite excreta ever observed on the mesh?

Mr. J. S. Waid. Mites and objects looking like their excretal pellets were often seen on gauzes that had been exposed for some time in soil. It was not possible to confirm that other types of humus particle besides mite excreta were present.

Dr. H. Katznelson. I was interested to learn that similar results were obtained by

Mr. Waid with his technique (with nylon mesh) as we obtained many years ago by dilution procedures for fungi, bacteria, and other groups of organisms. We found, too, that fungi first appeared in large numbers in soil treated with organic matter within a few days from treatment; these numbers then decreased, and this was accompanied by a marked increase in bacterial counts, which decreased after a few more days, followed by actinomycetes and these by cellulose-decomposing bacteria. A similar sequence of organisms colonizing glass surfaces was obtained by the use of the Rossi-Cholodny technique.

Mr. J. S. Waid. These observations agree with those of other investigators, such as those of Winston (1956) and of Tribe (1957).

Dr. E. Grossbard. Has Mr. Waid compared his nylon-mesh technique with other standard techniques, such as the dilution technique or others using the same sample of soil?

Mr. J. S. Waid. Fungi beneath grass turf and in a fallow allotment soil were estimated by the dilution plate and the nylon-mesh techniques. The ratio of the counts obtained in the grass turf compared to the allotment soil were 1·8 and 7·8 respectively for the two methods of sampling. The nylon-mesh technique appeared to demonstrate the type of hyphal activity that would be expected in the two contrasting types of soil conditions, whereas the dilution-plate technique failed to demonstrate very marked differences in the content of viable fungal propagules in the two soils.

Dr. D. Park. Isolation techniques are not so important for the study of ecology. One can study synecology without identification by, for example, the nylon-mesh technique, and autecology by *specific* isolation techniques. Thus differences of opinion on the utility of techniques is not an insuperable difficulty.

Dr. W. B. Kendrick. Has Mr. Waid compared the growth of mycelia in mull and mor humus, or were all soils he investigated of the mull type?

Mr. J. S. Waid. Fungal activity was studied in a variety of soils in Roudsea Wood Nature Reserve, Lancashire, where nylon gauzes were buried for varying periods up to a total of 410 days. Initially fungal development in the litter and in soil beneath the litter was slower in mull soils than in mor, but after 410 days' exposure little difference could be recorded in the quantity of mycelium accumulated on nylon gauze buried in the two types of soil humus. The majority of hyphae occurring on the meshes after 410 days' exposure were pigmented, and clamp-bearing hyphae were very abundant on several mor sites.

Dr. W. B. Kendrick. Did you find any tendency for mycelium to accumulate in mor rather than mull?

Mr. J. S. Waid. Hyphae appeared to accumulate steadily on the nylon gauze throughout the exposure period on all the sites that were sampled. The least accumulation of hyphae on nylon gauze occurred in a salt marsh 'soil' and in peat bearing either birch or Calluna. The mull and mor soils were very similar in the amounts of mycelium that accumulated on nylon gauze.

Dr. M. Witkamp. In answer to the question of Dr. Kendrick concerning the amount of mycelium present in more and mull. In general there is ten times as much mycelium in terms of mycelium length in mor than in mull. During summer, fluctuations in mycelium content appear to be due to fluctuations in moisture content.

Mr. R. Barton. What happened to hyphae after decay? Had chlamydospores been formed?

Mr. J. S. Waid. Hyphae collapsed at the time when they were first colonized by bacteria, and chlamydospores developed shortly after the first appearance of bacteria on the hyphal surfaces. It is not known whether the bacterial populations parasitized living hyphae or decomposed them when they were moribund. At a late stage of decomposition the mycelium could be detected as chains of chlamydospores suspended by strands of collapsed hyphae.

Dr. J. Bywater. Has Mr. Waid noticed any spots of condensed water on the nylon mesh?

Mr. J. S. Waid. Water can be held by capillarity in the individual pores and in the angles formed in the nylon meshwork, but I have not observed water droplets or a water film on the surfaces of the nylon threads.

Miss J. Bywater. Is this water in contact with soil water?

Mr. J. S. Waid. Presumably so because the meshwork is in very close contact with the soil. The grids are inserted into oblique rather than vertical slits cut in the soil, so that the soil can be pressed back into position easily and soil 'gaping' is prevented in dry weather. When meshes are removed from a soil face the impression of the meshwork can be seen very painly.

Prof. A. Burges. Soil sectioning has given information on hyphal growth. I am unhappy about the use of nylon mesh because it may cause disturbance of fungistasis patterns or aeration of soil. I would like to ask Dr. Juliet Brown to describe her survey of the fungal flora of sand dunes.

Dr. J. Brown. I have found relatively large amounts of mycelium in young sand dunes, where spores might be expected to predominate, using the impression-slide technique. The samples were taken immediately the soil is disturbed so that there is no possibility of spore germination or a release of fungistasis affecting the results.

Dr. D. Park. The increase in the numbers of hyphae on the nylon mesh over the first 6–7 days of exposure in soil, then a decrease in the numbers counted suggests that there is a sampling zone round the mesh. These events parallel those observed during the colonization of other types of organic substratum.

Mr. J. S. Waid. It is possible that whilst hyphae of soil fungi develop outwards from decomposing organic substrates, they encounter the meshwork of the nylon gauzes which offer fresh surfaces for 'colonization'. The development of bacteria on the hyphae that colonize the meshes must prevent the accumulation of hyphae which are susceptible to bacterial decay. Perhaps that is why pigmented hyphae (which appear to be resistant to bacterial decay) are so abundant on gauzes buried for several months, whilst the hyphae of Phycomycetes and septate hyaline hyphae disappear once bacteria colonize the meshwork.

Dr. J. Webster. The explanation of the order of mesh colonization could lie in the relative growth rates of the organisms concerned (Phycomycetes colonize first, etc.).

Dr. G. J. F. Pugh. Is there a possibility of a 'wick' action by the nylon mesh which results in the upward movement of water in the soil horizon.

Mr. J. S. Waid. Yes, but it is probably no more pronounced than the 'wick' action caused by root residues, leaf fragments, and other surfaces in the soil.

Prof. J. Ziemiecka. My study of the development of different groups of soil fungi by an application of the Rossi-Cholodny method showed that the development of soil fungi on buried slides may last a few hours and not weeks. Is not 20 days' exposure too much?

Mr. J. S. Waid. I believe Prof. Ziemiecka buried glass slides coated with a nutrient agar containing glucose. We found that when gauzes were buried in a soil moistened with a solution of 1 % (w/v) glucose and 0·1 % (w/v) sodium nitrate in distilled water that the rate of fungal development on the nylon meshes after a 24 hr. incubation period at 25° was eight times as great as that of a soil moistened with an equivalent quantity of distilled water. The response of soil fungi to these soil treatments could not be detected 48 hr. after the time they were applied. By following the course of colonization of the nylon mesh over prolonged periods, it might be possible to obtain information about the rate of development and disappearance of mycelium in soils as well as some of the ecological factors involved.

Dr. H. Katznelson. The addition of organic residues with a relatively high amount of water-soluble constituents such as amino acids and carbohydrates results, as

Mr. Waid found on addition of glucose, in a rapid increase within a matter of 24 hrs. of Phycomyceteous types, followed by other forms. However, the addition of more difficultly decomposed material (such as straw) yields a different picture.

Dr. G. J. F. Pugh. Is there a great deal of evidence for seasonal variations in the numbers of isolation? My findings indicate that temperature and water content of the substrate play a part in this complex problem.

Dr. C. G. Dobbs. Dr. Bywater has demonstrated seasonal variation in fungistasis.

Dr. W. B. Kendrick. There are contradictory reports of seasonal fluctuation of fungi in pine-leaf litter.

Dr. G. W. F. Sewell. Trichoderma viride was isolated with 100% frequency in summer and with zero frequency in winter from a podzol.

Dr. J. Brown. I found the same seasonal variation in the growth of *Trichoderma viride* as Dr. Sewell. In January during frosty weather the isolation of this species was practically nil. Isolations of Fusaria increased, possibly because competition from *Trichoderma* was reduced.

Dr. R. Caldwell. Has Mr. Waid carried out comparable experiments using glass-fibre tape in place of his nylon material? It is possible that his observation of a time of maximum mycelial growth on the nylon mesh followed by gradual disappearance is due to nutritive materials coated on the nylon threads.

Mr. J. S. Waid. We did not use glass-fibre tape at all in our investigations. It is possible that the accessibility of the nylon pores does not restrict colonization by hyphae of the biologically inert material forming the gauze and later the destruction of the hyphae by other organisms.

Dr. G. Wallis. Have you been able to trace the source of mycelial development? If so, does the size of this food base correlate with the length of time mycelium remains active and free from bacteria?

Mr. J. S. Waid. I can give no information about this topic at all apart from the fact that the presence of either living roots or glucose in the soil leads to the development of larger hyphal populations on the nylon gauzes than are found in fallow untreated soils incubated and sampled under similar conditions to the treated soil. This seems to indicate that the availability of organic food substances in the soil affects the size of the hyphal population which colonizes the nylon gauze.

Dr. B. Mosse. In relation to the paper of Drs. Winter, Peuss, & Schönbeck, I would like to comment on two aspects of endotrophic mycorrhizal infections. The first concerns their effect on plant growth. Dr. Peuss has shown that growth of tobacco may be stimulated by such infections, and I have published some work indicating that, under certain conditions, the growth of apple seedlings may be improved. I would like, however, to make a plea for the study of mycorrhizal infections, not because they make plants grow better or worse—because either is possible—and in my experience mycorrhizal plants may actually grow worse once they become pot-bound and are kept under what amount to starvation conditions. Endotrophic mycorrhizal infections are not a completely isolated phenomenon. To a very considerable extent they will exert effects on root metabolism similar to that of any other invading soil fungus. Endotrophic infections ought to be studied simply because they are so extremely widespread in a large proportion of naturally occurring and cultivated plants, and anyone who has looked closely at such infections cannot fail to realize that root metabolism must be altered by them. All one can hope to do at present, and this is now possible, is to find out something about their effects on root respiration, nutrient uptake, and other clearly defined root functions under any given conditions, with the intention of building up some picture of the conditions that ultimately influence the balance between parasitism and symbiosis. It is highly probably that this will be influenced by the other organisms present in the rhizosphere, and in this connexion Dr. Peuss' illustrations of the apparent associations between different soil fungi are most fascinating. With the possibility of obtaining a reasonable amount of growth from an *Endogone* sp. that causes vesicular-arbuscular mycorrhiza, some information could be obtained about the interaction of this fungus with other soil organisms.

The other point I would like to make is to draw attention to the extraordinary amount of active hyphae of the endophyte which frequently occurs in the rhizosphere of mycorrhizal roots. Earlier discussions have been largely concerned with the presence of active hyphae in soils, but it is worth remembering that the extramatrical mycelium of the endophyte, which possibly furnishes the largest amount of active hyphae of any fungus in the soil, or at least in the rhizosphere, is almost entirely ignored in these surveys.

Dr. T. Nicholson. What is the amount of the external phase of endophytes in various soils? In my own observations on endotrophic mycorrhiza in grasses, the only samples showing extensive external mycelium were from sand dunes. In samples from other soils and habitats which I examined, the external phase was rarely highly developed. Do the vesicular-arbuscular endophytes have a truly saprophytic existence in soil (developing without being subject to root influences)?

Dr. B. Mosse. I do not know whether this falls within the meaning of the question on the saprophytic existence of endophytes in soil, but there is no doubt that the *Endogone* sp. with which I am working has very marked ability to break down organic matter in soils when it has a mycorrhizal base within a living root. In connexion with an earlier discussion on the seasonal variation in soil fungi, a curious instance of this also occurs in the fungi causing vesicular-arbuscular infections. Magrow first recorded the markedly greater success of his attempts to culture the endophyte from root material collected in the spring. Gerdemann noticed that the large resting spores, with which he was able to induce vesicular-arbuscular infections in maize, germinate readily in the spring, hardly at all in the summer, and slightly during the autumn months. Germination of resting spores of the *Endogone* with which I am working occurs readily when spores are placed on damp filter-paper between about March and May. At other times spore germination can be induced by placing chilled spores on 'Cellophane' discs overlying non-sterile soil-agar plates.

Dr. R. H. Estey. When *Rhizoctonia* is isolated from the surfaces of roots or from soil, it is generally in very close association with what appears to be a particular type of bacterium. This bacteria-*Rhizoctonia* association is such a common occurrence as to suggest some sort of relationship akin to symbiosis, although it is more probable that the bacteria are making some use of exudates from the fungus hyphae just as rhizosphere fungi utilize exudates from the roots of higher plants.

Dr. D. J. F. Pugh. Dr. Sewell mentioned the possibility of mites and springtails eating spores of *Verticillium* when this was sporing on the root surface. Is there any evidence that mites pass viable spores in faeces?

Dr. D. W. F. Sewell. I have not investigated this point.

Dr. D. J. F. Pugh. Is there any minimum size of spore inoculum necessary to secure successful infection with *Verticillium*?

Dr. D. W. F. Sewell. The rate of wilting is related to the spore load, but one spore can certainly penetrate and probably cause infection.

Prof. A. Burges. Was Dr. Nicot able to contrast the fungal flora of desert soils during dry and wet periods?

Dr. J. Nicot. Les echantillons preleves apres des pluies d'une intensite exceptionnelle tombees en decembre 1955 mettent en evidence un bouleversement des niveaux floristiques particulierement sensible au voisinage de la surface. *Aspergillus fumigatus* domine dans les prelevements superficiels, alors qu'a 10 cm. de profondeur la flore s'est fortement enrichie en formes dematiees, entrainees par la pluie, qu'on retrouve aussi sporadiquement melees aux especes caracteristiques dans les couches plus profondes.

Dr. J. Brown. I have found in the fore dunes of sand dunes the community consists almost entirely of species such as members of the Sphaeropsidales as described by Dr. Nicot in desert soils. Phycomycetes and common soil forms such as *Trichoderma* do not come in until the conditions become less 'desert-like' in the fixed dune soils.

ANTAGONISMS IN SOIL

ANTAGONISTIC AND COMPETITIVE MECHANISMS LIMITING SURVIVAL AND ACTIVITY OF FUNGI IN SOIL

P. W. BRIAN

Akers Research Laboratories, Imperial Chemical Industries Ltd., Welwyn

INTRODUCTION

There is abundant evidence, which I shall only touch upon here, that antagonistic relations develop between different kinds of micro-organism in soil. Commensal and symbiotic relationships are as common as antagonisms and equally important biologically, but it is the antagonisms, and particularly the mechanisms by which they are expressed, that I shall discuss herein. I shall further restrict my subject by confining my attention to antagonistic influences limiting the activity of soil fungi.

The micro-organisms with which we are mainly concerned are those characterized by Winogradsky as 'zymogenous'; that is, they are organisms dependent for activity on localized soil substrates that are more or less rapidly exhausted. The quantity of such organisms may thus increase rapidly while the substrate is being exploited, only to decline again as it becomes exhausted. Familiar examples are saprophytes actively decomposing organic particles of plant or animal origin, or utilizing organic compounds escaping from plant roots in the rhizosphere; root parasites and mycorrhizal organisms are more specialized examples. Between these phases of activity metabolism is reduced to a low level, and many organisms fail to survive; fungi characteristically survive, if at all, in the form of spores, sclerotia, or other resting stages. Antagonism and competition have their place in the phase of active colonization of substrates and in the subsequent phase of quiescence.

Our knowledge of microbiological antagonisms in soil stemmed in the first place from studies of root disease, and in particular from those of Garrett (1956). Root parasites can be regarded as organisms which have, as it were, escaped from the rigours of saprophytic existence in soil by adaptation to a new substrate—the living tissues of plant roots—

inaccessible to most soil organisms. Because of their unique capacity to colonize this substrate they can frequently exist, during the life of the host plant, as more or less pure cultures, in which problems of inter-specific competition and antagonism do not arise. On the death of the host plant they find their way back into the soil, as mycelium in frag-ments of host tissue, or as spores, sclerotia, or other resting stages. They may be adapted to remain in resting stages until a suitable host plant is again available, as, for instance, in the case of *Sclerotium cepivorum*, whose sclerotia fail to germinate except in response to substances diffus-ing from roots of species of *Allium* (Coley-Smith & Hickman, 1957). Such a property is of great adaptive significance, all the more so since mycelia of *S. cepivorum* cannot compete saprophytically in soil with the normal soil microflora, and rapidly die (Scott, 1956). But some root parasites have not developed any such specialized resting stage, and are forced to adopt a saprophytic existence for a time; in such circumstances they are usually at a disadvantage in competition with soil saprophytes, having limited competitive saprophytic ability. Why cannot such root parasites compete successfully with saprophytes? Antagonisms also exist between groups of saprophytes. Park (1955, 1956a, b, 1957a, b) has recently shown that fungi 'native' to a soil survive better than 'alien' saprophytes, i.e. that in a particular soil the natives have a greater competitive saprophytic ability. What is the physiological or biochemical basis of this ability? The following suggestions can be made.

A soil saprophyte, X, will compete successfully with another organism, Y, if:

(1) It can withstand the starvation conditions of soil when no coloniz-able organic substrates are available better than Y can.

(2) If it can withstand, more successfully than Y, toxic conditions arising from the activities of other micro-organisms, from substances leached from higher plants or from inorganic soil constituents.

(3) If, when an organic substrate is present, it can convert the sub-strate more rapidly into living matter than Y can, as a result of a generally more rapid metabolic turnover.

(4) Where X has a greater rate of hyphal extension than Y.

(5) Where metabolic products of X, accumulating outside the pro-ducing cells, inhibit growth or some metabolic processes of Y.

These seem to me to be the main possible bases for antagonism and competition; they are considered further below, first in relation to the phase of active saprophytic colonization of substrates, secondly to the intervening period of inhibition.

ANTAGONISM DURING COLONIZATION OF SUBSTRATES

When organic matter is introduced into soil, naturally or experimentally, the dormant or semi-dormant fungi, largely present in the form of spores, become metabolically active. Spores germinate in the vicinity of energy-providing materials. The organic supplements have selective effects, some organisms increasing in quantity enormously, if only temporarily, whereas others rapidly decline. This differential effect appears to result from two processes: (a) a very early selective lysis and (b) a more prolonged competition of a more complex nature, but it is possible that this distinction is only a reflection of different methods of observation.

Lysis

Lysis of young mycelia has been observed by direct observation methods (Chinn, 1953; Chinn, Ledingham, Solanns & Simmonds, 1953; Novogrudsky, 1948; Park, 1955; Stevenson, 1956a; Tribe, 1957). How is this lysis brought about? Lysis of fungal hyphae has been less systematically studied than bacterial lysis, but it is probable that they are basically similar. We may expect lysis to occur as a result of purely internal metabolic changes (autolysis), as a result of exposure to enzymes produced by neighbouring micro-organisms, as a result of exposure to toxic materials secreted by micro-organisms, or as a result of a combination of more than one of these processes.

Autolysis of fungi is usually a consequence of nutrient deficiency. In pure culture, autolysis occurs when all available energy-yielding substrates have been exhausted. Exhaustion of other nutrients (nitrogen, minerals, micronutrients) may reduce or stop net protein synthesis but, as long as an energy-yielding source (i.e. carbon source) is available, none of the characteristic features of autolysis—disappearance of cell contents, erosion of cell walls, release of ammonia and minerals into the medium—will develop. Once the carbon sources in the medium and the available carbohydrate and fat reserves in the mycelium have been used, protein breakdown and autolysis occur whether other essential nutrients are available or not. Autolysis is therefore essentially a result of energy-source starvation. Thus the lysis occurring immediately after addition of organic amendments to soil is unlikely to be autolysis of this kind.

Autolysis may also occur if utilization of energy sources is prevented by oxygen-lack, or as a result of accumulation of metabolic products

toxic to the organism producing them. Oxygen-lack may be an effective
cause of lysis, particularly in the lower levels of soil. Accumulation of
autotoxic products is probably not a general phenomenon, since organisms tend to be tolerant of their own metabolic products however toxic
they may be to others. This is most true of the more complex toxic
metabolic products, such as the antibiotics, less true of simpler substances such as carbon dioxide.

Many toxic materials will induce lysis. Respiratory inhibitors, such
as azide, cyanide, or some of the antibiotics, will do so by blocking
energy-yielding metabolism. Other toxic substances will do so by dis-
ruption of the organization of the cell or cell membranes, and similar
effects can be induced by some bacterial enzymes.

I think it likely that much of this early lysis of fungal sporelings is due
to bacterial action. Park (1956b) found that the lytic properties of a soil
were unimpaired by treatment with propylene oxide, and from the much-
simplified microflora he was able to isolate an organism—*Bacillus
macerans*—which would actively lyse fungi *in vitro*, apparently by production of extracellular lytic materials. Stevenson (1956a) found that
Streptomyces antibioticus lysed *Helminthosporium sativum* in mixed
culture in soil, the lysis being apparently due to combined action of an
antibiotic (actinomycin) and some other factor. Tribe (1957) found that
fungi invading buried cellulose films died out, being succeeded by
bacteria. Novogrudsky (1948) found that certain bacteria characteristically settle on fungal hyphae, forming a bacterial sheath; lysis usually
followed, either as a result of deprivation of the fungus of oxygen or
nutrients, or as a result of secretion of lytic principles. He considered
this process one of the most important factors regulating the activity
of soil fungi. He also considered that fungi which produce anti-bacterial
antibiotics are less susceptible to this kind of bacterial action.

It seems clear, however, that lysis in soil is not entirely due to bacterial
action. Park (1957b) introduced spores of native and alien saprophytes
into autoclaved soil. The aliens, with one significant exception, disappeared fairly rapidly, but the natives maintained themselves. Lysis of
the aliens was observed. In this case, where observations extended over
several weeks and the soil was unsupplemented, though autoclaving
must have increased available nutrients to some extent, lysis as a result
of energy-source exhaustion may well have occurred. This raises the
question, why should the aliens suffer from energy-source exhaustion
more than the natives? This is dealt with in the next section. Lysis as a
result of antibiotic production cannot be ruled out; one of the native
fungi studied by Park (1957b) was *Trichoderma viride*, which can *in*

vitro produce toxic metabolites, gliotoxin, and viridin, which cause lytic changes in other fungal mycelia (Weindling, 1934, 1941). The possibility of such substances being produced in soil is discussed in the next section.

Thus this early lysis of fungi developing in response to addition of nutrients to soil can probably be attributed to a great extent to competition and antagonism by soil bacteria, but other micro-organisms, including fungi, may also be involved. The antagonism probably results partly from deprivation of the fungi of oxygen and nutrients by heavy superficial growth of bacteria, and partly from production of toxic metabolic products and lytic enzymes. No explanation has yet been offered of the greater capacity of certain ecological groups of fungi to survive such conditions. The key to differential survival probably lies more in differing capacities to colonize organic particles. Nevertheless, the possibility, envisaged by Novogrudsky (1948), that the capacity to produce antibiotics may protect some fungi from bacterial lysis, should not be overlooked, nor the possibility that fungi differ, even in the stage of freshly germinated spores, in their resistance to toxin- or enzyme-induced lysis. The relative importance of these factors cannot at present be estimated.

Competitive saprophytic ability

The situation I wish to discuss here is well established and at first sight not unduly complex. We start with a soil containing colonizable substrates. Some fungi can colonize such substrates quickly and effectively in the presence of other organisms, some cannot. By and large, soil saprophytes can colonize dead substrates more effectively than root parasites. The root parasites differ among themselves, some colonizing dead material almost as easily as soil saprophytes, whereas others have scarcely any competitive saprophytic ability; comparisons of these two types have been made by Butler (1953a, b, c). Saprophytes also differ in their competitive ability, those native to soil being more successful than those alien to the soil habitat (Park, 1955, 1956a, b, 1957a, b). Survival in such substrates once colonized is similarly differential. What mechanisms are involved?

(1) *Competition for nutrients* is obviously involved because the situation ends with one organism or group of organisms 'in possession' of the available substrates. The rate of utilization of carbon sources would probably be the limiting factor since uptake of all other nutrients is an energy-requiring process, and an organism that could use a given carbon source unavailable to another would consequently have the

opportunity not only to utilize and exhaust that particular nutrient but also supplies of nitrogen and minerals in the vicinity. But there is little evidence that great efficiency in conversion of substrates into living mycelium is a major cause of competitive success. Park (1955) showed that a number of alien saprophytes were able to colonize plant fragments in pure culture more or less as effectively as a number of native soil saprophytes, but under normal conditions of mixed culture the natives were far more effective at colonization. Some root parasites are more exacting in their nutrient requirements than most soil saprophytes; for instance, *Ophiobolus graminis* requires thiamin for growth, and in some circumstances this might account for its failure to compete with some less-exacting saprophytes. But Butler (1953c) has shown that another root parasite, *Helminthosporium sativum*, is as unsuccessful a saprophyte as *O. graminis*, yet its nutrient requirements are as simple as those of any saprophyte.

(2) *Capacity for rapid hyphal extension.* This is possibly a character of value in such fungi as *Trichoderma viride* and many of the Mucorales, but many successful saprophytes grow no faster than some unsuccessful ones.

(3) *Parasitism.* It is perhaps significant that quite a number of soil saprophytes appear to be capable of parasitizing other fungi. *T. viride* (Aytoun, 1953; Boosalis, 1956; Campbell, 1956; Weindling, 1932), *Papulospora* sp. (Warren, 1948), and *Penicillium vermiculatum* (Boosalis, 1956) have been recorded as parasitic upon *Rhizoctonia solani*, and in the studies of Boosalis (1956), which were carried out in natural soils, it was clear that there was a great reduction in the viability of host hyphae. It might seem likely that under natural conditions parasitic activity of this kind might severely influence the survival of *Rhizoctonia*, but in Boosalis' experiments, while parasitism was obvious at 28°, none was observed at the more normal soil temperature of 18°. Moreover, *R. solani* itself is apparently parasitic on quite a considerable range of Phycomycetes (Butler, 1957). In any case, parasitism of this kind verges upon chemical antagonism, especially with the important antagonist *T. viride*; hyphae of this fungus twine themselves round hyphae of *Rhizoctonia*, and whereas disintegration of host hyphae is frequently observed without any sign of penetration of the host hyphal walls, active penetration is infrequent. Furthermore, apparent parasitic activity occurs only under those pH conditions where the antibiotics which *Trichoderma* is capable of producing are most stable (Aytoun, 1953; Weindling, 1932). *P. vermiculatum* seems to be more truly parasitic.

(4) *Production of antibiotics.* Where there are two organisms, with no

parasitic relationship, with apparently similar rates of nutrient utilization and similar rates of hyphal extension, it is difficult to explain the success of one and failure of the other in colonizing a substrate unless one postulates some form of chemical antagonism. And this is by no means an uncommon situation. I do not propose to review in detail the evidence for and against production of antibiotics in soil, as I have recently done this elsewhere (Brian, 1957). Whether or not antibiotics can accumulate in such quantity as to be detectable throughout the soil, the evidence for production in localized environments, such as fragments of plant material or seed coats, or in the rhizosphere, is, I think, convincing. I am thinking in particular of the identification of antibiotics in such loci by paper chromatography (Kalyanasundaram, 1958; Wright, 1956a, b), and by highly specific bioassay based on morphogenetic effects on fungal germ-tubes (Stevenson, 1956a, b). If a fungus is able to produce such substances in food substrates, it will be able to reduce the growth rate and rate of nutrient uptake of susceptible organisms even if it does not inhibit their development entirely. In fact, this becomes an aspect of competition for foodstuffs. It is a fact that a high proportion of soil fungi can produce antibiotics. At one time (Brian, 1951) I thought the data insufficient to be sure whether soil fungi as a class were more able to produce antibiotics than plant parasites; after seven more years' experience, I now feel certain that it is the case. Similarly soil bacteria and soil actinomycetes more frequently produce antibiotics than organisms of this group from other habitats. Since organisms producing antibiotics are themselves usually more resistant to the antibiotics they themselves produce (Jefferys, Brian, Hemming & Lowe, 1953), there seems to me to be a good basis here for explaining some soil antagonisms. However, there is no doubt that it does not afford a universal explanation; many of the most widespread soil saprophytes, notably the Mucorales, apparently do not produce such substances.

(5) *Resistance to chemical inhibitors.* If production of an antibiotic can give an organism an advantage in the exploitation of a substrate particle, then resistance to such inhibitors would also be advantageous. Organisms do, in fact, differ in their resistance. This may be achieved by several mechanisms: (*a*) Production of an enzyme which will destroy the inhibitor, e.g. the penicillinases produced by some bacterial species which will destory penicillin; such enzymes may be very specific— many penicillinases will destroy the penicillins produced by *Penicillium chrysogenum*, but not the more hydrophilic penicillins produced by *Cephalosporium* spp. (*b*) Production of metabolites which will antagonize or neutralize the effects of the antibiotic; thus some species of *Pseudo-*

monas produce antagonists of streptomycin (Lightbrown & Jackson, 1956) and of chlortetracycline (Stanecki, Fast & Krzywy, 1958). (*c*) Development of resistance by development of new biosynthetic pathways not inhibited by the antibiotic. (*d*) Development of barriers to the entrance of antibiotics into the cell. I suspect that the latter may be of great importance, since many soil fungi notably resistant to antibiotics are also notably resistant to many synthetic fungicides. An excellent example of this is *Trichoderma viride*, the dominance of which in soils partially sterilized by formalin or carbon disulphide is probably due to this resistance (Evans, 1955; Garrett, 1957; Mollinson, 1953). Garrett (1950) first pointed out that many plant pathogens, especially root parasites, appear to be more sensitive to antibiotics than soil saprophytes, and this has since been amply confirmed (Butler, 1953*b*; Jefferys, Brian, Hemming & Lowe, 1953). Park (1956*a*) has extended this observation to show that saprophytes alien to soil are less resistant than native soil saprophytes. Thus resistance to antibiotics is also probably an important factor in determining competitive success. Indeed, Butler (1953*b*) has produced convincing evidence that the great saprophytic colonizing ability of the cereal foot-rot organism, *Curvularia ramosa*, as compared with the weak saprophytism of *Helminthosporium sativum*, is associated with the generally greater resistance of *Curvularia* to antibiotics. However, resistance to chemical inhibitors can only be of importance where inhibitors are present. In my view, the only inhibitors of importance are likely to be antibiotics, using the word in a wide sense to include all metabolic products of micro-organisms which inhibit other micro-organisms, thus including such substances as carbon dioxide, which may well be of importance on occasion.

To summarize, it may be said that quite a number of mechanisms of antagonism and competition can be plausibly suggested, each of which could theoretically explain differential survival of fungi in soil. However, it must also be said (*a*) that no one of them has been unequivocally implicated, by direct evidence, in any antagonism in natural soil conditions, and (*b*) that no one of them alone can possibly explain all cases of differential survival. It seems certain that microbial antagonisms are complex and of varied origin. Nevertheless, I believe that further understanding will best be achieved by an analytical approach, involving an unravelling of the complex interactions of specific mechanisms.

'WIDESPREAD FUNGISTASIS'

It has long been suspected, and Warcup (1955) has proved, that most of the colonies of fungi developing in soil-dilution plates develop from spores. The question therefore arises, why have these spores not already germinated in the soil? Many spores will not germinate *in vitro* unless supplied with nutrients. Frequently the nutrient requirements are complex, approximating to those necessary for growth, as in *Penicillium expansum* (Brian, 1933) and *Glomerella cingulata* (Lin, 1945), but in some cases only a carbon (energy) source is required, as in *Sclerotinia fructicola* (Lin, 1940). Spores with such requirements might well not germinate in the extremely poor nutrient conditions prevailing in soil, or in restricted soil localities devoid of organic plant or animal remains. But most of the fungi whose spores have such requirements are plant parasites, and the spores of most soil saprophytes will germinate satisfactorily in water. Dobbs & Hinson (1953), by the use of a most ingenious experimental technique, have shown that such spores still fail to germinate in contact with soil, though sufficient water is present. This failure to germinate in contact with soil has been observed in many types of soil in many parts of the world (Caldwell, 1958; Chinn, 1953; Chinn & Ledingham, 1957; Dobbs, Hinson & Bywater, 1957; Jackson, 1957, 1958; Park, 1955), amply justifying Dobbs & Hinson's description of the phenomenon as a 'widespread fungistasis'. It may well appear inappropriate for me to discuss this phenomenon here. However, there is some suspicion that it may be due to accumulation of inhibitory substances of biological origin, i.e. that it may be a form of microbial antagonism—a 'cold war' as distinguished from the 'hot war' discussed in the preceding paragraphs.

The failure to germinate may be due to absence of some essential substance or to the presence of an inhibitory influence. Though spores capable of germination in water *in vitro* are inhibited, the possible absence of a factor essential for germination must still be considered, for two reasons: (*a*) It is conceivable that, in soil, nutrient requirements are greater than on the microscope slide; oxygen lack may be involved. (*b*) The fungistasis can, in fact, be overcome by addition of nutrients. We must therefore examine a little more closely the ways in which the degree of fungistasis can be modified; our knowledge is mainly due to Dobbs & Hinson (1953). The inhibition can be removed or reduced by the following procedures:

(*a*) Heat treatment of soil or prolonged drying. (*b*) Treatment with organic solvents. (*c*) Elution with citrate-phosphate buffer, but not with water, hydrochloric acid, or phosphate buffer. (*d*) Addition of nutrients to the soil; Dobbs & Hinson (1953) found glucose satisfactory, but Chinn & Ledingham (1957) found pure glucose ineffective, crude glucose more effective, but particulate crude organic materials, such as soybean meal, more effective still. Germination also takes place in the vicinity of roots (Jackson, 1957), probably as a result of leakage of sugars (Rovira, 1956). (*e*) Addition of charcoal to the soil.

There is no clear-cut evidence which enables us to decide whether we are dealing with lack of an essential factor or presence of an inhibitor. Lack of oxygen is not a likely cause, since addition of organic materials would probably still further increase the demand for oxygen. But observations (*a*) to (*d*) inclusive are all compatible with a necessary nutrient being unavailable, since treatments in (*a*) and (*b*) would increase available food materials as a result of chemical change and killing of micro-organisms, the citrate in the effective elution treatment (*c*) might act as an energy source for germination, and the effect of adding nutrients (*d*) would be simply explained. Observation (*e*) is incompatible with this hypothesis. On the other hand, if it is assumed that a labile toxic substance is present, observations (*a*), (*b*), and (*e*) can be understood. The effect of nutrients (observation (*d*)) would best be explained as a 'neutralization' of the toxic substance; it has often been observed that antifungal substances have reduced activity in the presence of sugars (Dimond, Horsfall, Heuberger & Stoddard, 1941; Watkins & Klemme, 1948). The success in removing the toxin from soil by washing with a citrate buffer, but not with water, hydrochloric acid, or phosphate buffer (observation (*c*)), is difficult to explain. The only substances I know with properties like this are certain basic copper compounds, which are soluble in amino-acids or citrate, but not in mineral acids or water (Wain & Wilkinson, 1943).

The balance of evidence is probably slightly in favour of the view that we are dealing with a real inhibition, but the evidence is purely circumstantial. If the inhibitory influence could be extracted from the soil, one could feel more confident. Solvent extractions have produced no convincing results. Expressed soil water may show some toxicity to fungi (Dobbs & Hinson, 1953; Park, 1956*a*), but unfortunately this toxicity is lost after Seitz filtration. This latter observation is difficult to interpret since the Seitz filter-pad is anything but an inert filter, many substances being retained by adsorption and some chemically altered.

If we assume that the toxicity is chemical, thus due to one or more chemical compounds, what is its origin? It seems unlikely that it is an inorganic soil constituent. If it is organic it must derive either from higher plants or animals or from soil micro-organisms. Jackson (1958) has shown fungistasis to be marked in a soil which had been kept fallow for 2 years; a toxicity derived from vegetation, such as that observed in forest litter by Melin & Wiken (1946), therefore seems unlikely. We are consequently driven to consider a microbial origin for the fungistasis, in other words, that we may be dealing with a case of microbiological antagonism. Again it will be noted that there is no direct evidence that this is the case; in particular, attempts to regenerate toxic conditions by reinoculation of soil detoxified by heat have not been successful (Dobbs & Hinson, 1953).

At this point it is convenient to digress a little and recall an example of soil toxicity described before the recent interest in soil fungistasis had developed. This was the toxicity to fungi in Wareham Heath soil (Neilson-Jones, 1941). This was noted in the first place as a toxicity to mycelia of mycorrhizal fungi, but it was in all respects similar to the fungistasis described by Dobbs & Hinson, though more intense. It could be alleviated by similar means, but was successfully reinduced in heat-sterilized soil by inoculation with a small volume of untreated soil. The inhibitory influence was diffusible, preventing fungal growth in nutrient agar poured on the surface of the soil. It was therefore reasonably interpreted as a chemical inhibition arising from microbial activity. This example lends support to the otherwise rather dubious conclusion that the cases of fungistasis more recently studied are also chemical inhibitions resulting from microbial activity.

What kind of substance could be involved? Let us first consider simple substances. Carbon dioxide is an obvious possibility. It can accumulate in soils to levels which may be inhibitory to fungi, and has been considered to be one of the factors influencing the distribution of fungal species in soil profiles (Burges & Fenton, 1953). Abeygunawardena & Wood (1957) have shown that the failure of sclerotia of *Sclerotium rolfsii* to germinate in soil may be due to CO_2 accumulation; the sclerotia can be induced to germinate by forced aeration of the soil. But it will be recalled that organic supplements reduce toxicity, yet they would undoubtedly increase CO_2 production in the soil. Neilson-Jones (1941) suggested that production of hydrogen sulphide by anaerobic sulphate-reducing bacteria might be the origin of the toxicity in Wareham Heath soil. Though H_2S was never specifically detected, two further pieces of evidence were compatible with the view that it might be the cause of the toxicity, viz.: (*a*) addition of sodium sulphate to the soil increased toxicity, whereas sodium chloride had no effect, and (*b*) aeration of the soil-reduced toxicity. Nevertheless, the evidence tending to involve H_2S

in the Wareham Heath toxicity is not conclusive, and there is still less reason to suppose that it is involved in the widespread fungistasis described by Dobbs & Hinson. There are few other structurally simple metabolic products of micro-organisms which one can envisage as a cause of fungistasis except, just conceivably, such substances as the methylated arsines produced by many fungi in the presence of traces of arsenic salts.

The next and most obvious possibility to consider is that the toxicity is caused by accumulation of those more complex metabolic products usually called antibiotics. Brian, Hemming & McGowan (1945) examined the microflora of a toxic sample of Wareham Heath soil, and found, in confirmation of the observations of Neilson-Jones, that it was very restricted. Actinomycetes were rare, bacterial numbers low, and the fungi were virtually restricted to a few species of *Penicillium*. The most abundant species were *P. nigricans*, *P. albidum*, and *P. terlikowskii*, since shown to produce the antibiotics griseofulvin, albidin, and gliotoxin respectively. They suggested that the fungistasis might be due to accumulation of these substances, and in this connexion it should be noted that gliotoxin is a sulphur-containing compound, so that addition of sodium sulphate might stimulate production of this substance as well as H_2S. However, though Wareham soil untreated except for incorporation of organic matter will support accumulation of gliotoxin (Wright, 1954), the general body of experimental work on antibiotic production in soil (Brian, 1957) indicates the improbability of this occurring in nature, and though it might conceivably happen in the rather unusual Wareham Heath soil, it is most unlikely to do so in the many other types of soil in which fungistasis has been detected. I come to this conclusion with some reluctance because antibiotic production has seemed to me by far the most likely explanation of fungistasis; perhaps it is as well to remember that as yet no detailed studies of production in soil of the polypeptide antibiotics of bacteria or the antifungal polyenic antibiotics produced by actinomycetes have yet been made, and their chemical properties are in many ways rather distinct from those of the antibiotics which have so far received most attention.

What remains? Park (1956a) has drawn a parallel between fungistasis in soils and staling in pure cultures. This does not seem to me a very fruitful comparison. There have been no modern investigations of staling, but it seems fairly certain that it is either due to production of autotoxic antibiotics, which we have already dealt with, or nutrient exhaustion, which in the case of carbon-source exhustion would rapidly lead to autolysis and release of breakdown products such as ammonia, or accumulation in high concentration of such mildly toxic metabolites as bicarbonate. I cannot see that any of these occurrences are likely to afford an explanation of soil fungistasis.

I must confess that I find it quite impossible to suggest any convincing mechanism for soil fungistasis. There are still too many uncertainties concerning basic features of the phenomenon. We need information that will enable us to decide unequivocally whether the fungistasis is a positive effect, i.e. a definite inhibition, rather than due to absence of essential factors for germination and growth. Assuming that it can then be decided that it is a real inhibition, we need more definite proof that it is a chemical toxicity. Finally, we need to know more definitely whether it is of biological, and specifically of microbial, origin.

It may be that we have here a completely new kind of phenomenon, something more 'subtle' than antibiotic production, as Dobbs & Hinson (1953) have described it. That remains to be seen, but it is perhaps relevant to note that a fungistasis in a much simpler system—viz. involving a fungal parasite and some saprophytes on a leaf surface—has also so far so been found inexplicable in nutritional terms or on the basis of antibiotic production (Newhook, 1957).

REFERENCES

ABEYGUNAWARDENA, D. V. W., & WOOD, R. K. S. (1957). Factors affecting the germination of sclerotic and mycelial growth of *Sclerotium rolfsii* Sacc. *Trans. Brit. mycol. Soc.*, **40**, 221–31.

AYTOUN, R. S. C. (1953). The genus *Trichoderma*: its relationship with *Armillaria mellea* (Vahl ex Fries) Quel and *Polyporus schweinitzii* Fr., together with preliminary observations on its ecology in woodland soils. *Trans. Bot. Soc., Edin.* **36**, 99–114.

BOOSALIS, M. G. (1956). Effect of soil temperature and green manure amendment of unsterilized soil on parasitism of *Rhizoctonia solani* by *Penicillium vermiculatum* and *Trichoderma* sp. *Phytopathology*, **46**, 473–8.

BRIAN, P. W. (1933). Experimental study of moulds responsible for the wastage of apples. *Rept. Food Investigation Board for* 1932, 66–8.

BRIAN, P. W. (1951). Antibiotics produced by fungi. *Bot. Rev.*, **17**, 357–430.

BRIAN, P. W. (1957). The ecological significance of antibiotic production. *Microbial Ecology Symposium Soc. Gen. Microbial*, Cambridge University Press, 168–88.

BRIAN, P. W., HEMMING, H. G., & McGOWAN, J. C. (1945). Origin of a toxicity to mycorrhiza in Wareham Heath soil. *Nature, Lond.*, **155**, 637.

BURGES, A., & FENTON, E. (1953). The effect of carbon dioxide on the growth of certain soil fungi. *Trans. Brit. mycol. Soc.*, **36**, 104–8.

BUTLER, E. E. (1957). *Rhizoctonia solani* as a parasite of fungi. *Mycologia*, **49**, 354–73.

BUTLER, F. C. (1953a). Saprophytic behaviour of some cereal root-rot fungi. I. Saprophytic colonization of wheat straw. *Ann. appl. Biol.*, **40**, 284–97.

BUTLER, F. C. (1953b). Saprophytic behaviour of some cereal root-rot fungi. II.

Factors influencing saprophytic colonization of wheat straw. *Ann. appl. Biol.*, **40**, 298–304.

BUTLER, F. C. (1953c). Saprophytic behaviour of some cereal root-rot fungi. III. Saprophytic survival in wheat straw buried in soil. *Ann. appl. Biol.*, **40**, 305–11.

CALDWELL, R. (1958). Fate of spores of *Trichoderma viride* Pers. ex Fr. introduced into soil. *Nature, Lond.*, **181**, 1144–5.

CAMPBELL, W. P. (1956). The influence of associated micro-organisms on the pathogenicity of *Helminthosporium sativum*. *Canad. J. Bot.*, **34**, 865–74.

CHINN, S. H. F. (1953). A slide technique for the study of fungi and actinomycetes in soil, with special reference to *Helminthosporium sativum*. *Canad. J. Bot.*, **31**, 718–24.

CHINN, S. H. F., & LEDINGHAM, R. J. (1957). Studies on the influence of various substances on the germination of *Helminthosporium sativum* spores in soil. *Canad. J. Bot.*, **35**, 697–701.

CHINN, S. H. F., LEDINGHAM, R. J., SOLANNS, B. J., & SIMMONDS, P. M. (1953). A mechanism for the control of common root rot of wheat. *Phytopathology*, **43**, 701.

COLEY-SMITH, J. R., & HICKMAN, C. J. (1957). Stimulation of sclerotium germination in *Sclerotium cepivorum* Berk. *Nature, Lond.*, **180**, 445.

DIMOND, A. E., HORSFALL, J. G., HEUBERGER, J. W., & STODDARD, E. M. (1941). Role of the dosage-response curve in the evaluation of fungicides. *Connecticut Agric. Exp. Sta. Bull.*, **451**, 635–67.

DOBBS, C. G., & HINSON, W. H. (1953). A widespread fungistasis in soils. *Nature, Lond.*, **172**, 197–9.

DOBBS, C. G., HINSON, W. H., & BYWATER, J. (1957). Mycostasis in soil. *J. gen. microbiol.*, **17**, xi.

EVANS, E. (1955). Survival and recolonization by fungi in soil treated with formalin or carbon disulphide. *Trans. Brit. mycol. Soc.*, **38**, 335–46.

GARRETT, S. D. (1950). Ecology of the root-inhabiting fungi. *Biol. Rev.*, **25**, 220–54.

GARRETT, S. D. (1956). *Biology of root-infecting fungi*. Cambridge University Press.

GARRETT, S. D. (1957). Effect of a soil microflora selected by carbon disulphide by fumigation on survival of *Armillaria mellea* in woody host tissues. *Canad. J. Bot.*, **3**, 135–49.

JACKSON, R. M. (1957). Fungistasis as a factor in the rhizosphere phenomenon. *Nature, Lond.*, **180**, 96–7.

JACKSON, R. M. (1958). An investigation of fungistasis in Nigerian soils. *J. gen. Microbiol.*, **18**, 248–58.

JEFFERYS, E. G., BRIAN, P. W., HEMMING, H. G., & LOWE, D. (1953). Antibiotic production by the microfungi of acid heath soils. *J. gen. Microbiol.*, **9**, 314–41.

KALYANASUNDARAM, R. (1958). Production of fusaric acid by *Fusarium lycopersici* Sacc. in the rhizosphere of tomato plants. *Phytopath. Zeit.*, **32**, 25–34.

LIGHTBROWN. J. W., & JACKSON, F. L. (1956). Inhibition of cytochrome systems of heart muscle and certain bacteria by the antagonists of dihydrostreptomycin: 2-alkyl-4-hydroxyquinoline *N*-oxides. *Biochem. J.*, **63**, 130–7.

LIN, C. K. (1940). Germination of the conidia of *Sclerotinia fructicola* with special reference to the toxicity of copper. *Cornell Univ. Agric. Exp. Sta. Mem.*, **233**, 1–33.

LIN, C. K. (1945). Nutrient requirements in the germination of the conidia of *Glomerella cingulata*. *Amer. J. Bot.*, **32**, 296–8.

MELIN, E., & WIKEN, T. (1946). Antibacterial substances in water extracts of pure forest litter. *Nature, Lond.*, **158**, 200–1.

MOLLINSON, J. E. (1953). Effect of partial sterilization and acidification of soil on the fungal population. *Trans. Brit. mycol. Soc.*, **36**, 215–28.

NEILSON-JONES, W. (1941). Biological aspects of soil fertility. *J. agric. Sci.*, **31**, 379–411.

NEWHOOK, F. J. (1957). The relationship of saprophytic antagonism to control of Botrytis cinerea Pers. on tomatoes. *N.Z. Journ. Sci. Tech.*, **A38**, 473–81.

NOVOGRUDSKY, D. M. (1948). The colonization of soil bacteria on fungal hyphae. *Mikrobiologiya*, **17**, 28–35.

PARK, D. (1955). Experimental studies on the ecology of fungi in soil. *Trans. Brit. mycol. Soc.*, **38**, 130–42.

PARK, D. (1956a). On the role of amendments in the biology of fungi in soil. *Rapports VIe Cong. Internat. de la Science du Sol*, **3**, (5), 23–8.

PARK, D. (1956b). Effect of substrate on a microbial antagonism, with reference to soil conditions. *Trans. Brit. mycol. Soc.*, **39**, 329–59.

PARK, D. (1957a). Behaviour of soil fungi in the presence of bacterial antagonists. *Trans. Brit. mycol. Soc.*, **40**, 283–91.

PARK, D. (1957b). Behaviour of soil fungi in the presence of fungal antagonists. *Trans. Brit. mycol. Soc.*, **40**, 358–64.

ROVIRA, A. D. (1956). Plant-root excretions in relation to the rhizosphere effect. I. The nature of root exudate from oats and peas. *Plant and Soil*, **7**, 178–94.

SCOTT, M. R. (1956). Studies on the biology of *Sclerotium cepivorum* Berk. I. Growth of the mycelium in soil. *Ann. appl. Biol.*, **44**, 576–83.

STANECKI, J., FAST, J., & KRZYWY, T. (1958). Inactivation of the bacteriostatic action of chlortetracycline by substances produced by bacterial metabolism. *Antibiotics and Chemotherapy*, **8**, 167–70.

STEVENSON, I. L. (1956a). Antibiotic activity of Actinomycetes in soil as demonstrated by direct-observation techniques. *J. gen. Microbiol.*, **15**, 372–80.

STEVENSON, I. L. (1956b). Antibiotic activity of Actinomycetes in soil and their controlling effects on root-rot of wheat. *J. gen. Microbiol.*, **14**, 440–8.

TRIBE, H. T. (1957). Ecology of micro-organisms in soils as observed during their development upon buried cellulose film. *Microbial Ecology. Symposium Soc. Gen. Microbiol.*, Cambridge University Press, 287–98.

WAIN, R. L., & WILKINSON, E. H. (1943). Studies upon the copper fungicides. VI. The solution of copper from Bordeaux and Burgundy mixtures. *Ann. appl. Biol.*, **30**, 379–91.

WARCUP, J. H. (1955). On the origin of colonies of fungi developing on soil-dilution plates. *Trans. Brit. mycol. Soc.*, **38**, 298–301.

WARREN, J. R. (1948). An undescribed species of *Papulospora* parasitic on *Rhizoctonia solani* Kühn. *Mycologia*, **40**, 391–401.

WATKINS, G. M., & KLEMME, D. E. (1948). Some effects of dextrose concentration upon the action of a fungicide, 2, 2′-methylenebis-(4-chlorophenol). *Amer. J. Bot.*, **35**, 622–7.

WEINDLING, R. (1932). *Trichoderma lignorum* as a parasite of other soil fungi. *Phytopathology*, **22**, 837–45.

WEINDLING, R. (1934). Studies on a lethal principle effective in the parasitic action of *Trichoderma lignorum* on *Rhizoctonia solani* and other soil fungi. *Phytopathology*, **24**, 1163–79.

WEINDLING, R. (1940). Experimental consideration of the mould toxins of *Gliocladium* and *Trichoderma*. *Phytopathology*, **31**, 991–1003.

WRIGHT, J. M. (1954). The production of antibiotics in soil. I. Production of gliotoxin by *Trichoderma viride*. *Ann. appl. Biol.*, **41**, 280–9.

WRIGHT, J. M. (1956a). The production of antibiotics in soil. III. Production of gliotoxin in wheat straw buried in soil. *Ann. appl. Biol.*, **44**, 461–6.

WRIGHT, J. M. (1956b). The production of antibiotics in soil. IV. Production of antibiotics in coats of seeds sown in soil. *Ann. appl. Biol.*, **44**, 561–6.

INHIBITION OF FUNGAL GROWTH
IN SOILS

C. G. DOBBS, W. H. HINSON, AND
JOAN BYWATER[1]

University College of North Wales

PART I[2]

A preliminary account of a widespread inhibition of spores was published by Dobbs & Hinson (1953) under the title 'A widespread fungistasis in soils'. This paper emphasizes some aspects and details which have not been stressed in the accounts so far published. For several reasons the term mycostasis is now preferred to fungistasis.

The general dormancy of spores in the soil and the failure of fungal inocula to establish on undisturbed soils is well-known, but the usual explanations—lack of nutrients, oxygen or water, or excess of carbon dioxide—did not seem to explain the germination of spores in buried slide traps.

It was necessary, first of all, to make sure that mould spores did not, in fact, germinate in moist soil. Accordingly *Penicillium nigricans*, which has easily recognizable spiny conidia, was chosen and spores were mixed into sieved forest soil (A_2 horizon under beech) which was examined again after a month's incubation. The interior of the mass was then found to be full of recognizable spores without a single germ tube, although spores were seen to have germinated in minute crumbs detached from the mass or projecting from the surface. In a similar test with autoclaved soil about a third of the spores in the interior had germinated in a few days, and the outside of the mass of soil was soon covered with conidiophores.

All the more obvious explanations were then eliminated in turn. It was not found possible to germinate soil spores by any treatment of the soil affecting aeration or moisture—wetting and drying or exposing to air. Theoretical considerations appeared to rule out carbon-dioxide concentration as a limiting factor under the conditions of the test, though

[1] Now Mrs. N. W. Daniels, present address: School of Agriculture, Cambridge.

[2] This part incorporates material from a thesis by W. H. Hinson approved in 1954 for the Ph.D. degree of the University of Wales.

it may be of importance in the lower layers of the soil (Burges & Fenton, 1953). The work of Neilson-Jones (1941) on Wareham Heath soil, and of Brian, Hemming and McGowan (1945) suggested the possibility of an inhibitor in the soil solution.

A variety of methods of testing this hypothesis were tried. Seitz-filtered soil extract did not inhibit germination in a hanging drop, as compared with water, but there are some unexplained facts about the germination of spores in water drops (mainly limited to spores in the meniscus) which cannot be satisfactorily explained on the basis of aeration alone. Agar, as used in A. G. Morton's nutrient agar test for Wareham Heath soil (Neilson-Jones, 1941), was used, but after much experiment, with variable results, it was discarded. It is impossible to make a really thin agar film, some agar after autoclaving seems to contain inhibiting substances, and the growth of fungi and other organisms into it confuses the interpretation of results, though it has been found useful, especially when separated from the soil by some other material (Molin, 1957; Jackson, 1958). Soil solution was shown to be able to diffuse through pipe-clay and through sintered glass and to reduce the germination of spores, but for an effective test we returned to cellulose film.

The cellulose-film tests

Figs. 1, 2, and 3 show the cellulose-film test in its three forms, referred to as the 'open', the 'closed', and the 'partly open' film test. Thin cellulose film of about 20μ thickness is essential, and it must be of the non-moistureproof type, with dressing removable by boiling. This film is cut into 2-in. squares, autoclaved in water, and smeared, sprayed, or dusted on one side with the test spores, the method of application varying with the type of spore. It is then folded with the spores inside. For the 'open' film test the 'fold' is first pressed under a lump of moist soil against a glass slide (Fig. 1A) then inverted and carefully opened up (Fig. 1B). For the 'closed' test it is pressed between two lumps of soil (Fig. 2) and for the 'partly open' a 'closed' fold is pulled slightly apart to admit air (Fig. 3). In every case the soil contact must be perfect if patchy results are to be avoided. The free 'margins' of the folds act as the controls for the 'open' and 'partly open' tests. For the 'closed' form kaolin and other inert materials have been used.

These three forms of test differ in sensitiveness. The 'closed' form is the most sensitive, and imitates more closely than the others the conditions of moisture and aeration which must obtain within the soil. With some control materials, both kaolin and coarse sand for instance, there is a tendency for water to collect between the films, flooding the spores and causing a 'submergence' effect which may depress germination. This may be as low as 5% with kaolin, but is never reduced to zero, as it is with living soil. The 'open' form is the least sensitive of the three, and this fact has been used, later, to differentiate soils which give 100% inhibition with the 'closed' film. The 'partly open' test is intermediate in sensitiveness, and has been useful for some purposes, as it avoids the poor aeration of the 'closed' form and the danger of condensation on the surface, especially in fluctuating temperatures, and also of undue evaporation, which are disadvantages of the 'open' test.

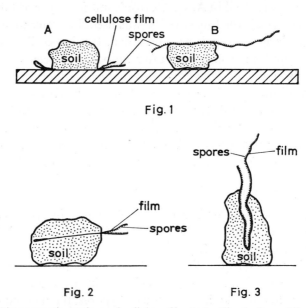

Figs. 1–3. Diagrammatic sections of cellulose film tests. Fig. 1. Open Film test; A, the folded film pressed under moist soil, B inverted with the film opened out. Fig. 2. Closed film test; Fig. 3. Partly-open film test.

In addition to these, the student of mycostasis now has available a range of methods mainly of less sensitivity, all based on the use of agar. These include the attractive method of Chinn (1953) of coating slides with a spore suspension in a very weak agar, the agar-disc method of which variants have been used by Molin (1957), Jackson (1958), and ourselves, the agar slabs placed direct on the soil profile by Jefferys and Hemming (1953), and the original nutrient agar-plate method of Morton (Neilson-Jones, 1941). We have tried out all these and find that they have their place for differentiating the phenomenon at the appropriate level of sensitiveness, but that the cellulose-film method is the most effective for demonstrating the inhibition at its lower levels of intensity.

Soils and subsoils tested

All soils tested showed complete inhibition of germination of the test fungus, *Penicillium frequentans* ('closed' film test), with the exception of some deep subsoils. It is clear that mycostasis is not merely widespread but is a normal phenomenon in most surface soils.

The subsoils showed various effects: two woodland profiles showing undiminished inhibition down to the parent rock at 1 m. and less, as also did other shallow soils; but occasionally there was a little germination on the 'open' film. Fresh deep exposures of subsoil are not frequently available, and old pits, however deep, do not escape the inhibition on their exposed sides or bottoms. Eventually the deep subsoils problem was solved in three ways:

(i) Four samples of gritty subsoils taken at depths from 1–7 m. (opencast coal working near Aberdare) showed no sign of the inhibition.

(ii) The excavations for the new Botany Building at Bangor provided

TABLE 1

Closed cellulose-film test with spores of Penicillium frequentans
Locality; Maesgeirchen Cemetery, Bangor, Caerns

Depth of samples (cm.)	Approx. percentage germination	Approx. length of germ-tubes (μ)
15	0	—
30	0	—
45	0	—
60	1	100–300
90	0	—
120	5	100–300
140	1	100–300
170	2	100–700
200	2	100–1000
215	5–10	100–1000
Kaolin control	5–10	100–2000

Description: Vegetation, mown grass. Surface layers disturbed by former ploughing. Soil horizons not distinguishable.

0–10 cm. Heavy light-brown loam with abundant grass roots and small stones.

10–30 cm. Silty clay with larger stones and a few grass roots.

30–210 cm. Silty clay with larger stones, mottled and showing signs of impeded drainage.

Parent material of drift origin.

Water-table varies between 30 and 120 cm.

an exposure of silty loam and clay down to 2–3 m. Tests with the 'partly open' fold gave full inhibition at 30 cm., a few germlings at 60 cm., 5–10 % germination at 90 cm., 20–40 % at 120 cm., and at 150, 180, and 240 cm. depths 30–45 %, which was equal to the control values.

(iii) Table 1 gives data for another type of fresh subsoil. Ten samples taken down to about 215 cm. showed a decrease in inhibition (with a slight irregularity at 90–120 cm.) until it disappeared at about 215 cm.

When plated out, the levels at which germination reached control value were found to be almost sterile of fungi; they were beyond the visible reach of roots, and below or within reach of the water-table. It was noticed in several cases that freely drained soils showed the complete inhibition to a greater depth than soils with impeded drainage.

It is interesting to compare these germination profiles in North Wales with those of Jackson (1958) in Nigeria, in which, using the agar-disc method, he found that germination reached control level at about 35 cm. depth, and showed distinct stimulation below that. Though no conclusions can of course be drawn from a couple of profiles in each country, especially as different methods were used, the possibility that the inhibition may generally permeate a greater depth of soil in a temperate than in a tropical climate is worth bearing in mind.

Species of fungi tested

Hinson standardized his cellulose-film germination tests on *Penicillium frequentans* as a test fungus, after experimenting with a wide range of fungi from soil, including mixed inocula from soil plates, as well as stock cultures. A few of the fungi tested (e.g. *Chaetomium globosum* and *Trichoderma viride*) were known to be able to attack cellulose, but there were no signs of such attack on the film during the period of the test; the majority tested were common 'sugar fungi'. In no case was it possible to find a fungus of which the spores would germinate readily, without added nutrient, on the 'margins' of the films, which did not respond to the inhibition in the soil-contact area. When test films were exchanged between non-sterile and autoclaved soil, the germ tubes formed over the latter were also inhibited from further growth, while the spores which had remained ungerminated over the former proceeded to germinate normally without showing any signs of having been subjected to any toxic influence. The film tests were, of course, not available for a large range of fungi of which the spores will not germinate in the time required under the test conditions, notably the Basidiomycetes; and a different technique had to be found for these and for testing the growth of mycelia (see Part II).

Killing and other treatments

The absence of the inhibition from the majority of autoclaved soils may be due to the destruction of the inhibitor or of its biological source, but must also be affected by the release of nutrient from killed organisms, as evidenced by the strong stimulation of growth and often of sporing. We have not yet been able to distinguish the effects of these two factors. Moist soil kept at 40° for 1 hr. showed the inhibition unaltered, at 50° it was much reduced (under 5% germination), but 3 days later had returned in full, at 60° there was stimulated germination (60–70%) and growth, which however fell to less than 5% in 3 days. After 8 days the full inhibition had returned.

This obviously suggests a biological effect—but the reinoculation of an autoclaved soil with a fresh soil, also with soil moulds, and its exposure to air infection, failed to restore the inhibition even after 60 days. Further evidence about re-inoculation is provided in Part II of this paper.

Exposure of the soil to toxic vapours—acetone, ether, and propylene oxide—for 18 hr. (which did not quite render them sterile of fungi) temporarily removed the inhibition (as tested after the vapour had evaporated), but 3 days later it had returned. Acetone-treated soil continued to allow germination when kept moist for $13\frac{1}{2}$ hr. at laboratory temperature, and after shaking in water for 3 hr., but the inhibition was restored by $13\frac{1}{2}$ hr. of shaking in water.

Some very old stored specimens of soils lacked the inhibition, but 10 weeks of air-drying of a sieved fresh soil failed to get rid of it. On the other hand, when some clods of soil were kept in the laboratory, after 7 weeks, one of them suddenly gave a high germination rate, which fell off again 3 days later, while other clods kept their full inhition for 9 weeks. Perhaps the death of some soil organism released nutrient in the one clod.

Active garden soil, mixed with two brands of powdered activated charcoal (1:3 of soil) lost all inhibition and grew moulds; other surface-active materials, alumina and kaolin, had no such effect.

Nutrient

Obviously nutrient was an important factor, but mixing the soils with solutions of the ordinary mineral salts used in culture media did not reduce the inhibition as tested; neither did asparagine plus salts until the concentration reached the high level of 2% (w/v), which then gave less than 0·5% germination.

Glucose, by itself or with salts, gave obvious results. On the woodland

soils 0·1% (w/v) glucose gave some germination, though complete inhibition returned in a few days and was preceded by a drop in germination. The more glucose added the longer it took to restore the inhibition.
It returned also earlier when salts were added than with glucose alone.

e.g. 4% (w/v) glucose plus salts, complete inhibition had returned by
    12th day.
    4% (w/v) glucose alone, complete inhibition had not returned by
    24th day.
    1% (w/v) glucose plus salts, complete inhibition had returned by
    3rd day.
    1% (w/v) glucose alone, complete inhibition had not returned by
    12th day but had returned by 18th day.

Replicates of these tests with glucose gave disappointingly variable
results, and our hopes of finding here an accurate method of assaying
the inhibitor in terms of glucose threshold value were not fulfilled.

The reducing power of an untreated forest soil (beech A2 horizon)
was determined by a copper reagent (Shaffer & Hartmann, 1921) and
found to be equivalent to only 0·0075 mg. glucose per ml. soil extract.

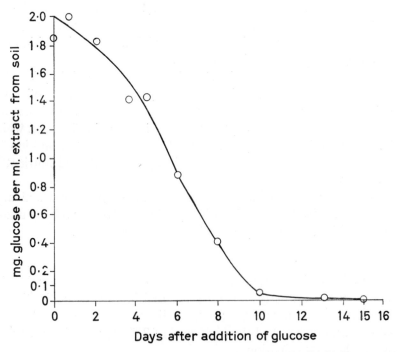

Fig. 4. Graph showing the fall in glucose content of extracts of soil initially treated with
glucose.

This soil was moistened to a slurry with 2% glucose solution, and the reducing power of samples determined daily for 13 days, by which time it had sunk to zero (Fig. 4). This was about the time taken for the inhibition to restore itself completely in other samples—evidently owing to the attenuation of the glucose.

Different soils varied widely in their glucose reaction—e.g. the beech-wood soil began to give some germination with only 0·1% (w/v) solution, but a garden soil not till 4% (w/v). Fig. 5 shows the percentage germination for these two soils plotted against the percentage glucose in the added solution (with some points also incorporated from the attenuation curve)—both on a logarithmic scale.

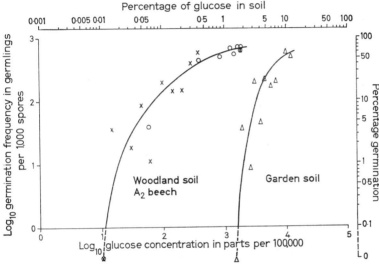

Fig. 5. Inter-relation between glucose in soil and germination in film tests, in two soils: on the left, A_2 horizon under beech, on the right a garden soil. The points marked with triangles and crosses show percentage glucose in solutions used to moisten the soil samples (4 cc. to 30 gm.); the circles show equivalent glucose remaining in the soil as calculated from residual reducing power (see Fig. 4) during attenuation.

Citrate was the only other substance which by accident was discovered to remove the inhibition in a manner similar to glucose. This occurred during tests on the effect of leaching with buffer solutions over a range of pH's. There was no effect on the inhibition when the soil was shaken up with HCl, phosphate-HCl, and Sorensen's phosphate buffers, with pH's from 1–8, but when McIlvaine's phosphate-citrate buffers were used, every soil gave stimulated germination with the film tests and afterwards grew moulds on the surface. We have not followed up this line of work so far, but Jackson (1958) has done so by incorporating a range of nutrients in agar discs.

Soil extracts

It was found impossible to affect the inhibition by leaching with water or percolating even for a month, nor did the percolate or leachate inhibit germination. The same applied to Seitz-filtered extracts of soil. In general, they behaved like water in allowing germination of test spores on slides and on cellulose films pressed between pads of filter-paper soaked in the extract. The same applied to extracts made by repeated extraction of fresh soil with the same water, others made by hydraulic pressure on moist natural soils, and others made by suction on a Buchner funnel. Some woodland soils showed a slight reduction of germination which was just significant, and a delay in germination as compared with water. Only the garden soil mentioned before showed an appreciable depression in germination. It seemed probable that the inhibitor might be either volatile or unstable in air, and that a different test method would have to be used.

Vial tests

Fig. 6 shows Hinson's McCartney vial test, in which a relatively large amount of extract is kept in contact with a small area of cellulose film bearing the test spores, under varying conditions of aeration. Form A was used merely to show that neither boiled water nor saturated carbon-dioxide solution in the vial would depress the germination of test

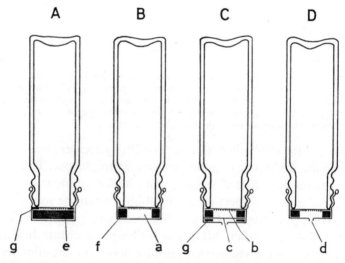

Fig. 6. Diagrammatic sections of the four forms of W. H. Hinson's McCartney Vial method of testing the effect of soil extracts upon the germination of test spores. a—air space; b—cellulose film bearing spores; c—cellulose film limiting diffusion of air; d—aperture in metal cap; e—3 mm. neoprene pad; f—3 mm. neoprene washer; g—0·5 mm. fibre washer.

spores (*M. hiemalis* and *P. frequentans*) in the minimum air space which could be made. Form B was used for most tests on extracts—this has a larger, but enclosed, air space in the cap. When filled with a soil suspension, the vial inverted with sediment in contact with the film, germination was depressed to 2%, whereas it was 35–40% with the vial on its side, sediment not in contact.

Forms C and D gave progressively more aeration, which was found to reduce the effect of the extract. Thus, with a woodland soil, Form B gave 38% germination, Form C 40%, Form D 48%, water control 47%. Form B thus gave a significant reduction, which was much more marked with the garden soil. The effect of Seitz-filtering the extract is also of interest:

P. frequentans—*percentage germination on film in vial (means of* 3)
(*garden soil*)

Extract not Seitz-filtered	Seitz-filtered		Water control
	'Sterimat'	6 thicknesses 'Whatman's No. 50' filter-paper	
14	22	15	45

After storage the activity of the extract falls off—for instance, after 50 hr. Seitz-filtered extract gave 36% germination. It is clear that the inhibitor is unstable in water, and that the poor results with extracts must be partly due to the delay involved in germination tests. However, the vial tests definitely establish that the soil extracts tested contain an inhibitor capable of diffusing through cellulose film, while the ordinary film tests show that such an inhibitor must be widespread, and perhaps almost universally present in surface soils, since no other explanation will fit the facts.

The possibility that the inhibition might be due to the diffusion from the spores of some substance necessary for their germination was considered, but rejected as a general explanation, since the test spores will germinate on cellulose film over deep subsoil, over kaolin and other absorbent materials, on a 20μ-thick cellulose film dialysis tube filled with distilled water, and on the film in a McCartney vial filled with distilled water. As for the nature of the diffusable inhibitor (or complex of inhibitors), since it diffuses through cellulose film it cannot be a very large molecule, it appears to be partially removed by the Seitz filter (especially when Ford 'Sterimats' are used), it is unstable in water at ordinary temperatures, thermo-labile, and almost certainly biological in origin. There seems to be no evidence so far that it is toxic to fungi, but its 'competitive' behaviour with glucose, with citrate, and to some extent with aeration suggests that it should be regarded as an anti-metabolite.

PART II

When this work was continued with the aid of a grant from the Forestry Commission, three general lines of approach were adopted: (1) to find some means of assaying and comparing soils in respect of the inhibition and ability to support mould growth; (2) to extend the range of fungi tested for susceptibility to soil inhibition, especially to include Basidio-mycetes; and (3) to identify further the nature of the inhibiting factor or factors concerned. Most of the work so far has been concerned with the first of these approaches, and this part must be regarded as an interim report.

1. The germination assay

The assay method finally adopted was a variant of the 'open' film method. The soil was packed into 25-ml. cylindrical 'Oxoid' caps, and covered with the prepared cellulose-film bearing spores of *Mucor ramannianus*, which was found to be a more suitable test organism than *Penicillium frequentans* for assay purposes. The whole was incubated in a moist container for 48 hr. at 27°. The margins of the films extending beyond the soil-contact area were used as controls. The percentage of spores not germinating on the soil-contact area, as estimated by spore counts on a grid in randomly chosen fields, was taken as a measure of the degree of inhibition. The controls were found to maintain a fairly constant level of about 95% germination. Where the growth of the germ tubes exceeded that on the margins, the degree of stimulation was assessed quantitatively by eye.

In view of the complete inhibition invariably found by Hinson, during preliminary tests early in 1957 we were surprised to find some samples of forest humus which not only allowed germination in the soil-contact area, but even, in some cases, stimulated growth and sporulation of the test fungus. However, this proved to be temporary, and after a month or two these soils began to recover their inhibiting power. This led us to investigate the possibility of a seasonal variation in the inhibition by assaying a group of forest soils at approximately monthly intervals. The soils selected were from four sites, two of them near sea-level beside the Menai Straits, under mature beech-oak mixture and under mature Scots pine respectively, and two under mature beech-oak mix-ture and under 30-year spruce, on a hillside about 500 ft. above sea-level.

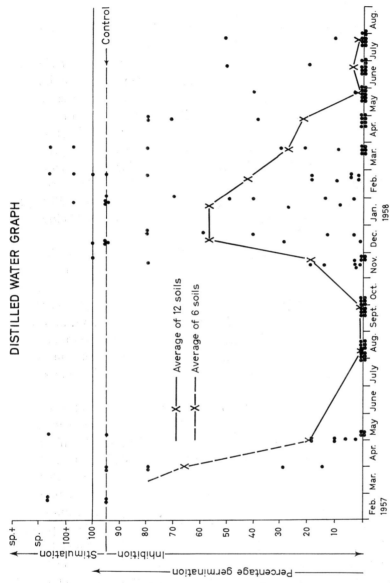

DISTILLED WATER GRAPH

Fig. 7. Germination assay points for *Mucor ramannianus* on twelve forest soils, taken from four sites at three levels, from May 1957. Points occupying the same position are shown in contact. The values above 100 per cent. are arbitrary estimates of stimulated growth, thus : 100+—germ tubes united into a network ; sp.—mycelium sporing moderately ; sp. +—mycelium sporing abundantly.

At each site samples were taken at three levels: surface litter (A_0) at 0–1 in., dark amorphous humus (A_1) at 1–2 in., and mineral soil, often somewhat bleached, (A_2) at 6–10 in. depth.

In addition to this series of tests in which the soil was moistened with distilled water, a parallel series of tests was carried out in which the soil was moistened with glucose solutions at several concentrations.

Seasonal variation. The results of the distilled-water assays are shown in Fig. 7. It can be seen that there is a strong seasonal variation in germination in most of the soils tested. There was, in fact, some seasonal variation in all of them. In each soil inhibition was complete in August and September 1957, but decreased during the winter, reaching a minimum in December and January 1958, after which, as in the spring of 1957, it has been increasing again towards the high level of the summer months. During the winter months there was a wide 'scatter' of germination levels, even including mycelial growth and sporulation, although the average percentage germination remained at all times well below the controls.

As might be expected, the glucose solutions in general gave higher germination counts than the distilled water, though there were several apparently anomalous results with individual soils. With the lowest concentration used (0·1 % (w/v) glucose), the graph runs roughly parallel to the distilled-water graph at a higher level of germination, and still shows a marked seasonal variation, but when the soils were moistened with 1·0 and 3·0 % (w/v) glucose solutions, the assay points came very high and the seasonal variation became less distinct and in some cases was obliterated.

Inhibition at the four sites and two localities was compared by averaging the distilled-water results for the three forest soil layers at each site. The curves in Fig. 8 show that the inhibition did not fall off so far during the winter at the higher locality (Marian-y-Winllan) as at the lower (Church Island), or under the beech-oak mixtures as under the conifers. In the particular soil layers, the site difference was most marked in the mineral layers in which, at Marian-y-Winllan, germination never exceeded 15%, while at Church Island inhibition disappeared completely in mid-winter. It was noticeable also that, on three of the humus layers, germination and growth reached its maximum in November and December, but on all four surface litters the maximum was reached after the New Year. The impression given is that the three soil layers behaved independently as regards level of inhibition.

The pronounced seasonal variation suggested a temperature effect, and so a test was set up in which the 12 forest soil samples, before assay

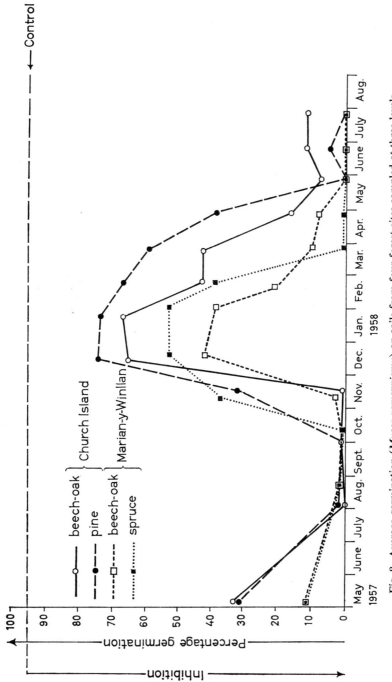

Fig. 8. Average germination (*Mucor ramannianus*) on soils from four forest sites sampled at three levels.

at the usual incubation temperature of 27°, were kept for 8 days at a range of 9 temperatures from −18 to 52°. The results showed that temperatures of 12·5–27° inclusive had little or no effect on inhibition which stayed at the usual high summer level. At 39° and above, inhibition was lost and the soil supported growth—with one exception at 39°. At 9° and below, inhibition progressively decreased until at 18° all the soils except one supported growth. As might be expected, the extreme temperatures did markedly reduce inhibition, but the temperatures within the normal out-of-doors range produced a much smaller variation in inhibition than the seasonal variation. It seems probable, therefore, that the seasonal variation may be attributed only partly to seasonal temperature changes. There is, of course, the possibility that, if the soils had been kept for longer than 8 days at the different temperatures, greater variation might have been shown.

A collection of about 40 soil samples from various sites in North Wales and the south of England were assayed for germination mainly during the high-inhibition summer period. With distilled water every sample showed complete or almost complete inhibition, but a range of glucose solutions brought differences to light. Broadly it is possible to distinguish between two main categories of soils—those in which the addition of glucose results in appreciable germination and growth of the test fungus, and those in which it does not.

The first category comprises most of the soils tested including forest soils under both hardwoods and conifers with pH 4–5, some under grass turf and acid heath, including several samples from Wareham Heath and Sugar Hill nursery, a garden soil with pH 5·5, and a Barton sand subsoil from Denny sandpit, New Forest.

The second category comprises chalk subsoil pH 8·5 and dark humus pH 7·5 from chalk rendzina under beech, both from Whiteleaf Hill, Chilterns; surface and deeper samples from Newborough Warren sand dunes, Anglesey, from both creeping willow and marram grass zones; also a sample of dune sand from Lligwy Bay on the opposite side of Anglesey.

Four soils were intermediate between these two categories. They were a sample of the notorious 'toxic' soil pH 4·0 from Gore Heath, near Wareham, studied by Neilson Jones and others; a garden soil from a shrubby border pH 7·1 which may have been limed as it effervesced with acid; clay from Chiltern plateau (pH 4·3) and sand with pH 7·4 from beneath grass turf on a fixed dune planted with Corsican pine on Newborough Warren. A series of germination tests with *Mucor ramannianus* on water agar and on beech-oak humus soil, adjusted to a range of pH values, showed no effect upon the inhibition within the range of pH found in any of the soils so far tested.

2. *Extension of tests to mycelia of Basidiomycetes*

As mentioned in Part I, the ordinary cellulose-film test is not generally applicable to mycelia or to the spores of Basidiomycetes and other fungi, which will not germinate under the control conditions. During a preliminary search for a method suitable for mycelia we found, in 1955, that lumps of moist soil placed upon a cellulose film covering a growing mycelium of *Polystictus versicolor* reduced growth in the contact area. Later, a variant of the agar-disc method used by Molin (1957) and Jackson (1958) was adopted. In our method standard 2-mm. plugs of inoculum were placed upon discs of water agar lying upon a cellulose film in intimate contact with the moist soil. For controls, glass cover-slips were inserted under the agar discs. These gave the same diameter growth of *Polystictus versicolor* as did the substitution of water agar and of kaolin for the soil. Tested in this way on a range of 12 forest-soil samples (4 test and 3 control discs on each), a group of 11 Basidiomycetes and a wood-rotting Pyrenomycete (*Xylaria hypoxylon*) showed an over-all average reduction in diameter-growth of 84%. Average percentage reductions for each species were as follows: *Coniophora cerebella*, 48; *Mycelium radicis atrovirens*, 54; *Polystictus versicolor*, 77; *Xylaria hypoxylon*, 83; *Poria vaillantii*, 84; *Merulius lacrymans*, 89; *Collybia velutipes*, 91; *Hydnum coralloides*, and *Armillaria mellea*, 93; *Lentinus lepideus*, 97; *Fomes annosus*, 98; *Polyporus schweinitzii*, 100.

Molin (1957) using discs of 1% (w/v) malt agar, with sterilized soil as a control, obtained complete suppression of growth in 4 Basidiomycetes, including *Fomes annosus* and *Lentinus lepideus*, two fungi which were also almost totally inhibited in our tests. We found, however, that the lower values for inhibition were associated with wide variations in growth of the fungus on different soils. In the case of *Coniophora cerebella* these ranged from no growth to growth equal to the controls.

3. *The nature of the inhibition*

The work hitherto described has so far allowed little time for any systematic attempt to isolate and identify the inhibitor, or to define its nature more closely. The inhibitory effect has been shown to travel up filter-paper from wet soil, in company with bacteria from which it has not been found possible to separate it except by the unsatisfactory

S.E.S.F.—10

method of Seitz filtering; and it has not so far been found possible to distinguish the effects of variation in the inhibition from those of variation in carbohydrates available in the soil.

The results of the assay have revealed not only a seasonal variation but also a variation in the behaviour of soils, and made it clear that some soils possess a chemical inhibition with quite different characters from that with which we are mainly concerned. Some of the Newborough Warren sands, for instance, exert some inhibition on germination of spores of *Mucor ramannianus* under all circumstances, in summer and winter, after washing, freezing, autoclaving, with or without added glucose. The chalk subsoil also inhibited after autoclaving, whereas the majority of soils when heated lose all inhibiting power and stimulate growth and sporulation.

We have had trouble in finding a satisfactory control material which neither inhibits nor stimulates growth, but recently this has been provided by a deep sample of Barton sand which, when cleaned with chromic acid and thoroughly washed with water, allows the same germination with the 'open' film as the control margins of the cellulose. It has now been shown that the inhibiting power is restored to this control sand when it is mixed with 1 % (v/v) of untreated soil or sand and incubated for 6 or more days.

This restoration was more complete when the inoculating material was Newborough Warren sand (creeping willow zone), which reduced germination to zero, than with a forest soil (A$_2$ horizon under spruce), which reduced it to under 1 % in the same time when the control sand was moistened with distilled water, but to zero when very dilute malt and peptone was used.

This is in contrast with the results of Hinson who did not get appreciable restoration in sterilized mineral forest soil even 63 days after mixing with the untreated soil (1:30), although the stimulus due to sterilization had by then fallen off; whereas Park (1956) using point inoculations of fresh soil, obtained a patchy restoration of inhibition. These differences may very well be due to differences in the number and virulence of the organisms available in the inoculum and of nutrient in the inoculated material, resulting in a different ecological balance among the microorganisms. It is clear that further investigation is required.

There can be little doubt now that the widespread inhibition is of biological origin, but in view of the complexity of the soil population it may not be easy to distinguish the parts played by any particular organism which when isolated can inhibit fungal growth or germination, such as the strain of *Bacillus macerans* isolated by Park (1956) or of actinomycetes studied by Stevenson (1956). The best chance seems to lie in studying the situation in the simplest and least fertile soils, such as sands.

REFERENCES

BRIAN, P. W., HEMMING, H. G., & McGOWAN, J. C. (1945). Origin of toxicity in Wareham Heath soil. *Nature, Lond.*, **155**, 637.

BURGES, A., & FENTON, E. (1953). The effect of carbon dioxide on the growth of certain fungi. *Trans. Brit. mycol. Soc.*, **36**, 104–8.

CHINN, S. H. F. (1953). A slide technique for the study of fungi and actinomycetes in soil with special reference to *Helminthosporium sativum*. *Canad. J. Bot.*, **31**, 718–24.

DOBBS, C. G., & HINSON, W. H. (1953). A widespread fungistasis in soils. *Nature, Lond.*, **172**, 197–9.

HINSON, W. H. (1954). *A study in the biology of soil moulds.* Ph.D. Thesis, University of Wales.

JACKSON, R. M. (1958). An investigation of fungistasis in Nigerian soils. *J. gen. Microbiol.*, **18**, 248–58.

JEFFERYS, E. G., & HEMMING, H. G. (1953). Fungistasis in soils. *Nature, Lond.*, **172**, 872.

MOLIN, N. (1957). A study on the infection biology of *Fomes annosus*. *Medd. fr. Stat. Skogsf. inst.* **47** (3), 1–36.

NEILSON-JONES, W. (1941). Biological aspects of soil fertility. *J. agric. Sci.*, **31**, 379–411.

PARK, D. (1956). Effects of substrate on a microbial antagonism, with reference to soil conditions. *Trans. Brit. mycol. Soc.*, **39**, 239–59.

SHAFFER, P. A., & HARTMANN, A. H. (1921). The iodometric determination of copper and its use in sugar analysis. *J. biol. Chem.*, **45**, 365.

STEVENSON, I. L. (1956). Antibiotic activity of actinomycetes in soil as demonstrated by direct observation techniques. *J. gen. Microbiol.*, **15**, 372–80.

ANTAGONISM—THE BACKGROUND TO SOIL FUNGI

D. PARK

Department of Cryptogamic Botany, University of Manchester

As ecology is the central and centralizing discipline of biological science, it is fortunate that current works on general ecology show a considerable amount of agreement on terminology and understanding of the concepts used. Clarke (1954) and Odum (1954) discuss the possible forms of interaction between pairs of species, and both subscribe to the system of description evolved by Haskell (1949) in the field of social science, and later applied more widely by Burkholder (1952). *Antagonism* is one main subdivision (the other being *symbiosis*) and includes all those associations in which at least one of the interacting species is harmed. The mechanisms of antagonism are three; namely, *antibiosis* in which species A produces a chemical substance that is inimical to species B without species A deriving any direct benefit, *exploitation* in which species A inflicts harm by the direct use of species B for its own benefit, and *competition* which is found in the indirect rivalry of two species for some feature of the environment that is in short supply. There are obstacles to the complete acceptance of these definitions; an important one is that 'competition' has, in addition to the strict meaning given above, a wider meaning equating it with antagonism. This Darwinian usage is difficult to avoid in certain contexts, e.g. in the verbal form as when 'two species compete for a substratum'. Similarly the broad concept is implied in the phrase 'competitive saprophytic ability', the precise meaning of which has been amply set forth by its author (Garrett, 1956). In unavoidable cases such as these the context usually makes it clear that 'antagonism' is referred to, while for most purposes the more strict definitions are gaining acceptance.

Despite the lack of terminological standardization in the earlier literature, it is apparent that all three mechanisms have been cited by various authorities to account for the antagonisms among soil fungi, and probably all are responsible in some degree. Exploitation, as represented by the parasitism of fungal hyphae by others, has undoubtedly been demonstrated, yet most emphasis has been laid on competition and antibiosis. There has been much controversy over the relative importance of these two processes. This controversy has its origin, it would seem, not in the fact that the two processes are mutually exclusive but in that workers have applied Occam's razor, and looked for a single general mechanism to explain the universal phenomenon of fungal inhibition in soil. Since this fungistasis is such a universal phenomenon, associated, not with specific factors but generally with the distribution and intensity of fungal activity (Dobbs & Hinson, 1953; Jackson, 1958), this is a more logical procedure than to explain some examples by antibiosis and others by competition. Some arguments in favour of antibiosis rather than competition have been put forward by Park (1956b); these will be extended and stated in more detail here.

It is common experience that fungi, although heterotrophic, can grow in nutrient solutions containing only low concentrations of nutrients. Examples of such growth are found in the continuous growth that occurs in a medium of distilled water and agar, in the growth of fungal colonies in laboratory mineral reagents, and in the growth over clean glass surfaces (Smith, 1946). In the light of these facts, when considering the probability of competition for nutrients as a mechanism in the production of the fungistatic property of soils, the following comment by Odum (1954) seems apt:

In a study of a particular situation the ecologist can usually discover the probable weak links and focus his attention, initially at least, on those environmental conditions most likely to be critical or 'limiting'. If an organism has a wide range of tolerance for a factor which is relatively constant and in moderate quantity in the environment, that factor is not likely to be limiting.

In this connexion it seems to have slipped out of focus that fungi have an extraordinarily wide range of tolerance for low levels of nutrients. Moreover, it is easily demonstrated (Park, 1956b) that a soil solution does contain sufficient nutrients to support fungal growth. There is of course the possibility that low-nutrient status might emphasize the susceptibility of fungi to retarding factors other than competition, as demonstrated by Brown (1922); this could make low nutrients seem more directly responsible than is actually the case. The theory of competition for nutrients, has been supported, among others, by Thornton & Skinner (1953), who have accompanied their views with the statement that 'workers have too often tended to ignore this factor of competition for nutrients, and to attribute antagonism wholly to the action of antibiotic secretions. More experiments are needed that aim at distinguishing these two factors'. I would point out that in respect of this general antagonism in soil such experiments are unnecessary, since

it is known that the fungistatic factor maintains fungal structures in an
inactive condition. It is difficult to imagine that inactive propagules
should compete for nutrients, or should be inhibited by lack of nutrients
when most are able to resume activity without any external source of
nutrients. For these reasons, therefore, and for others given later,
competition for nutrients does not satisfactorily account for the widespread type of antagonism that occurs between fungi in soil.

Competition for space has been named as a mechanism operative in
fungal antagonism in soil. In an analysis of the validity of any concept,
it is necessary to take the words at their true meaning. Competition for
space, then, implies that organisms compete primarily for physical
dimensions that, in an otherwise more suitable environment, exist in
amounts insufficient to accommodate the bodies of the organisms
together. In motile organisms of a high degree of organization, the
space concept may be less simple, as may be illustrated by reference to
foraging animals or to animals with territorial breeding requirements,
but in non-motile individuals space properly refers to those dimensions
necessary to house the body of the organism. Among higher plants one
may find examples of competition for space in this strict sense—in a
radish plot where swelling tap-roots may lift plants completely out of
the ground, or among the rhizomes of the floating mat vegetation at the
borders of lakes, where the aqueous medium provides ample nutrients
and removes metabolic products. The condition of a substratum being
so intensively colonized by fungal mycelium as physically not to allow
of penetration by another hypha must be comparatively rare. Examples
may be found in the mummification of a parasitized substratum by such
fungi as *Sclerotinia fructigena* and *Cordyceps militaris*. Elsewhere
among microbes competition for space may be found among the organisms colonizing sewage filters in a continuous flow of nutrient medium
which also removes staling products, although even here it is difficult to
visualize a potential colonizer of such a closed community 'competing'
for space without employing some other means of antagonism to dis-
place or incapacitate its predecessor on the site.

A microscopic examination of soil or of decomposing organic
materials in soil shows that fungal structures are normally not sufficiently numerous to be able physically to prevent further fungal development there. Competition for space, in fact, is not conceivable as a
mechanism underlying the general antagonism in soil. Any space unoccupied by structures, and which is unsuitable for colonization, does
not itself act as a factor in antagonism, but as a medium through or in
which some other mechanism operates. It may be that with more space

available further development would occur, initially at least, but the additional space would be acting by attenuating the other inhibiting factor by, e.g., absorbing or diluting toxins. Thus the problem is one of *space-plus*, or *Lebensraum*, rather than of space in the strict sense. To argue that the term 'competition for space' does not imply space in a strict sense is merely to replace one indefinite concept by another, and defers the consideration of the real problem a stage further.

It is my aim here to show that antibiosis more easily accounts for the general antagonism in soil. Unfortunately the concept of antibiosis has become associated almost inseparably with the study of specific antibiotics. From Waksman's (1945) discussion of the term 'antibiotic', current ideas have narrowed and become more and more confined to considerations of potent, complex, and usually chemotherapeutic substances. Almost all recent discussions of the significance of antibiotics in Nature are limited, explicitly or implicitly, to well-characterized, specific compounds, while simpler and more general compounds, such as carbon dioxide and lactic acid which the original definition includes, are omitted or excluded. Problems relating to the production and activity in soil of the specific type of antibiotic have received much attention. This subject has recently been reviewed in detail by Brian (1957), and lists of references on the items in the following sentences may be found in that article. Many workers have shown that such specific compounds may be produced in detectable amounts in soil, which in most cases was sterilized or greatly amended with energy materials. Jefferys (1952) has shown clearly that some of these antibiotics are stable under certain conditions on addition to the soil, and may exert an effect there. On the other hand, much work has gone to show that a number of specific antibiotics are degraded biologically in soil, or are there inactivated by adsorption on to colloidal materials. Such data, which suggest that specific antibiotic substances are not produced or are not active in soil, have been used to support arguments to the effect that the action of antibiotics in soil is, if operative at all, small and local. These arguments have little bearing on the general significance of *antibiosis* in soil, which is more probably mediated by simple toxic compounds than by specific antibiotics. In the same way positive proof of the local action of specific antibiotics, although of interest in connexion with the particular situation under investigation, and of probable significance there, may have less relevance to the general phenomenon of antibiosis in soils in which some mechanism of widespread occurrence and general validity must be operative.

In this respect much early work in this field, performed before the acceptance of the 'antibiotic' conception, is relevant, and shows that non-specific substances may account for the soil antagonism and that this phenomenon may be explained without reference to highly complex antibiotics. Schreiner & Shorey (1910) and Waksman (1936) give lists of chemical compounds that may be found in soil; many of these compounds are toxic to fungi. Greig-Smith (1912), Neilson-Jones (1941), Waksman & Woodruff (1942), and Newman & Norman (1943) are among those who have demonstrated the presence of fungi-toxic substances at inhibitory levels in soils. Further, it is known that common compounds of relatively simple nature may occur in soils at levels high enough to exert toxic effects, e.g. nitrites (Waksman, 1931), cyanides (Timonin, 1941), and carbon dioxide (Garrett, 1936). In using examples from the familiar literature to show that substances having an antibiotic effect do, in fact, occur in normal soils in quantities sufficient to inhibit fungal development, it is not my claim to introduce anything new, merely to point out the significance of what has been overlooked both by those authors who argue against antagonism by antibiosis and by those who propose a general antibiosis mediated specifically by antibiotics of the restricted type. 'Espinasse (1944) has criticized the use of the term 'antibiotic' for what is an aspect of a broader phenomenon. The concept of 'external metabolites', suggested by Lucas (1947), develops this idea further, and might serve as a means of avoiding some of the confusion surrounding the discussion of antibiotic substances.

The normal inactivity of fungi in soils is most easily overcome by adding amendments of various sorts to soil. Evidence of this type has usually been taken to support theories of competition rather than antibiosis, more especially since the amendments have usually contained food materials. In cases such as these, however, it has not been thought necessary to show that that amendment was effective through a direct amelioration of nutrient deficiency; this has usually been assumed. Even if it could be shown that such a stimulation were due directly to a higher nutrient status, the antibiosis hypothesis might still be applicable on the basis of the maxim already recalled, that inhibitory substances have their greatest effect when the energy of growth is small, and that an increase in the amounts of available nutrients may enable an organism to overcome a positive inhibition (Brown, 1922). But the nutrient effect is not the most reasonable explanation of the action of amendments. It has repeatedly been found that insoluble amendments to soil have a greater stimulatory action on the inhibited soil microbia than do soluble amendments (Rayner, 1939; Katznelson & Chase, 1944; Bingeman, Varner & Martin, 1953; Park, 1955; Chinn & Ledingham, 1957). Park (1956a) has shown, in addition, that non-nutrient but insoluble amendments may stimulate activity in similar toxic habitats. These facts invalidate the hypothesis of competition for nutrients as a cause of the inhibition. There are two other possible interpretations. The first, that the insoluble additions provide space and relieve competition for this factor need not further be considered; the second, that the amendment provides a fresh physical substratum in which there is no accumulated level of antibiotic substances has been preferred (Park, 1956a, b).

A useful analogy may be made between the condition of fungi in soil and in old cultures on agar. In pure culture a fungus may fill the Petri dish before cessation of growth, but in this condition spaces in the agar remain unoccupied by hyphae. The fungus is inhibited by the accumulation of autotoxic metabolic by-products or staling substances, and not by the depletion of nutrients (Boyle, 1924; Pratt, 1924; Waksman & Foster, 1937) or of space. Tribe (1957) has given an ingenious demonstration of how the same process can occur in soil: here cellulose film buried in soil eventually became unsuitable for further growth of cellulose-decomposing fungi, although some cellulose remained. The staling of fungal cultures is by definition an example of antibiosis, and has, in fact, been considered by Waksman (1937) as iso-antagonism comparable with the hetero-antagonism found in soils. In a staled pure culture of a fungus, as in soils, a block of non-nutrient agar gel added to the surface stimulates the inhibited fungus to activity, and for the same reasons. If, then, soil is regarded in the light of a fungal culture medium in this way, normal field soil is a medium that has been inoculated with a complex mixed culture of fungi and other organisms, and incubated for long periods under varying cultural conditions. Obviously, in such a medium metabolic products of diverse types have accumulated, and have resulted in an intense example of the sort of inhibition that occurs even in a pure fungal culture in which the fungus is not a recognized antibiotic producer. On this basis the fungal population of any settled soil is normally in an advanced stage of what has been described as 'Altkultur', and shows the inhibited, abnormal, and disintegrating spores and hyphae characteristic of that state (Appel & Wollenweber, 1910). This condition has also been described from experimental cultures of individual fungi in sterilized soil. So-called 'sick soils' that are characterized by an unusually high level of toxins (Waksman, 1937) may be regarded as extreme examples of staled cultures.

In short, then, theories of competition for nutrients or space fail adequately to account for the phenomenon of antagonism in soils in a general sense. A basis for an explanation of the phenomenon lies in facts familiar to all microbiologists, so that it is superfluous to postulate in all cases of antagonism the action of specific antibiotic substances, the antibiosis being brought about by either a general toxic substance or by a complex of toxins produced by many organisms.

Implicit in the foregoing arguments are certain views on the significance of antibiotic production. Before expanding these, I should like to point out that discussions on this topic usually consider two separate aspects of significance; firstly, the immediate importance of the production to the species which produces the antibiotic, and secondly, the significance of the production in the biology of the habitat. Although separate, these two facts are conveniently discussed together. The idea of an antibiotic being of direct value to the organism producing it has been criticized on the grounds that it implies a purposiveness on the part of that organism; Brian (1957) has adequately disposed of this argument, which seems to be based on the misconception that to ascribe a function to a process in an organism is to accept that the organism evolved the process with a foreknowledge of the function that it would perform. Garrett (1956) has dealt with, and disposed of, three other main arguments against the antibiotic value of antibiotics to the organisms that produce them. Other arguments may be raised. An antibiotic is a toxic compound, and there are indications that organisms producing such compounds are not immune to their action, but merely possess a high degree of tolerance to high concentrations of them. It is, therefore, probable that the external secretion of compounds of this sort is essentially an elimination of autotoxic metabolites. The primary function, and hence value to the organism, of such 'secretion', then, may be the elimination of toxicity. Antibiotic production, on this view, has its individual significance for the producer-organism in excretion, and is independent of any possible action on other organisms.

Other arguments consider both types of significance together. Brian (1957) argues in the following way in support of the advantage conferred on organisms by the capacity to produce an antibiotic.

Organisms sensitive to antibiotics are at a disadvantage where they have to compete with antibiotic producers for limited substrates. If that conception is valid, I think it is reasonable to conclude that what is a disadvantage for one group of organisms may be an advantage for others. If that is so, the capacity to produce antibiotics must be expected to increase the likelihood of survival of a saprophytic species.

This statement expresses one of the main arguments of the supporters of the theory that antibiotics have an immediate beneficial effect on the organism which produces them, and is therefore worth examining in some detail. The major error in the argument is that the two types of organism that are compared—namely, those 'organisms sensitive to antibiotics' and the 'antibiotic producers'—are assumed to be two different and separate categories; in fact, this need not be so. Butler (1953) and Park (1956*b*) are among those who have shown that organisms not recognized as producers of antibiotics may have a higher tolerance of antibiosis than some organisms that exhibit antibiotic activity. Some misconceptions in this respect have arisen as a result of thinking in terms of artificially mixed cultures of only two organisms, and with those growing towards each other as colonies. This condition is remote from that usually occurring in Nature, where the colony as such may not exist, and where many more than two organisms are in the same sphere of influence and are probably simultaneously active on those occasions when conditions favour activity. If, in such a situation, fungus A produces an antibiotic at a concentration to which some associated organisms are sensitive, and to which others, including A, are tolerant, then the degree of advantage gained by A will not be simply determined, but will depend on many factors, among which the following are particularly relevant: (i) the relative numbers of the sensitive and the tolerant organisms; (ii) the distribution within these two categories of organisms able to inhibit A itself; (iii) the proportion of sensitive organisms that would, in the absence of the antibiotic produced by A, be able to inhibit the antagonists of A. Two hypothetical situations will illustrate this more clearly; in both of these, four organisms occur together, and have equal demands on the habitat.

1*st situation:* A grows and produces an antibiotic that inhibits B, C, and D. Thus A has the substratum to itself—an obvious advantage.

2*nd situation:* A inhibits B, but C and D are tolerant of A's antibiotic. B, when active, inhibits C and D, but has no adverse effect on A. In the presence of A, of course, B neither grows nor produces its antibiotic, and so C and D grow. A, therefore, shares the substratum with two organisms, whereas were it not to produce the antibiotic it would share it with only one organism.

The first type of situation is the one usually assumed by the protagonists of the hypothesis of an individual beneficial effect of antibiotic production. The second situation illustrates a perfectly possible type of set-up (cf. Lochhead & Landerkin, 1949) in which antibiotic production may be a disadvantage. Although this situation is hypothetical and a simplification, it is a much greater simplification to assume that because an organism produces an antibiotic it automatically has an advantage.

An extension of the above reasoning shows that an organism that has a wide tolerance of antibiotics, irrespective of any ability to produce antibiotics, has a high chance of success in mixed cultures. The fact that tolerance to antibiotics is an important character in ecological success is recognized by most authorities, and has been cited as such in a number of review papers (e.g. Garrett, 1950; Hawker, 1957), including the one containing the statement quoted (Brian, 1957). Garrett (1956), in his discussion of competitive saprophytic ability, lists this character as one of the four likely to favour a high competitive saprophytic ability. The other three are high growth rate and rapid germinability of spores, good enzyme-producing equipment, and the production of antibiotic toxins. The argument advanced in this present essay would, in reference to any toxic situation, relegate these three characters to a role subsidiary in importance to tolerance to antibiosis. An organism sensitive to the antagonism to which it is exposed might possess such characters but be unable to express them. A clear example has been given by Park (1956b) of an organism (*Trichothecium roseum*) having a high antibiotic activity yet being unsuccessful in mixed cultures due to its low tolerance to antagonism. So that although the capacity to produce antibiotics is a character conducing to fitness (Brian, 1957), it is a secondary character, tolerance to the antagonism existing in soil being the primary requirement of any soil fungus that inhabits situations in which the general fungistasis exists.

There are some conditions in which an organism producing an antibiotic has a clear-cut advantage, irrespective of its sensitivity to antibiosis from other organisms. These are those conditions of Nature which compare closely with laboratory conditions of culture. One of these is the situation of a pioneer or primary colonizer of a substratum which can grow and produce its antibiotic freely and without interference. Here, an organism that is sensitive to antibiosis and unable to colonize any substratum that is already occupied by other organisms may, when established in a newly available substratum, continue to be active and survive, and may even exclude those organisms to which it is, in other circumstances, sensitive (e.g. Simmonds, 1947; Wright, 1956; Tribe, 1957; Barton, 1960). In some of these cases it is noticeable, however, that the initial colonizers able to exclude other organisms are not recognized producers of antibiotics. It is in a situation of this type, in which the organisms are, in part, dependent upon a sustained high inoculum potential, that antibiotic activity may have considerable individual significance for the organism possessing it. Furthermore, under the conditions of this sort the other characters listed by Garrett (1956) as important in respect of competitive saprophytic ability (e.g. high growth rate, etc.) become primary and tolerance to antibiosis secondary. This is because the organism exists in a non-toxic environment. Despite the tendency, through the high inoculum potential, of such a system to be self-perpetuating, these organisms do eventually bring about a change in the substratum both through nutrient loss and through staling, so that it eventually becomes unsuitable for their continued development there. It is one of the causes of succession, therefore, that an organism may be more sensitive to its own antibiotic products than are other organisms that succeed it in time.

Clements (1916, 1935) has considered some topics that are appropriate to this discussion of background antagonism; in particular, his definitions of action, co-action and re-action are of direct relevance. *Action* is the effect of the abiotic habitat on the organism; *co-action* is the direct effect of one organism on another; *re-action* is the effect of the organism on the abiotic environment. The idea of antibiotic production directly and solely favouring those organisms that produce them seems to be based on the conception of antibiosis as a form of co-action. Co-action may occur, but is special and restricted. The arguments that have been put forward in this essay favour the view that antibiosis is an ecologically significant factor mainly in the form of a re-action that is followed later by action. In other words, the organisms in a habitat produce substances that are added to the abiotic environment, from which they subsequently affect the other organisms under the influence of that modified environment. Soil antagonism is in this sense a non-specific background effect, cumulative and common in its production by all the organisms present, and acting on all those organisms.

REFERENCES

APPEL, O., & WOLLENWEBER, H. W. (1910). Grundlagen einer monographie der gattung *Fusarium* (Link.). *Arb. Kaiserl. Biol. Anstalt f. Land- u. Forstwirtschaft*, **8**, 1–207.

BARTON, R. (1960). Antagonisms among some sugar fungi. *Ecology of soil fungi*, Symposium, Liverpool, 1958.

BINGEMAN, C. W., VARNER, J. E., & MARTIN, W. P. (1953). The effect of the addition of organic materials on the decomposition of an organic soil. *Proc. Soil Sci. Soc. Amer.*, **17**, 34–8.

BOYLE, C. (1924). Studies in the physiology of parasitism. X. The growth reactions of certain fungi to their staling products. *Ann. Bot. N.S.*, **38**, 113–35.

BRIAN, P. W. (1957). The ecological significance of antibiotic production. *Microbial Ecology, 7th Symposium Soc. gen. Microbiol.*, 168–88.

BROWN, W. (1922). On the germination and growth of fungi at various temperatures and in various concentrations of oxygen and carbon dioxide. *Ann. Bot. N.S.*, **36**, 257–83.

BURKHOLDER, P. R. (1952). Co-operation and conflict among primitive organisms. *Amer. Scientist*, **40**, 601–31.

BUTLER, F. C. (1953). Saprophytic behaviour of some cereal root-rot fungi. II. Factors influencing saprophytic colonization of wheat straw. *Ann. appl. Biol.*, **40**, 298–304.

CHINN, S. H. F., & LEDINGHAM, R. J. (1957). Studies on the influence of various substances on the germination of *Helminthosporium sativum* spores in soil. *Canad. J. Bot.*, **35**, 697–701.

CLARKE, G. L. (1954). *Elements of ecology*. New York: Wiley.

CLEMENTS, F. E. (1916). *Plant succession*. Washington: Carnegie Inst.

CLEMENTS, F. E. (1935). Experimental ecology in the public service. *Ecology*, **16**, 342–63.

DOBBS, C. G., & HINSON, W. H. (1953). A widespread fungistasis in soils. *Nature, Lond.*, **172**, 197–9.

'ESPINASSE, P. G. (1944). Effects of secretions. *Nature, Lond.*, **154**, 610.

GARRETT, S. D. (1936). Soil conditions and the take-all disease of wheat. *Ann. appl. Biol.*, **23**, 667–99.

GARRETT, S. D. (1950). Ecology of the root-inhabiting fungi. *Biol. Rev.*, **25**, 220–54.

GARRETT, S. D. (1956). *Biology of root-infecting fungi*. Cambridge University Press.

GREIG-SMITH, R. (1912). The agricere and bacteriotoxins of the soil. *Centrbl. Bakt.*, **34**, 224–6.

HASKELL, E. F. (1949). A clarification of social science. *Main Currents in Modern Thought*, **7**, 45–51.

HAWKER, L. E. (1957). Ecological factors and the survival of fungi. *Microbiol Ecology, 7th Symposium Soc. gen. Microbiol.*, 238–58.

JACKSON, R. M. (1958). An investigation of fungistasis in Nigerian soils. *J. gen. Microbiol.*, **18**, 248–58.

JEFFERYS, E. G. (1952). The stability of antibiotics in soils. *J. gen. Microbiol.*, **7**, 295–312.

KATZNELSON, H., & CHASE, F. E. (1944). Qualitative studies of soil micro-organisms. VI. Influence of season and treatment on incidence of nutritional groups of bacteria. *Soil Sci.*, **58**, 473–9.

LOCHHEAD, A. G., & LANDERKIN, G. B. (1949). Aspects of antagonisms between micro-organisms in soil. *Plant and Soil*, **1**, 271–6.

LUCAS, C. E. (1947). The ecological effects of external metabolites. *Biol. Rev.*, **22**, 270–95.

NEILSON-JONES, W. (1941). Biological aspects of soil fertility. *J. agric. Sci.*, **31**, 379–411.

NEWMAN, A. S., & NORMAN, A. G. (1943). The activity of subsurface soil populations. *Soil Sci.*, **55**, 377–91.

ODUM, E. P. (1954). *Fundamentals of ecology*. Philadelphia: W. B. Saunders & Co.

PARK, D. (1955). Experimental studies on the ecology of fungi in soil. *Trans. Brit. mycol. Soc.*, **38**, 130–42.

PARK, D. (1956a). Effect of substrate on a microbial antagonism, with reference to soil conditions. *Trans. Brit. mycol. Soc.*, **39**, 239–59.

PARK, D. (1956b). On the role of amendments in the biology of fungi in soil. *Proc. 6th Congr. Int. Soil Sci. Soc.*, **3**, 23–8.

PRATT, C. A. (1924). The staling of fungal cultures. I. General and chemical investigations of staling by *Fusarium*. *Ann. Bot.*, **38**, 563–95.

RAYNER, M. C. (1939). The mycorrhizal habit in relation to forestry. III. Organic composts and the growth of young trees. *Forestry*, **13**, 19–35.

SCHREINER, O., & SHOREY, E. C. (1910). Chemical nature of soil organic matter. *U.S. Dept. Agr. Bur. Soils Bull.*, **74**, 1–48.

SIMMONDS, P. M. (1947). The influence of antibiosis in the pathogenicity of *Helminthosporium sativum*. *Sci. Agric.*, **27**, 625–32.

SMITH, G. (1946). Presidential address: Mycology and the war. *Trans. Brit. mycol. Soc.*, **29**, 1–10.

THORNTON, H. G., & SKINNER, F. A. (1953). The interaction of actinomycetes with other micro-organisms in soil. *6th Int. Congr. Microbiol., Rome. Actinomycetales Symposium*, 174–90.

TIMONIN, M. I. (1941). The interaction of higher plants and soil micro-organisms. III. Effect of by-products of plant growth on activity of fungi and actinomycetes. *Soil Sci.*, **52**, 395–408.

TRIBE, H. T. (1957). Ecology of micro-organisms in soils as observed during their development upon buried cellulose film. *Microbial Ecology, 7th Symposium Soc. gen. Microbiol.*, 287–98.

WAKSMAN, S. A. (1931). *Principles of soil microbiology.* London: Baillière, Tindall & Cox.

WAKSMAN, S. A. (1936). *Humus: origin, chemical composition, and importance in nature.* London: Baillière, Tindall & Cox.

WAKSMAN, S. A. (1937). Associative and antagonistic effects of micro-organisms. I. Historical review of antagonistic relationships. *Soil Sci.*, **43**, 51–68.

WAKSMAN, S. A. (1945). *Microbial antagonisms and antibiotic substances.* New York: The Commonwealth Fund.

WAKSMAN, S. A., & FOSTER, J. W. (1937). Associative and antagonistic effects of micro-organisms. II. Antagonistic effects of micro-organisms grown on artificial substrates. *Soil Sci.*, **43**, 69–76.

WAKSMAN, S. A., & WOODRUFF, H. B. (1942). The occurrence of bacteriostatic and bactericidal substances in the soil. *Soil Sci.*, **53**, 233–9.

WRIGHT, J. M. (1956). The production of antibiotics in soil. IV. Production of antibiotics in coats of seeds sown in soil. *Ann. appl. Biol.*, **44**, 561–6.

ANTAGONISM AMONGST SOME SUGAR FUNGI

R. BARTON

Department of Cryptogamic Botany, University of Manchester

The experiments presented for discussion in this paper form part of an investigation into the ecology of *Pythium mamillatum* in soils. Their implications concerning the biology of this parasite can conveniently be left for some later date, but as they also contribute towards an understanding of antagonistic mechanisms between soil fungi, they are put forward for consideration here in this respect.

Although better known as vigorous parasites on juvenile or senescent parts of plants, *Pythium* spp. have been regarded as soil saprophytes since the end of the last century (de Bary, 1887). These fungi typically occur as pioneers in the sequence of ecological succession on decaying organic materials (Barton, 1958), exemplifying to an extraordinary degree the physiological characteristics associated with their substrate group, namely the sugar fungi (Burges, 1939a; Garrett, 1951, 1956). For instance, they are able to develop abundant mycelium very rapidly, and possess a marked capacity for producing resting bodies from vegetative hyphae, such features being an adaptation for exploiting situations only intermittently available in soil.

A quantitative experimental method for assessing the saprophytic colonizing ability of *Pythium* has been based on the well-known technique of baiting soils described by Butler (1907). Wood obtained from dead oak twigs was cut into cubes (about 2-mm. cube), soaked in a 2% (w/v) glucose solution, and autoclaved. Amended in this way, the fragments were readily colonized by *Pythium* in soil and had the additional advantage of being easily handled. Twenty-five of these pieces were placed in each of three 50-g. batches of the test soil and incubated for 3 days. After washing in 6 changes of sterile water, the wood fragments were finally plated on to oat agar. Incubation at 20° C. for a further 3 days allowed the colonizers to grow out on to the agar. Microscopic observation at low magnification of plates flooded with formalin/alcohol enabled the numbers of fragments colonized by *Pythium* to be recorded, these being clearly observed as centres of oospore production.

To facilitate this inspection *Pythium mamillatum*, a species character-ized by a spiny oogonial wall, was chosen as test fungus.

This method was used in conjunction with a modification of the Cambridge method (Butler, 1953*a*; Lucas, 1955; Garrett, 1956) to obtain information concerning the saprophytic colonizing ability of *P. mamillatum* at different inoculum levels, and the effect of using virgin and pre-colonized organic material as baits. A garden soil containing a low natural inoculum of *P. mamillatum* was adjusted to the appropriate inoculum levels by mixing with sand/maize-meal inoculum of the fungus in the following ratios, 100:0, 95:5, 90:10, 75:25, 50:50, 25:75, 0:100.

In one series tests were carried out at each inoculum level with sterile amended wood, and in another series with sterile fragments which had been left for 3 days in a woodland soil known not to contain *Pythium*. It is evident from the results (Table 1) that *P. mamillatum* is a very active saprophyte in the garden soil, heavily colonizing the virgin organic material even at low inoculum levels. In contrast, pre-coloniza-tion of such material by other soil saprophytes significantly reduced the percentage of pieces colonized; in fact, from the natural inoculum of the garden soil there was no colonization at all. It is reasonable to assume that after 3 days in woodland soil the invading saprophytes consist mainly of sugar fungi, together with some bacteria and members of the soil fauna. In this communication attention is directed to the fungi involved.

TABLE 1

Saprophytic colonization of virgin and pre-colonized substrates by Pythium mamillatum *at different inoculum levels*

	Percentage of inoculum in soil						
Percentage colonization in	*100*	*75*	*50*	*25*	*10*	*5*	*0*
Sterile substrate	100	100	100	99	66	48	35
Pre-colonized substrate	99	100	66	45	26	9	0

Leading on from the establishment of a definite antagonistic effect comes the question of interpreting the underlying mechanism. From the findings of other investigators it is possible to suggest three alterna-tives that might be important here.

(*a*) *Nutrient effect*. It is possible that the antagonistic organisms have decomposed or otherwise removed the available carbohydrates in the wood. This possibility is substantiated by the fact that only a limited

S.E.S.F.—11

amount of glucose is impregnated into the material in the first place, and furthermore, *P. mamillatum* is unable to colonize wood in the absence of added nutrients of this kind (Fig. 1).

(*b*) *Toxic effect.* The production of chemical substances inhibitory to *P. mamillatum* might well limit colonization. Many soil fungi (including sugar fungi) have been shown to produce specific antibiotics which limit the activities of *Pythium* spp. In addition, inhibition might also be caused, directly or indirectly, by simpler chemical compounds produced as a result of general metabolic activity, such substances being included in the general category of external metabolites suggested by Lucas (1949). Although evidence for the functioning of specific antibiotics in natural soils is limited, in the present case the conditions would be particularly favourable for their production (Wright, 1956*a*, *b*). The antagonists are confined to a relatively small zone of organic material in which adequate nutrients occur, and, in addition, after only 3 days' growth are in an active metabolic state.

(*c*) *Physical effect.* It is possible that the antagonistic organisms, in a sudden burst of vegetative activity, have occupied most of the available space in the interior or at the surface of the organic material, influenceing, solely by physical means, the entry and further development of *Pythium* hyphae.

The following experiment was undertaken to determine the relevance of some of the above factors. Samples of 150 fragments of wood were subjected to one of the treatments enumerated below:

A. Autoclaved in distilled water.
B. Autoclaved in a 2% (w/v) solution of glucose (treatments A and B were set up as controls).
C. Autoclaved in glucose, then left in *Pythium*-free soil for 3 days.
D. Autoclaved in glucose, left in *Pythium*-free soil for 3 days, then resterilized by exposing to propylene oxide vapour for 24 hr.
E. Autoclaved in glucose, left in *Pythium*-free soil for 3 days, then soaked in 2% (w/v) glucose solution for 24 hr.
F. Autoclaved in glucose, left in *Pythium*-free soil for 3 days, sterilized in propylene-oxide vapour, then soaked in 2% (w/v) glucose for 24 hr.

The 150 fragments in each treatment were divided, 25 being placed in each of 6 100-ml. flasks containing, in 3 cases, garden soil at its natural inoculum level, and in the other 3 flasks, garden soil plus 15% (w/w) sand/maize-meal inoculum. After 3 days in these flasks the pieces were assessed for colonization by *P. mamillatum* (Fig. 1).

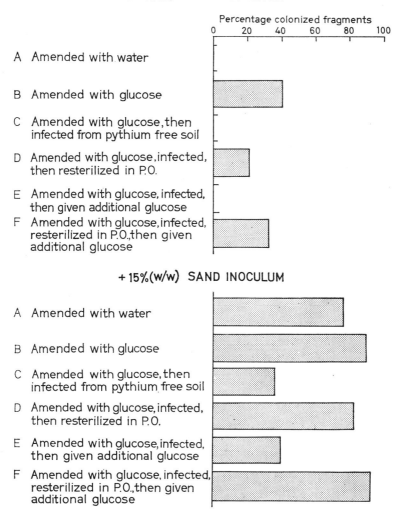

Fig. 1. Saprophytic colonization of variously treated wood
fragments by *Pythium mamillatum*.

Comparing treatment B with treatment E, the latter having at least as much nutrient material as B but also being colonized by other organisms, it is evident that lack of sufficient nutrients is not preventing the colonization of preinfected fragments by *P. mamillatum*. Sterilization by propylene-oxide vapour interferes less with the stability of labile chemical substances, including specific antibiotics, than methods involving heat. The fact that *P. mamillatum* colonized a considerable proportion of wood fragments in treatment D, indicates that highly potent specific antibiotics are unlikely to have been produced in the substrate. A similar conclusion can be drawn from treatment F, where the wood fragments, after being sterilized in a similar manner, are given additional glucose.

Some of the sugar fungi that were likely to have been limiting saprophytic colonization of wood fragments by *P. mamillatum* were isolated from soil on wood baits for screening tests. Each isolated fungus, after being established in pure culture, was used to infect wood fragments autoclaved in a 2% (w/v) glucose solution, then these pieces were placed in a garden soil and assessed for colonization by *P. mamillatum* in the manner already outlined. Of the 12 sugar fungi[1] investigated in this way, each one limited saprophytic colonization to such an extent that at the natural inoculum level of the garden soil, *P. mamillatum* did not succeed in becoming established in any of the fragments. The underlying antagonistic mechanism seems, from this, to be of a general nature involving all of the sugar fungi examined, and argues against the operation of specific antibiotics.

To investigate this implication further, the ability of *P. mamillatum* to colonize pieces of wood soaked in growth media staled by these fungi was determined. The same 12 sugar fungi were grown in a liquid medium containing inorganic salts and 2% (w/v) glucose, for periods of 3 and 14 days. After being Seitz filtered, the staled medium from each fungus was allowed to diffuse into autoclaved wood fragments, which were then placed in garden soil and examined for colonization by *P. mamillatum*. Staled growth media from the sugar fungi did not significantly exclude *P. mamillatum* from wood pieces except in one case. The antagonist involved was a fungus which has not yet been identified, for although forming cleistothecia or perithecia in abundance, conidia or

---

[1] *Trichoderma viride* 1   *Mucor silvaticus*
  Trichoderma viride 2   *Mucor microsporus*
  Trichoderma viride 3   *Rhizopus nigricans*
  Trichoderma viride 4   *Cephalosporium curtipes*
  Penicillium frequentans   *Fusarium oxysporum*
  Dicoccum asperum   Perithecial producer (unidentified)

ascospores have not yet been detected. Within the limits of accuracy of the method employed, it is possible to conclude that toxic substances, likely to retain their effectiveness at considerable dilutions when impregnated in wood, e.g. specific antibiotics, are not found in the staled-growth media of most of these sugar fungi.

Conclusions from the above experiments suggest that the antagonistic mechanism operating between some sugar fungi and *P. mamillatum* during the colonization of fresh organic material is not dependent on the production of specific antibiotics. The summation of evidence for this view is, firstly, the general nature of the antagonism, and secondly, the non-detection of potent toxins in growth media or in the pre-colonized organic matter. Other chemical substances of a more general, and possibly less potent, nature may play a part, gaseous toxins such as carbon dioxide or ethylene would not diffuse to any great extent into the wood fragments from staled-growth media, and other staling substances might be rendered ineffective by the dilution involved. The alternative of physical restriction by the established antagonists remains to be considered. Competition for available space has been suggested as an antagonistic mechanism by Wright (1955) and Skinner (1956), such a phenomenon might become especially prominent in cases involving organic material rich in nutrients and limited in size. It is self-evident that, short of parasitism, the space occupied by one hypha cannot be occupied by another so long as the original hypha remains in a healthy condition; therefore, physical restriction will be determined by the density of the mycelium of the antagonist, and will vary according to the quantity and activity of inoculum of the colonist. In the fragments of organic material used in the above experiments, the quantity of space actually occupied by the mycelium of the antagonistic sugar fungi must be very high, but it is doubtful if a complete physical barrier, sufficient to preclude the entry of active colonizing hyphae, is formed. On the other hand, a high density of mycelium will result in a much more effective distribution throughout the organic material of toxic staling substances emanating from living hyphae. In other words, to have prevented the entry of *P. mamillatum* into a fragment of wood of the size used here, the staling substances must have been disposed in functionable quantities at least all round, and perhaps all through the material. Therefore an antagonistic mechanism based on the toxic effect of generally produced staling substances, together with the proviso that these substances are favourably disposed throughout the substratum relative to the density and degree of colonization by the mycelium of the antagonistic sugar fungus, seems to be the best explanation for the preclusion of *P. mamillatum* from pre-colonized wood fragments. However, the issue is by no means closed, further experiments are being undertaken to establish the relationship between these sugar fungi and *P. mamillatum* in culture, and to examine the effect of known antibiotics in limiting the colonization of wood pieces by the parasite, both of which have some bearing on the arguments advanced here.

Considerable attention has been given to the role of specific antibiotics in antagonistic phenomena in soils. Recently, Brian (1957) has reviewed the evidence for the production and functioning of these substances, concluding that antibiotics are likely to be produced, and have their greatest effect, in or around organic material in soil. I have suggested, however, that *P. mamillatum* can be excluded from organic material occupied by sugar fungi by antagonistic mechanisms other than specific antibiotics. The two statements are not contradictory, the relevant question being, should one of these antagonistic sugar fungi have the ability to produce a potent antibiotic, would it become even more effective as an antagonist above and beyond its effectiveness obtained from other sources? Wright (1956c) has, in fact, shown this to be the case with *Trichoderma viride* strains antagonistic towards *P. ultimum*. There is good reason for suggesting, then, that antagonism from specific antibiotics and from more generally produced staling substances must be regarded as complementary to each other, the difference being one of degree rather than essence.

REFERENCES

BARTON, R. (1958). Occurrence and establishment of *Pythium* in soils. *Trans. Brit. mycol. Soc.* **41**, 207–22.

BARY, A. DE. (1887). *Comparative morphology and biology of the Fungi, Mycetozoa, and Bacteria.* Oxford: Clarendon Press.

BRIAN, P. W. (1957). The ecological significance of antibiotic production. *Microbial Ecology. 7th Symposium Soc. Gen. Microbiol.,* Cambridge University Press, 168–88.

BURGES, A. (1939). Soil fungi and root infection. *Broteria,* **8**, 64–81.

BUTLER, E. J. (1907). An account of the genus *Pythium* and some of the Chytridiaceae. *Mem. Dep. Agric. India (Bot. Ser.* 1), No. **5**.

BUTLER, F. C. (1953). Saprophytic behaviour of some cereal root-rot fungi. I. Saprophytic colonization of wheat straw. *Ann. appl. Biol.,* **40**, 284–97.

GARRETT, S. D. (1951). Ecological groups of soil fungi: a survey of substrate relationships. *New Phytol.,* **50**, 149–66.

GARRETT, S. D. (1956). *Biology of root-infecting fungi.* Cambridge University Press.

LUCAS, C. E. (1949). External metabolites and ecological adaptation. *Symposium Soc. exp. Biol.,* **3**, 336–47.

LUCAS, R. L. (1955). A comparative study of *Ophiobolus graminis* and *Fusarium culmorum* in saprophytic colonization of wheat straw. *Ann. appl. Biol.,* **43**, 134–43.

SKINNER, F. A. (1956). The effect of adding clays to mixed cultures of *Streptomyces albidiflorus* and *Fusarium culmorum*. *J. gen. Microbiol.*, **14**, 393–405.
WRIGHT, J. M. (1955). The production of antibiotics in soil. II. Production of griseofulvin by *Penicillium nigricans*. *Ann. appl. Biol.*, **43**, 288–405.
WRIGHT, J. M. (1956a). Production of gliotoxin in soils. *Nature, Lond.*, **177**, 896.
WRIGHT, J. M. (1956b). The production of antibiotics in soil. III. Production of gliotoxin in wheat straw buried in soil. *Ann. appl. Biol.*, **44**, 461–6.
WRIGHT, J. M. (1956c). Biological control of a soil-borne *Pythium* infection by seed inoculation. *Plant and Soil*, **8**, 132–40.

(This work was carried out during the tenure of an award from the Agricultural Research Council.)

SOIL FUNGISTASIS AND THE RHIZOSPHERE

R. M. JACKSON

Soil Microbiology Department, Rothamsted Experimental Station, Harpenden, Hertfordshire

INTRODUCTION

Since Hiltner introduced the term 'rhizosphere' in 1904, a considerable volume of work has been devoted to studies of the region of enhanced microbial activity immediately surrounding plant roots. The most obvious reason for the stimulation of micro-organisms in the rhizosphere is the presence of an increased supply of nutrients in the form of soluble inorganic and organic root excretions and the breakdown products of sloughed-off dead root cells. As pointed out by Starkey (1929), other factors may be responsible for the modified microflora near roots, including the lowering of the concentration of certain mineral elements in the soil due to their absorption, partial desiccation of the soil resulting from water absorption, and increase in soil carbonates following carbon dioxide production by the roots. While a direct stimulation of growth by the increased nutrient content of the root zone, as compared with soil away from the roots, may provide the most satisfactory explanation for the often considerable increase in bacterial numbers in the rhizosphere, it would seem likely to provide only a partial explanation for the behaviour of fungi.

It has been shown conclusively that a very high percentage of the fungi present in the soil, as determined by the dilution-plate method, are represented by inactive propagules (Hinson, 1953; Warcup, 1955, 1957). Germination of these inactive fungal propagules is not generally limited by lack of nutrients, as may be readily demonstrated by plating soil suspensions on water agar. The reason for this inactivity must rather be sought in the almost universal presence in natural soils of an inhibitory or fungistatic factor, which is particularly potent in preventing spore germination (Dobbs & Hinson, 1953; Hessayon, 1953; Park, 1956; Jackson, 1958). It is apparent that any change which reduces or removes the fungistatic effect of the soil will result in an increase in fungal activity irrespective of any alteration in the nutrient status of the soil. For the nutrients released into the soil by plant roots to be effective in stimulating the activity of inhibited fungal propagules, there must be an accompanying removal or amelioration of the dormancy imposed by soil fungistasis. It has, in fact, been found by Chinn (1953), Dobbs & Hinson (1953), Park (1955), and others that the addition to soil of organic amendments such as soya-bean meal results in increased germination of previously inhibited fungal spores or may reduce lysis; glucose and sodium nitrate have been shown to have similar effects. In this contribution some work, already briefly reported (Jackson, 1957), is described which was undertaken to determine whether or not the roots of seedling plants are capable of inducing germination of previously inhibited fungal spores, and to examine in more detail the stimulation of inhibited fungal spores by known compounds.

EXPERIMENTAL

The use of buried glass plates to study the effects of seedling roots on fungal spores in soil

Technique. The method used was derived from Chinn's buried-slide technique (Chinn, 1953) and from that used by Glathe (1955) for making observations of the rhizosphere. Glass plates are coated with melted, cooled agar (2% (w/v) agar plus 0·5% (w/v) peptone) in which are suspended spores of the fungus being studied. The coated plates are buried at an angle of approximately 45° with their top edge just below the surface of the soil in flower-pots containing moist, sieved, fresh soil. Seeds are then sown in the soil immediately above the plates, so that the seedling roots grow down and into contact with them. After the required period of growth the plates are carefully removed from the soil, allowed to dry, freed from the larger adherent soil particles by gentle tapping, and stained with acetic-aniline-blue (Jones & Mollison, 1948).

Results

Using the buried slide technique, the effects of pea seedling roots on *Absidia* sp., *Fusarium* sp. 1, *Gliocladium roseum*, *Paecilomyces marquandii*, and *Acrostalagmus cinnabarinus* were studied. These fungi were chosen after tests on the sensitivities to soil fungistasis of a range of different fungi, because their reaction to fungistasis was intermediate between the most sensitive and the most insensitive, being inhibited on Chinn buried slides, but only partially or not at all in the agar-disc test (Jackson, 1958). It was considered more likely that fungi such as these would be able to germinate in the soil in the presence of a low concentration of a counteracting substance than would highly sensitive species. Plates coated with spore suspensions in agar were placed in position in the soil and three pea seeds, variety Laxton's Superb, placed in the soil above each plate. Further plates were incubated in moist chambers as 'no-soil' controls. After 4 days' growth in the greenhouse, the pea plumules had not emerged, but radicles had grown into contact with and along each plate. At this stage one set of plates was removed and examined, and the 'no-soil' control plates were also examined. The second set of plates was removed 8 days after the beginning of the experiment, by which time the plumules had emerged to an average height of 1 cm. above soil level and well-developed primary and secondary roots were present, making contact with the glass plates. The results of this experiment are summarized in Table 1, from which the *Absidia*

TABLE 1

The behaviour of fungi on glass plates buried beneath pea seedlings

Treatment	*Fusarium* sp. 1	*Gliocladium roseum*	*Paecilomyces marquandii*
'No-soil' control: incubated in moist chamber for 4 days	Thick sterile mycelial growth	Thick mycelial growth, frequent conidiophores with conidia	Thick mycelial growth, frequent conidiophores with conidia
In soil beneath pea seedlings for 4 days	About 50% of conidia with short germ tubes germinated by chlamydospores	No germination	No germination
In soil beneath pea seedlings for 8 days	All conidia with germ tubes and chlamydospores, themselves germinating within 2 mm. of roots; 2-day germ tubes growing towards roots	No germination away from roots, good germination within 1 mm. of roots; germ tubes growing towards roots	No germination away from roots, good germination within 1 mm. of roots; germ tubes not growing towards roots

sp. and *Acrostalagmus cinnabarinus* have been omitted; these fungi germinated well in the 'no-soil' controls, but showed no germination on the buried slides even in the root zone. Two of the 5 fungi tested whose spores showed no germination by 8 days away from the roots did germinate in the roots' immediate vicinity, while a third fungus (*Fusarium* sp. 1), although it germinated well on plates in the soil, always produced short germ tubes terminated by chlamydospores, which did not develop further without the stimulation of a root. The germ tubes produced by the conidia of *Gliocladium roseum* and the chlamydospores of *Fusarium* sp. 1 exhibited a strong tropic growth towards the pea roots, while those produced by the conidia of *Paecilomyces marquandii* showed no such directed growth.

The use of root observation cells to study the effects of seedling roots on fungal spores in soil

Technique. Although quite suitable for large-seeded species, the buried-plate method suffers from the disadvantage that continuous observations cannot be made. As an alternative, root-observation cells, rather similar to those used by Linford (1942), may be used for making continuous observations on the effects of the seedling roots of small seeded plants on fungal spores in soil. Glass cells 50 × 25 × 4 mm. are constructed by cementing three pieces of glass tubing or rod to standard microscope slides. The cells are prepared for use by filling with moist fresh soil passed through a 2-mm. sieve and placing cover-glasses (which function as the lids of the cells) in position after coating with spore suspensions in melted, cooled agar. The cover-glasses are conveniently held in place by rubber bands. Seeds are placed in the soil at the open end of the cells, which are then incubated in the greenhouse, open end upwards in lightly plugged boiling tubes, the lower part of the tubes being partially shaded. The cells may be removed and examined at any time without disturbing the seedlings. Examination is carried out by incident illumination preferably with equipment such as the Leitz Ultropak illuminator, which allows objectives of up to × 55 magnification to be used.

Root-observation cells were used in an experiment to study the behaviour of spores of *Fusarium* sp. 1, *Fusarium oxysporum* f. *pisi*, *Fusarium solani*, *Gliocladium roseum*, and *Paecilomyces marquandii* in the presence of roots of radish (French Breakfast), tomato (Moneymaker), and lettuce (All-the-Year-Round) seedlings. After filling and placing the cover-glasses in position, the water content of the soil in the cells was brought to approximately 50% of water-holding capacity with distilled water, and maintained at this level throughout the experiment. Four cells were used for each fungus. Two seeds per cell of radish and three seeds per cell of tomato and lettuce were sown 12 hr. after the cells were set up, one cell of each group of four remaining unsown as a soil control. Observations were made with the Ultropak at 2-day intervals. At the end of 20 days the experiment was terminated, and the cover-glasses from the unsown soil-control cells removed, irrigated with a 1% (w/v) solution of glucose in distilled water and incubated at 25° for a further 16 hr. 'No-soil' controls comprised inoculated cover-glasses which were examined after 42 hr. incubation in moist chambers at 25°.

Results

The results of the observations are summarized in Table 2. Good germination occurred in all the 'no-soil' controls, while in the soil-control cells germination of conidia either did not occur or, in the case of the Fusaria studied, was followed by the production of chlamydospores. On incubating the ungerminated conidia and chlamydospores with glucose at the end of the experiment excellent germination resulted

TABLE 2

The behaviour of fungi in root observation cells containing seedlings of radish, tomato, and lettuce

	Fusarium sp. 1	Fusarium oxysporum pisi	Fusarium solani	Gliocladium roseum	Paecilomyces marquandii
'No-soil' control	Good germination	Good germination	Good germination	Good germination	Good germination
Soil control	Good germination	Good germination	Good germination	No germination	No germination
Radish	Germinated chlamydospores, tropic growth	A few germinated chlamydospores, tropic growth	A few germinated chlamydospores and conidia without chlamydospores, tropic growth	Many germinated conidia with tropic growth; sporulation	Many germinated conidia; sporulation
Tomato	No stimulation	A few germinated chlamydospores, tropic growth	A few germinated chlamydospores, tropic growth	A few germinated conidia	No stimulation
Lettuce	A few germinated chlamydospores, tropic growth	A few germinated chlamydospores, tropic growth	—	Frequent germinated conidia	No stimulation

in every case, indicating that the inhibited spores had retained their viability. Differences in the degree of fungal stimulation produced by the three types of seedlings were obvious and probably related, at least in part, to the differences in the size and vigour of the seedlings; thus, the radish seedlings, which were the most vigorous of the three species tested, produced the greatest over-all stimulation. Subsequent to stimulation by the seedling roots, the Fusaria all produced germ tubes which grew towards the roots, and gave rise to varying amounts of mycelial development close to and on the root surfaces, but in no case in this or in other similar experiments was sporulation observed. In contrast with this behaviour, *Gliocladium roseum* and *Paecilomyces marquandii* started to sporulate vigorously within the root zone of radish after rather a short period of vegetative development. It is perhaps significant that while species of *Fusarium* have been reported as abundant in the mycelial condition on the surfaces of healthy roots, where they may constitute a high proportion of the fungi present (Simmonds & Ledingham, 1937; Peterson, 1957), they are usually infrequent on dilution plates prepared from rhizosphere soil unless they are being actively parasitic or the roots are senescent. *Gliocladium roseum* may become predominant on dilution plates prepared from the rhizosphere, as has been shown with red clover by Peterson (1957), indicating that sporulation is occurring, while being absent or very infrequent on the root surface. These observations emphasize that dilution plate counts of rhizosphere fungi only reflect reproductive activity and cannot be expected to give any indication of the amount of vegetative growth taking place.

Substances stimulating germination of inhibited fungal spores

Reference has already been made to the stimulatory effect on inhibited fungal spores of various substances, including glucose, sodium nitrate, and such soil amendments as soya-bean meal, which has been noted by a number of workers. In most cases the substances being investigated were added to the soil, where, in addition to any direct effect which they may have had on the fungal spores or the inhibitory factor, there will have been the likelihood of secondary effects through their general action on the soil microflora. Further, a more or less rapid reduction in the concentration of a nutrient would be expected on addition to unsterile soil. In order to reduce the possibility of secondary interactions and to avoid the rapid dissipation of nutrients added to the soil, the effects of a range of sugars and other compounds on the inhibition of spore germination was tested by incorporating them in the agar used in the agar-disc test. Most of the tests were carried out with conidia of a strain of *Penicillium citrinum* which had previously been used as a test organism in work on soil fungistasis (Jackson, 1958).

The effects of a range of sugars at concentrations of 0·01, 0·1 and 1% (w/v) on the germination of *Penicillium citrinum* conidia on agar discs over soil is shown in Table 3. The monosaccharide sugars all had a

TABLE 3

The effect of incorporating different concentrations of sugars in the agar-disc medium on the germination of Penicillium citrinum *conidia in the absence of soil and over soil. The figures represent mean counts of 4 fields on 4 discs for each treatment*

Sugar	% (w/v)	% germination		Sugar	% (w/v)	% germination	
		No soil	Soil			No soil	Soil
Glucose	0	80·6	21·7	Mannose	0	90·2	19·8
	0·01	95·7	72·8		0·01	89·1	25·2
	0·1	96·9	94·7		0·1	94·3	50·7
	1·0	97·4	100·0		1·0	97·6	79·0
Fructose	0	91·1	15·4	Sucrose	0	77·8	21·0
	0·01	95·2	25·5		0·01	78·5	13·1
	0·1	91·8	38·2		0·1	87·2	47·9
	1·0	77·7	84·0		1·0	96·8	90·6
Arabinose	0	84·1	15·4	Maltose	0	68·9	21·2
	0·01	89·6	24·0		0·01	61·3	19·4
	0·1	95·0	36·6		0·1	74·1	17·8
	1·0	99·2	79·5		1·0	86·6	48·3
Galactose	0	90·6	15·6	Lactose	0	77·0	9·5
	0·01	85·8	27·7		0·01	68·9	18·6
	0·1	97·4	64·2		0·1	77·4	25·8
	1·0	99·8	91·4		1·0	95·3	59·1
Xylose	0	81·8	23·7	Raffinose	0	61·0	15·7
	0·01	86·9	31·7		0·01	72·6	9·2
	0·1	92·3	78·9		0·1	70·8	8·4
	1·0	96·2	89·6		1·0	80·6	36·1

similar effect in counteracting soil fungistasis although to slightly differing degrees, glucose being most effective, 0·01% increasing germination over soil from 20–73% and the 1% concentration to 100%, while mannose was the least effective of those tested. The disaccharides generally had less effect than the monosaccharides, and the trisaccharide raffinose had least effect. Asparagine, alanine, leucine, 'Difco' Casamino acids, and 'Difco' Peptone were all found to be without significant effect on fungistasis up to 0·5%, the highest concentration tested. It was because of the lack of effect of 0·5% peptone on soil fungistasis, although increasing control germination to a high level, that it was normally included in test agar. Of a number of mineral salts commonly used in fungal media which were tested, only ammonium sulphate at a concentration of 1% or above and ammonium chloride at 5% resulted in increased germination in the presence of soil. The effect of these two ammonium salts may have been due to a reduction in the pH of the agar.

DISCUSSION

The results obtained in the experiments described clearly demonstrate that seedling roots may stimulate germination of fungal spores previously prevented from germinating by the fungistatic effect of the soil. Although the mechanism of this stimulation has not yet been definitely elucidated, the most likely explanation would appear to be the excretion by the roots of a substance or substances which counteract the effects of fungistasis. Sugars, which have been shown to be capable of inducing the germination of inhibited fungal spores, may be present in the root excretions produced by seedlings in quantities considered sufficient to have a stimulating effect on the soil population (Lundegårdh & Stenlid, 1944; Rovira, 1956). It would therefore appear very likely that sugars are responsible, at least in part, for the observed effect of seedling roots on spores in soil. Whether more mature root systems could affect fungal spores by the same mechanism is open to some doubt. According to Rovira (1956), glucose and fructose excretion by seedling pea and oat roots only takes place during the first 10 days of growth, after which there appears to be a re-absorption or synthesis of oligosaccharides, as these sugars can no longer be detected by 21 days. It is, nevertheless, possible that excretion of sugars by the young meristematic regions of the root system may continue throughout the growth of the plant, re-absorption by other parts of the root system making this difficult to demonstrate in nutrient solution or sand cultures.

There is no evidence for specificity in the effects of roots on fungi from the results of the work reported here, and if such substances as glucose, fructose, and sucrose are involved, no high degree of specificity would be expected. However, preliminary experiments indicate that there are certain differences between the behaviour of *Penicillium citrinum* and *Gliocladium roseum* with respect to the sugars effect, but extensive tests will have to be made before it will be possible to determine the differential responses of different fungi. It is probably where host-parasite relationships are concerned that the more complex interaction between root and fungus should be sought, such as the differential effect of root excretions of varieties of peas on different races of *Fusarium oxysporum* g. *pisi*, recently described by Buxton (1957).

REFERENCES

BUXTON, E. W. (1957). Differential rhizosphere effects of three pea cultivars on physiologic races of *Fusarium oxysporum* f. *pisi. Trans. Brit. mycol. Soc.*, **40**, 305–17.

CHINN, S. H. F. (1953). A slide technique for the study of fungi and actinomycetes with special reference to *Helminthosporium sativum. Canad. J. Bot.*, **31**, 718–24.

DOBBS, C. G., & HINSON, W. H. (1953). A widespread fungistasis in the soil. *Nature, Lond.*, **172**, 197.

GLATHE, H. (1955). Die direkte mikroskopische Untersuchung des Bodens. *Z. PflErnähr. Düng.*, **69**, 172–6.

HESSAYON, D. G. (1953). Fungitoxins in the soil: II. Trichothecin, its production and inactivation in unsterilized soil. *Soil Sci.*, **75**, 395–404.

HINSON, W. H. (1954). *A study of the biology of soil moulds.* Ph.D. Thesis. University of Wales.

JACKSON, R. M. (1957). Fungistasis as a factor in the rhizosphere phenomenon. *Nature, Lond.*, **180**, 96–7.

JACKSON, R. M. (1958). An investigation of fungistasis in Nigerian soils. *J. gen. Microbiol.*, **18**, 248–58.

JONES, P. C. T., & MOLLISON, J. E. (1948). A technique for the quantitative estimation of soil micro-organisms *J. gen. Microbiol.*, **2**, 54–69.

LINFORD, M. B. (1942). Methods of observing soil flora and fauna associated with roots. *Soil Sci.*, **53**, 93–103.

LUNDEGÅRDH, H., & STENLID, G. (1944). On the excretion of nucleotides and flavanones from living roots. *Arkiv. Botanik*, **31A**, 1–27.

PARK, D. (1955). Experimental studies on the ecology of fungi in soil. *Trans. Brit. mycol. Soc.*, **38**, 130–2.

PARK, D. (1956). Effects of substrate on a microbial antagonism, with reference to soil conditions. *Trans. Brit. mycol. Soc.*, **39**, 239–59.

PETERSON, E. A. (1957). *Studies on rhizosphere fungi.* Ph.D. Thesis. University of London.

ROVIRA, A. D. (1956). Plant-root excretions in relation to the rhizosphere effect. 1. The nature of root exudates from oats and peas. *Plant and Soil*, **7**, 178–94.

SIMMONDS, P. M., & LEDINGHAM, R. J. (1937). A study of the fungous flora of wheat roots. *Sci. Agric.*, **18**, 49–59.

STARKEY, R. L. (1929). Some influences of the development of higher plants upon the micro-organisms in the soil. 1. Historical and introductory. *Soil Sci.*, **27**, 319–34.

WARCUP, J. H. (1955). On the origin of colonies of fungi developing on soil-dilution plates. *Trans. Brit. mycol. Soc.*, **38**, 298–301.

WARCUP, J. H. (1957). Studies on the occurrence and activity of fungi in a wheat-field soil. *Trans. Brit. mycol. Soc.*, **40**, 237–62.

DISCUSSION

*Dr. H. Katznelson.*In connexion with lysis of hyphae of *Helminthosporium sativum* in soils treated with various substances, could it not be due to the production of lytic substances by micro-organisms which develop in enormous numbers as a result of the soil treatment. Such microbial growth which includes fungal, actinomycete, and bacterial development may be demonstrated readily in the soil. It is possible, of course, that carbohydrate oxidation may lower the oxygen tension or reduce the oxidation-reduction potential to the point where lysis may be initiated. This hypothesis may be supported by the fact that lysis of hyphae of *H. sativum* occurs when ascorbic acid is added to soil.

Competition for nutrients would seem to be an important factor in any consideration of the relationships of organisms to each other. It is quite conceivable that high rates of growth and metabolic turnover may result in the depletion of nutrients to the extent that the development of certain organisms may be inhibited. Competition for limited quantities of nutrients may be particularly extreme when such materials as growth factors and trace elements are involved (perhaps the latter more than the former).

In regard to fungistasis in the soil, our experience with *H. sativum* indicates that its spores germinate quite readily in water or on moist filter-paper. When introduced into soil, they do not germinate. Since nutrients are apparently not involved in germination one must conclude that fungistatic substances are present whose effects may be overcome by partial or complete soil sterilization, or by the addition of substances such as soya-bean meal, and glucose.

Dr. D. Park. Is not a biological approach to the study of antagonism in the soil necessary before the biochemical, which can only fill in the grammar of the story? Competition for micro-nutrients need not necessarily involve chemical substances because the soil solution contains sufficient micro-nutrients for microbial (fungal and bacterial) growth. Thus biological methods of studying such problems are able to demonstrate that competition for nutrients cannot be a significant factor in most instances.

One should consider both general soil fungistatis and specific antibiotic effects, because they both play a part in competition. I feel that the general definition of antibiotics (Waksman, 1945) is pleasing, but unfortunately too much emphasis is being placed on specific and medical definitions.

With respect to staling, I think it is fruitful to compare staling effects with specific antibiotics. Staling is not a negative but a positive factor, i.e. it does not involve the absence of or the removal of anything from the substratum, as has been shown as early as 1912 and 1913 by Dox. But staling is the addition to the substratum of something positive, e.g. something that can prevent conidial germination and vegetative mycelium from developing further.

WAKSMAN, S. A. (1945). *Microbial antagonisms and antibiotic substances.* New York: Commonwealth Fund.

Dr. R. Caldwell. With respect to the production of antibiotics by *Trichoderma viride*, only about 50% of the isolates I have studied are able to produce gliotoxin or viridin.

Dr. P. W. Brian. Antibiotic producers vary in their production capacity—high-yielding strains are rare. Strains of *T. viride* which produce little if any gliotoxin or viridin are often effective antagonists. This would indicate that antibiotic production cannot be the only basis of antagonism.

Dr. R. M. Jackson. Autoclaved soil from which fungistasis has disappeared shows a return of fungistasis on inoculation with unsterile soil and subsequent incubation. Also, when soil is partially sterilized by steaming, fungistasis disappears and returns on incubation. It is possible to demonstrate that the inhibitory effects of the returned fungistasis of a treated soil is similar to that of untreated soil.

Mr. J. H. Clarke. As the fungistasis appears to return some time after total or partial sterilization of the soil, this is possible circumstantial evidence for the fungistasis being due to a biotic, perhaps a microbial, cause, as the soil microflora similarly takes a time to redevelop after such treatment.

Dr. M. Witkamp. Small branches lying on the forest floor and covered with *T. viride* mycelium when placed on nutrient agar show a considerable inhibitive effect on the growth of *Bacillus subtilis*. Similar branches without visible growth of *T. viride* showed only slight inhibitive effects in 3 out of 10 cases (branches with *T. viride* showed inhibition in 10 out of 10 cases).

Water washings of ground branches plated out in a nutrient agar (to which acti-dione had been added to prevent fungal growth) gave rise to bacterial growth when washings of branches without *T. viride* were added. On the other hand, almost no bacteria developed from similarly plated washings from branches with visible *T. viride* growth. Colony counts were in the ratio 300:1 respectively.

Dr. C. G. Dobbs. We have obtained spread of mycostatic activity in chromic acid-washed sand mixed with soil inoculum. There seems no doubt that a biological factor is concerned in the production of mycostasis.

Dr. J. Webster. I should like to point out that *T. viride* is probably an aggregate name used to cover a number of distinct entities.

Bisby, G. R. (1939). *Trichoderma viride* Pers. ex Fries, and notes on *Hypocrea. Trans. Brit. mycol. Soc.*, **23**, 149–68.

Dr. P. W. Brian. T. viride is a complex not a species, in which it is possible to distinguish many strains. With experience one can pick out high-yielding strains by their morphological features.

Dr. E. Grossbard. Regarding the recovery of fungistasis in re-contaminated auto-claved soil, I wish to inquire whether experiments were made on the effect of the extracts from autoclaved soil on the inhibition of germination of fungal spores. I have myself not worked on fungistasis, but when in 1946 I was working on anti-biotic production in re-inoculated soil, I noticed that extracts from autoclaved soil had an inhibitory effect on *Escherichia coli*, and if glucose had been added to such a soil prior to autoclaving, the extracts gave rise to zones of inhibition as if an anti-biotic had been formed.

Dr. W. Gams. I have some preliminary results about the fungistatic activity of autoclaved soil extract: by using the dilution-place method three media were com-pared—a rich malt agar, tap-water agar, and soil extract agar. The water agar gave a quarter to a half the number of colonies as the malt agar, i.e. it is probable that spores were germinating upon the water agar. The colonies were of course smaller and were counted under a binocular microscope. But the soil-extract agar gave only half the number of colonies as the water agar indicating the presence of a fungistatic factor in autoclaved soil.

Dr. F. Schönbeck. Dr. Winter and his colleagues found soil extracts were able to inhibit *Ophibolus graminis* in varying degrees, depending on the soil type. The addition of glucose to such a soil will counteract the effects. Our general conclusion is that biological effects are important in fungistasis.

Dr. J. L. Harley. One aspect which has not been mentioned is stimulation as opposed to inhibition. May I ask if anyone has thought that perhaps some aspects of the 'inhibition' of germination may be due to lack of factors required for germination rather than to inhibitors. I am led to compare the cases stated with the biological stimulation of germination described for various seeds and spores by a great many workers.

Dr. H. Katznelson. I wonder if a change in soil reaction may be responsible for the lysis of hyphae in soil. Fungi are quite tolerant of acid conditions, but this phenomenon of lysis might be active where young hyphae are concerned. We have had some experience with an actinomycete grown in pure culture on a medium containing $(NH_4)_2SO_4$ in which after a few days of growth the hyphae lysed completely. Concurrently there was a marked reduction in reaction (from pH 6·8 to pH 4·5), probably due to the preferential uptake of ammonium ions by the actinomycete and the consequent accumulation of sulphate ions. When potassium nitrate was used as nitrogen source, no lysis was observed. Similarly the addition of calcium carbonate to the medium resulted in the prevention of lysis. In both cases the medium did not become acid in reaction.

Dr. J. L. Harley. The same phenomenon is seen in fungal cultures supplied with ammonium chloride or ammonium sulphate as the source of nitrogen. As the pH falls to a low value, autolysis and the release of pigments and other substances from the hyphae often occurs. These events occur before the available carbohydrates in the medium are exhausted.

Dr. C. G. Dobbs. There are undoubtedly all these various factors, positive and negative, affecting fungal growth and germination, but none of them, *except* the presence of a water-soluble chemical inhibitor, explains the phenomenon of nongermination of spores or growth of hyphae on cellulose film or other materials permeable to the soil solution.

Dr. F. A. Skinner. Dr. Park's remarks on various mechanisms of antagonism were particularly interesting to me because I had experience of them all when working on the relationships between mixed cultures of fungi and actinomycetes some years ago. The actinomycetes could produce an antibiotic which was very active against my test strain of *Fusarium culmorum*. However, the intensity of this antibiotic effect was greatly dependent on nutrient status. Thus, antibiotic antagonism was severe only when there was an abundance of carbohydrate present. Growth of the fungus could still be depressed (as compared with controls) in the presence of clays which eliminated the antibiotic when the carbohydrate status was high, but rarely at all when carbohydrate was low. The important point is that neither antibiosis nor competition for nutrients could be called effective in preventing survival of either organism, when the carbohydrate status was unfavourable to the luxuriant growth of either.

It may well be that Dr. Park is correct in not assigning such an important role to nutrient competition in soil. My own experience suggests that unfavourable nutrient conditions would favour the survival of several species mixed together in the same environment, even though each would be making poor growth in terms of weight of cell substance formed per unit of time.

It is worth considering the view that the very diversity of the soil micro-flora is an indication of the unsuitability of soil as a medium for any one of the numerous species which it supports.

Mr. D. N. Crawford. In the discussion of the influence and interactions of antibiotics on organisms, most attention has been devoted to biological processes, and nonbiological processes have been only briefly mentioned. It is possible that sorption on to clay or organic matter surfaces may inactivate some antibiotics by chemical or physical changes—has this been examined and ruled out as of no importance, or is it being unjustifiably ignored?

Dr. P. W. Brian. Antibiotics are absorbed on soil colloids (humus, clays), sometimes with inactivation, sometimes not. Chemical and biological degradation all take place limiting the ecological effects of any antibiotic produced. We thus have to take account of the balance of rates of production and degradation of antibiotic substances in soil.

Dr. D. Park. One must visualise not a generally uniform habitat in soil, but 'islands' of, for example, different levels of activity and different levels of inhibition occurring in localized areas. It is in some of these islands that nutrients will occur at a high level, and thus permit the operation of antagonistic mechanisms other than competition.

Dr. F. A. Skinner. I agree with Dr. Park when he emphasizes the heterogeneity of the soil. No doubt each soil crumb differs in nutrient status from its neighbours, and that some will contain sufficient nutrients to support enhanced microbial activity.

Dr. C. G. Dobbs. Bacillus macerans, actinomycetes, and others are organisms which lead to toxic effects, but there is no indication that the mycostatic factor is toxic. Spores survive in the soil, and do not appear to have been subjected to toxins. The few facts we have suggest it to be an antimetabolite.

Dr. R. Caldwell. Experiments with *Trichoderma viride* in regard to long-term survival in soil showed that chlamydospores, and to a large extent conidia, survive burial and germinate readily when returned to nutrient media, and even germinate in small numbers in soil during the burial period.

Dr. J. L. Harley. In this case they differ markedly from a good many ascospores, which appear to become progressively unable to germinate after a relatively few months.

Dr. R. Caldwell. Large numbers of *Trichoderma* spores are killed, I was speaking of the proportion of the surviving spores.

Prof. L. G. Silvestri. It is a very important observation that soil consists of islands of different zones of nutrient and inhibition. We consider a large block of soil, but if we devise research methods to pick off the small situations, it would be easier to observe antagonistic phenomena which are obscured when a large soil block is studied.

Dr. C. G. Dobbs. Soil masses of below a certain size do, when separated, always allow germination. There seems to be a minimum quantity of soil that exert inhibition in its centre.

Prof. A. Burges. If soil is broken up it usually seems to lose its fungistatic activity. Is this general? Is the fungistatic factor likely to be gaseous?

Dr. C. G. Dobbs. It is not possible by any treatment of normal air-drying or moistening to effect this inhibition. When soil is scattered on the bench and then gathered up and goes mouldy, parts of it were probably killed by desiccation.

Dr. J. Bywater. The soil sieved in the preparations for all the assay test in my work was finely divided and fully exposed to the air, yet it exerted inhibition in the tests.

Dr. R. M. Jackson. When soil is dried under vacuum for 24 hr. and re-moistened, it shows inhibition.

Mr. J. H. Clarke. In relation to Dr. Jackson's work, it would be interesting to select, say, five fungi common in the chosen soil, and see if these were present on the pea-root surface by a washing technique, then use Chinn slides to show that the germ tubes of the spores of these species showed a tactic response towards the root.

Dr. R. M. Jackson. The fungi were chosen on the basis of sensitivity to fungistasis in previous tests. With *Fusaria* I think the story with a number of them is that they colonize the root surface, and sporulation does not occur till the tissues begin to die and the *Fusaria* start to invade the tissues, then sporulation may occur.

But in other fungi, *Gliocladium* and *Paecilomyces*, as I examined them they sporulated quite abundantly when the roots were quite healthy, the *Gliocladium* is a form recorded as abundant in rhizosphere soils.

Dr. G. W. F. Sewell. Your method of recording spores is to include as non-germinated some spores which have produced a short germ tube (which does not exceed the diameter of the conidium). Have you evidence that spores which are arrested at this stage lose their viability more quickly than those which are in fact ungerminated, and what percentage of the spores do reach this stage?

Dr. R. M. Jackson. Although the criterion of germination is a germ tube which has exceeded the diameter or length of the spore, this is merely a convenient criterion, because if a germ tube is just produced it is difficult to decide whether the spore has germinated or not. Now, I don't say that if there is a germ tube which I can see is less than the diameter of the spore that growth has been arrested; in fact, if I incubate for longer these spores will generally form longer germ tubes. In fact, I find that in agar discs over soil using a fairly sensitive fungus, a small percentage of the spores may germinate but their germination rate is somewhat delayed, so that I may be looking at these delayed spores after my arbitrary incubation period of 16 hr. at 25°.

Dr. G. J. F. Pugh. Increasing amounts of glucose stimulate germination, as do the exudates from the pea roots. Could this be due to the presence of sufficient food rather than the overcoming of the inhibitor?

Dr. R. M. Jackson. I want to try to make the distinction clear, the spores present in soil in an ungerminated condition are not ungerminated only because of lack of nutrients; apparently there are sufficient nutrients in the soil solution for them to germinate, perhaps they wouldn't develop very far if they did germinate. Before they can germinate, this inhibitory factor, whatever it may be, must be overcome in some way, and an increase in readily available carbon compounds (e.g. sugars) seems one way in which they may germinate; even in the presence of the inhibitor. As I say, I don't quite know whether the action is directly on the spore, but the germination must occur before nutrient substances can be of any use to the fungus.

Dr. R. Caldwell. It would seem desirable to compare studies made on fungistasis in soils by the use of Chinn slides, 'Cellophane' film, and glass material (devised by Legge, 1952). Only on the last-named are spores observed on a truly inert material.

Dr. C. G. Dobbs. About the inadvisability of using cellulose film as it is not inert. During the short periods of the assay tests (2 days) no cellulose decomposition occurred in most soils. When it does occur, etching of the film is visible.

DYNAMIC EQUILIBRIA OF
SOIL POPULATIONS

DYNAMIC EQUILIBRIA IN THE SOIL

N. A. BURGES

Department of Botany, University of Liverpool

So many studies in soil microbiology have been concerned with counting or with listing the organisms present in the soil that an impression has arisen that the soil is essentially a static system. The very stability of the soil population re-enforces this idea. It is important therefore to emphasize from time to time that this stability is the stability of a dynamic equilibrium. An equilibrium in which the individual units of the system are constantly changing, but compensating changes in other components maintain the over-all balance. The most familiar example of this is the nitrogen cycle where interconversions between free nitrogen, nitrates, nitrites, proteins, ammonia, etc., take place, where nitrogen is lost by leaching or added by biological or electrical fixation, yet despite all these changes the over-all amount of nitrogen in a natural system remains relatively constant, as indeed do the amounts of the individual components. Because of the great stress which has been laid on the nitrogen cycle both in teaching and in agriculture, the importance of other interchanges is often overlooked.

In soil mycology the changes associated with the annual leaf and branch fall are an outstanding example of a dynamic equilibrium so far as the soil is concerned. Several studies have given quantitative data on the changes involved, and they all give a similar picture provided the system being studied has reached the stable condition. Blow (1955) examined in detail the litter and litter fall in oakwoods in America. He showed that just before leaf and branch fall began, the amount of litter on the soil surface corresponded to about 4·2 tons per acre. Fall of leaves started in August, and the amount of new litter reached a maximum in December and January. The freshly fallen litter amounted to 1·4 tons per acre. Rapid decomposition occurred during the winter and early spring, so that although the amount of litter had risen to over 5 tons per acre immediately following leaf fall, by July it was back again to the summer value of 4·2 tons per acre. Observations on pine litter in England and the litter from stands of *Casuarina* in Australia show similar changes. The decomposition and leaching losses balance the annual increment from leaf fall; litter addition and decomposition are in a state of dynamic equilibrium.

In Blow's work the annual fall was 1·4 tons per acre, whereas in some tropical forests it may reach 30 tons per acre, but even under these conditions decomposition is sufficiently rapid to prevent any marked accumulation.

The above work refers to the over-all picture. If a single leaf is considered, a wide range of variation is seen. A leaf falling in a tropical rain-forest may be completely disintegrated in less than three months, but a pine needle in a Northern European forest takes 6–7 years at least before it is completely disintegrated. Despite this long period of decay, in a well-established pine forest the amount of litter does not change appreciably from year to year. Again, an amount of litter equal to the annual leaf fall is decomposed or leached away each year. Failure to appreciate this has led to many confusions, and particularly in connexion with discussions on mull and mor. It is frequently stated that decomposition is rapid in mull and slow in mor humus. While it is true that an individual oak leaf falling on to a mull soil may be decomposed in a year and a pine needle on mor may take 7–8 years to reach a similar state, in mature stands both systems may decompose comparable amounts of material per year. It is similar to an observer watching two trains pass, both travelling at the same speed but one with a single carriage, the other with thirty. The observer still sees the long train for some time after the short one has passed, although both were travelling at the same speed. Decomposition in mull and mor has many features in common with the two trains.

In studying the dynamic equilibria in the soil, we need to know the rates of the individual changes in the system and the nature of the compensating processes. The annual burst of decomposition associated with leaf fall is accompanied by an increase in microbiological activity, and it might be expected that this activity would be reflected in the changes in the number of micro-organisms present. Protozoal and bacterial numbers do fluctuate rapidly, and in some studies at least there is evidence of big increases in the populations of these organisms associated with the availability of fresh food reserves. Only occasionally has evidence for comparable fluctuations in fungal numbers been obtained. This may be because of the relatively long life of the fungal hypha or spore, compared with a bacterial or protozoal cell.

Our knowledge of the functional life of an individual fungal hypha is very meagre. In Rossi-Cholodny slides one can often see phycomycetous hyphae with densely cytoplasmic tips. A short distance back from the tips the cytoplasm becomes vacuolate, and farther back still the hyphae appear empty and are often enveloped in bacteria which seem to lyse the cell walls, leaving only slight traces of the hyphae. The evidence suggests that this kind of fungus progressively explores the soil, gradually accumulating a mass of cytoplasm at the growing tips until fruiting can be achieved. In an agricultural soil with a high bacterial count, the life of any individual piece of hypha is of the order of one or two days. This evidence is based on Rossi-Cholodny slides which represent somewhat artificial conditions; nevertheless, the available field evidence suggests that the time scale is of the right order. Warcup (1957), in his studies of Australian wheat-fields, found that *Rhizopus* and *Mortierella* produced sporangia 3 days after rain had fallen following the normal summer dry spell. The evidence here strongly suggests that from spore germination to sporing was 3 days. The fate of the vegetative hyphae was not recorded. Experience with Phycomycetes generally suggests that once sporing has been accomplished the vegetative hyphae cease to function, and in natural substrates such as dung or in composts, the hyphae are rapidly disintegrated. It is natural to think of each spore germinating, producing a mycelium with numerous sporangia each containing many spores, leading to a many hundred-fold increase. If this happens, then such increases ought to lead to tremendous and sudden variations in the number of colonies recorded in dilution-plate studies of such soils. The increases recorded, however, are surprisingly small, and an increase of the plate count by a factor of 20 represents one of the largest recorded. There may be several reasons why the increase is relatively slight. The general fungistasis may be very effective, and although one spore might give rise to 20,000 or so after a few days, if the initial population were of the order of 4,000 the germination and reproduction of only 9 spores out of the 4,000 would give a tenfold increase in the population.

Alternatively, it may be that when fresh substrates become available, a large proportion of spores lying dormant in the soil germinate and produce a mycelium which gives a greatly increased number of new spores, but these are quickly eliminated either by lysis, ingestion, or some other rapidly acting agency. At present we know practically nothing about the rate of destruction of spores. A third possibility is that the amounts of food materials immediately available at any one time are so small that any particular mycelium may produce only a few depauperate sporangia. Certainly when sporangia of mucors or sporing heads of Penicillia have been observed in the soil, they are very reduced when compared with the fruiting structures met in culture.

The life of Ascomycete and Basidiomycete mycelium seems to be very different. Growth rates, on the whole, are slower and hyphae function for greater periods. It is interesting that Phycomycetes as a group do not produce antibiotics and disintegration of their hyphae is often recorded. The long-lived mycelium of the Basidiomycetes, many of which produce antibiotics, seldom appears to be attacked by bacteria. Disintegration of the mycelium of Ascomycetes, Fungi Imperfecti, and Basidiomycetes seems to be accomplished more often by small animals such as mites and collembolas than by bacteria.

The above situations might be termed 'normal', where the hyphae when they have ceased to function are broken down. Abnormal situations also occur. Romell long ago showed that in mor humus there were characteristically large masses of relict mycelium. An extreme case is that investigated by Hepple (1958), who showed that in the B_1 of a podzol investigated by her a great deal of the hyphae had become virtually mummified by encrusting humic acid.

It is often very difficult to decide how many of the hyphae present in the soil are still active. Warcup (1957) found that on an average about 23% of the hyphae dissected from the soil were viable. This value rose to 75% soon after the crop residues were ploughed in, and fell to 3–15% during the dry summer. When the soil dries out below the wilting point most hyphae are killed, but clearly some can survive, as shown by Warcup, even for 6–8 weeks at a relative humidity of 30–50%. Such low humidity will also kill many spores. In Warcup's data we can see that a fall in soil-water content from 20% to 2% meant a killing of three-quarters of the spores in the soil. Other workers (e.g. Hepple (1958) with *Mucor rammannianus*) have found that McLennan's picture of hyphae being killed by desiccation and spores being resistant is not correct for many soil forms, although it is true for a number of the surface-living dry-spored species. The chlamydospores seem exceptional, and in many cases are the primary resistant element.

Clearly spores disappear from the soil, either by death or by germination, and their numbers are restored when the various mycelia produce new crops of spores. Initially these are produced in local aggregates, yet masses of spores are seldom seen in the soil. All the evidence suggests a rapid and efficient dispersal to give a surprisingly uniform distribution of the more abundant species. This was very well demonstrated by Hinson (1954). A similar study on soil from a pasture in the Wirral, Cheshire, confirmed Hinson's results. A large piece of soil was broken across to expose a fresh face and a 1 cm. grid superimposed on the surface. Samples were taken from each square and dilution plates prepared. The six most common fungi appeared in 80% of the grid squares. When Warcup soil crumbs were used, 62% of the crumbs contained at least 5 of the 6 commonest species. The work of Hinson suggests that animals may be primarily responsible for this efficient mixing.

When the soil is examined directly and particularly by means of soil sections (Hepple & Burges, 1956), it can be seen that different fungi exploit the soil in different ways and that a number of distinct growth patterns can be recognized. Some of these are set out below.

(i) *The Penicillium pattern.* A small piece of substrate is densely colonized by the fungus. Spore production occurs heavily over the surface of the substrate, and there is no extension of the mycelium into the surrounding soil. This growth pattern may sometimes be correlated with the ability to produce antibiotics and thus allow the fungus to dominate the localized habitat.

(ii) *The Mucor ramannianus pattern.* The fungus invades the substrate, e.g. a small dead root, utilizes the food materials, and then spreads into the surrounding soil, where it forms a zone of chlamydospores. The subsequent disintegration of the vegetative mycelium leaves a zone of resistant chlamydospores apparently unassociated with the original substrates. Hepple (1958) considers that this may give the negative rhizosphere effect reported by Thrower (1954).

(iii) *The Basidiomycete pattern.* The fungus colonizes the substrate with a long-lived mycelium, and then migrates to other substrates or to a position where it will produce fruit-bodies by means of rhizomorphs or well-developed mycelial strands.

(iv) *The Zygorrhynchus pattern.* In this the fungus appears to grow aimlessly through the soil as more or less isolated single hyphae, and does not seem to be associated with any particulate substrate. It is possible that it is growing at the expense of the small amount of organic matter dissolved in the soil solution.

(v) *The fairy-ring pattern.* The fungus migrates as a well-defined mycelial zone, causing profound microbiological and chemical changes in the soil. Careful examination does not reveal any apparent connexion between the fungus and any special substrate in the soil. A comparison (Warcup, 1951) of the soil in front of the mycelial zone and within the mycelial zone shows that about two-thirds of the soil fungi are killed by the fairy-ring, and other fungi not common in the unaffected soil become common in the mycelial zone.

It is not assumed that the above list of patterns is in any way exhaustive, and closer study will certainly reveal others. Even at this stage, however, it is clear that a proper understanding of the growth patterns is essential for an understanding of soil mycology. A single instance may suffice. In considering the rhizosphere fungi, we do not at present have a clear picture of the formation of the stimulated population. We could imagine a heterogeneous mass of spores lying dormant in the soil, and when a root grows through the area a localized stimulation leads to the establishment of a vegetative root flora. The results of Webley *et al.* (1952) on the rhizosphere of *Atriplex* support such a view. On the other hand, the observations of Robertson (1954) on pine roots indicate that the surface flora once established grows along the root as it extends through the soil.

One of the surprising aspects of soil mycology is the difficulty which species seem to find in colonizing soil even when the normal flora has been killed or impoverished. The difficulty of an intruding species invading a well-established community is understandable, and in the work of Park (1955) one can appreciate that the native flora has already been rigorously selected as best attuned to that particular environment, and would therefore have an advantage over any invader. Where soil has been sterilized and then exposed to air, one would not expect any difficulty, particularly in view of the ease with which sterile soil is invaded in the laboratory. It may be that the growth patterns of many species limit their ability to colonize the soil under natural conditions, and it is only the spreaders such as *Trichoderma* which can readily invade.

A further aspect of the growth pattern concept which requires consideration is the sphere of influence of the fungus. A root may influence the soil around it to a distance varying from a few millimetres to several centimetres from the root surface, a distance corresponding to less than ten times the diameter of the root. In thinking of a hypha growing through the soil, we must not transfer the mental picture of the root and its relatively restricted rhizosphere to a microscale. A hypha of *Sclerotinia sclerotiorum* will grow at about 1 cm. a day. This corresponds to about 40μ per hr. Hydrogen ions released from the hyphae will diffuse through agar several millimetres in an hour in sufficient concentration to be detected by ordinary pH indicators. This corresponds to a distance hundreds of times the diameter of the hypha. If we ignore the anomalies brought about by simply magnifying the image of the fungal hyphae, this would be equivalent to a bean root affecting the soil several feet away from its growing apex. With this in mind, a growth pattern of isolated hyphae growing widely separated in the soil becomes comprehensible. They may be successfully tapping the available substrate for a distance equal to hundreds of times their own diameter.

In touching on so many aspects, I have tried to emphasize the necessity for taking a dynamic view of soil fungi. Unless we know their growth patterns, their turnover rates, and their zones of influence, we cannot hope to advance beyond the counting and listing which has occupied us for so long.

REFERENCES

BLOW, F. E. (1955). Quantity and hydrologic characteristics of litter under Upland Oak Forests in Eastern Tennessee. *J. of Forestry*, **53**, 190–5.

HEPPLE, S. (1958). *Mucor ramannianus in a podzolized soil.* Ph.D. Thesis, University of Liverpool.

HEPPLE, S., & BURGES, A. (1956). Sectioning of soil. *Nature, Lond.*, **177**, 1186.

HINSON, W. (1954). *A study in the biology of soil moulds.* Ph.D. Thesis, University of Wales.

PARK, D. (1955). Experimental studies on the ecology of fungi in soil. *Trans. Brit. mycol. Soc.*, **38**, 130–42.

ROBERTSON, N. F. (1954). Studies on the mycorrhiza of *Pinus sylvestris*, I. *New Phytol.*, **53**, 253–83.

THROWER, L. B. (1954). The rhizosphere effect shown by some Victorian heathland plants. *Austr. J. Bot.*, **2**, 246–67.

WARCUP, J. H. (1951). Studies on the growth of Basidiomycetes in soil. *Ann. Bot. N.S.*, **15**, 305–17.

WARCUP, J. H. (1957). Studies on the occurrence and activity of fungi in a wheat-field soil. *Trans. Brit. mycol. Soc.*, **40**, 237–59.

WEBLEY, D. M., EASTWOOD, D. J., & GIMINGHAM, C. H. (1952). Development of a soil microflora in relation to plant succession on sand-dunes, including the 'rhizosphere' flora associated with colonizing species. *J. Ecol.*, **40**, 168–78.

OBSERVATIONS ON THE RHIZOSPHERE EFFECT

H. KATZNELSON

Microbiology Research Institute, Research Branch
Canada Agriculture, Ottawa

INTRODUCTION

Soil is the habitat of an extremely complex microbiological community in which occur all the phenomena operative in the struggle for existence, and, as may be expected, by analogy with ecological events on a macro-scale, certain groups and types of micro-organisms eventually establish themselves as dominant forms in the community and others are relegated to a subdominant level. Thus an equilibrium is established which is characteristic of the soil, and which shifts and fluctuates as the environmental factors (moisture, temperature, treatment, cropping system) change. The struggle for existence among the component microbial elements in the soil is intensified in the vicinity of the plant root, the rhizosphere, because of the large numbers of organisms in this zone. However, in addition to stimulating massive microbial growth, the plant, which is in effect another environmental factor though a complex one, gives direction to the microbial activity on its roots, and a microflora develops with certain recognizable features which differentiate it from that of the soil a short distance away from the root. The new equilibrium is also dynamic and varies with such factors as the type of crop, the age and vigour of the plant, soil moisture, and other environmental conditions (Katznelson, Lochhead, & Timonin, 1948). However, a basic microbial pattern is established even when the plant is only a few days old, and persists, with minor and temporary variations, as long as the plant is in an actively growing condition. The plant root, as well as the soil, seems to act as an effective microbial buffer.

The rhizosphere effect itself may be studied along two broad lines, one concerning the influence of the plant on the soil micro-population, the other dealing with the influence of the rhizosphere microflora on the plant. The former consists of quantitative and qualitative studies of the microflora in the root zone, studies on the relationships of the organisms to each other, and studies on the influence of environmental factors such as moisture and treatment of the soil, type and age of plant on them; it is a study of the microbial ecology of the rhizosphere. The latter consists of an examination of the role of the root microflora in relation to the growth and well-being of the plant. It is a study of the ability of various microbial species to provide plant nutrients, to compete with the plant for these, and to induce a pathological condition in the roots. Most of the work in our laboratory has dealt with the first of these two lines of investigation, that is, with the nature and composition of the rhizosphere microflora, and I should like to spend the remainder of my time in reviewing some of our results.

METHODS OF STUDY

We have employed a number of methods in our rhizosphere work. These include plating and ultimate dilution procedures with non-selective and selective media to determine numbers of specific types of organisms, and pure-culture techniques for morphological, taxonomic, nutritional and physiological studies. Rhizosphere soil is obtained by removing plants from soil, and after shaking gently to remove loosely adhering material, immersing and vigorously shaking the roots in sterile water blanks; the roots are then removed. Soil a short distance from the plant (6–10 in.) is used as control. Suitable dilutions are prepared from these soil suspensions and aliquots plated with soil extract agar for bacteria and actinomycete counts (Lochhead, 1940) and on rose bengal-aureomycin agar (Peterson, 1958) for fungi. One millilitre aliquots of each dilution are then transferred in quintuplicate to fluid or solid media designed to detect physiologically important groups of organisms such as ammonifiers, denitrifiers, nitrifiers, carbohydrate fermenters, cellulose decomposers, nitrogen fixers, and so on. The results may be expressed quantitatively by use of extinction dilution tables and calculating on an oven-dry soil basis. Recently we have carried our analysis of the rhizosphere effect one step farther by washing the roots thoroughly after removal from the original water blanks, in a number of changes of sterile water, comminuting aseptically in a Waring blendor, and preparing dilutions with this material. By this means organisms in very intimate association with the roots may be studied (Rouatt & Katznelson, 1958b). Pure culture studies are carried out by picking all colonies developing on plates of soil extract agar or representative portions of these, and examining the resulting cultures microscopically (Lochhead, 1940; Lochhead & Chase, 1943), determining their nutritional requirements in media of increasing complexity (Lochhead &

Chase, 1943), studying their growth rates and general physiological activity, and measuring by means of the Warburg apparatus their ability to oxidize various substrates (Katznelson & Rouatt, 1957a; Rouatt & Katznelson, 1957; Zagallo & Katznelson, 1957). Many other tests may be conducted with these isolates, such as determining their antibiotic potentialities, their ability to synthesize amino acids and growth factors, their ability to produce organic acids, and to carry out a variety of chemical reactions. This 'isolation' procedure permits calculation of the relative incidence of specific types of organisms, and is therefore useful in determining the microbiological equilibrium in both soil and rhizosphere.

An attempt has been made also to study rhizosphere and non-rhizosphere soils by means of manometric techniques (Katznelson & Rouatt, 1957b). The procedure consists of removing roots carefully, breaking up adhering soil clumps, and then shaking the remaining soil off on paper. This rhizosphere soil is then dried quickly with the aid of a fan for 30 min. and passed through a 1-mm. sieve. Four grams are weighed into each Warburg vessel, and water or a solution of substrate added directly to the soil to bring its moisture content to about 70% of its moisture-holding capacity. The vessels are then set up in the conventional manner in a water-bath, except that they are not shaken. Oxygen uptake and CO_2 evolution are then determined. A variety of substrates can be tested in this manner, the soil being treated as an ecological unit, the gas exchange being a reflection of the combined activity of all the organisms in it.

Direct microscopic examination of roots growing in soil by means of buried-slide techniques has also been used as a means of demonstrating microbial development in the rhizosphere (Rovira, 1956b; Starkey, 1938). We have done relatively little work along this line, although the method is of value in providing information on the localization of organisms on roots, their relative abundance, sequential activity, and morphology.

EXPERIMENTAL RESULTS

Data on the rhizosphere microflora of mangels and wheat are given in Table 1, as an example of the type of quantitative and qualitative information which may be obtained by plating and ultimate dilution procedures (Katznelson, 1946; Katznelson, Rouatt, & Payne, 1956). The results are expressed as rhizosphere soil: control soil or R:S ratios which are obtained by dividing the number of organisms in the rhizosphere soil by the number in soil apart from the root, all calculated on an oven-dry basis. A rhizosphere effect—that is, an increase in number of organisms in the rhizosphere over that in the control soil is indicated by an R:S ratio greater than 1. Such an effect occurs to various degrees with most of the groups of organisms listed in the table, except algae, nitrifying bacteria, *Azotobacter* or spore-forming types. A selec-

TABLE 1

Ratios of numbers of different types and groups of organisms in rhizosphere soil to numbers in control soil (R/S)

Group	Wheat	Mangels
Total bacteria	21	120
Actinomycetes	—	23
Fungi	10	19
Protozoa	3	23
Algae	1	2
Nitrifying bacteria	1	1
Spore formers	2	—
Aerobic cellulose decomposers	6	3
Anaerobic cellulose decomposers	4	—
Gas-producing anaerobes	12	14
Anaerobes	2	46
Ammonifiers	50	167
Denitrifiers	90	230
Azotobacter	—	2

tive or preferential effect of the root on specific bacterial groups is considered to take place when the R:S ratio is greater than that of the total bacterial count. Thus the only bacterial groups which appear to be selectively stimulated are ammonifying and denitrifying forms. According to this line of reasoning most of the other groups are relatively depressed, although their absolute numbers are greater at the root surface. It must be emphasized, of course, that these relationships will change with type and age of plant and the environmental conditions under which it is growing (soil moisture and treatment, temperature, light, etc.). We have also tested other groups of bacteria by the dilution procedure, and have found that organisms capable of reducing methylene blue or resazurin and those which ferment glucose with production of gas are selectively stimulated (Katznelson & Rouatt, 1957a). This was found to hold for oats, barley, corn, flax, red clover, as well as for wheat (Rouatt & Katznelson, 1958b).

An analysis of the macerated roots of these plants, or the rhizoplane

(Rouatt & Katznelson, 1958b), showed that on the basis of dry weight of roots there were lower bacterial and fungal counts than in the rhizosphere soil. This applied also to physiological groups such as ammonifying, denitrifying, acid and gas-producing and methylene-blue reducing bacteria.

Most of the work in our laboratory has dealt with bacterial isolates from rhizosphere and non-rhizosphere soil, although studies have been initiated recently on mycological aspects as well. Lochhead (1940) reported that Gram-negative bacteria were proportionally increased in the rhizosphere, whereas Gram-positive, coccoid, and spore-forming rods were less abundant. Furthermore, there appeared to be a greater proportion of bacteria producing good growth on nutrient agar, and of chromogenic and motile types at the root surface than in control soil. These results have been verified in general by Rovira (1956a). Studies on the nutritional requirements of the bacterial isolates, on media of increasing complexity (Lochhead & Thexton, 1947; Lochhead & Rouatt, 1955) yielded the interesting information that a selective action was exerted in the rhizosphere of all plants studied, on bacteria requiring amino acids for optimal growth, as may be noted in Table 2 (Katznelson, 1957).

When the amount of growth of such isolates on three media of increasing complexity was compared (Table 3), it was found that there was a pronounced shift in the rhizosphere towards rapidly growing types (Katznelson, 1957). Similar data have been obtained with other crop plants and with approximately 5000 cultures.

Representative isolates from rhizosphere and non-rhizosphere soil were also tested manometrically for ability to oxidize various substrates, as was reported in an earlier paper by Zagallo & Katznelson (1957). The results in Table 4 again support the thesis that the rhizosphere soil supports a metabolically more active bacterial flora than the soil apart from the root (Katznelson & Bose, 1958).

These and other isolates have been tested also for vitamin requirements, vitamin-synthesizing capacity (Lochhead, 1957; Lochhead & Burton, 1957), and most recently for ability to dissolve phosphate (Katznelson & Bose, 1958). I shall not dwell too long on this subject except to indicate that although the roots did not exert a selective action on vitamin-requiring or phosphate-dissolving bacteria, there appeared to be a preferential effect on vitamin-synthesizing types. However, the absolute numbers of the former two groups of organisms were very high in the rhizosphere in view of the much larger total number of bacteria in this zone.

TABLE 2

Rhizosphere effect on percentage incidence of amino acid requiring bacteria

	Plants			
	Barley	Oats	Wheat	Peas
Control	26	17	16	26
Rhizosphere	53	30	61	64

TABLE 3

Comparison of growth of isolates from rhizosphere and non-rhizosphere soil on different media*

Medium	Control soil	Rhizosphere soil	
		Barley	Peas
B (inorganic salts and glucose)	5	14	19
A (B + amino acids)	24	58	69
Y (B + yeast extract)	45	81	89

* Numbers represent percentage of cultures showing less than 90% light transmission in photoelectric colorimeter.

TABLE 4

Oxygen uptake (μl) of bacteria from wheat rhizosphere and control soil (after 2 hr.)

Source of culture	Number tested	Average endogenous values	Average* glucose values	Average* alanine values
Control soil	68	131	113	140
Rhizosphere soil	56	206	200	247

* Endogenous values subtracted.

The preceding paragraphs have dealt with bacteria only, as we have done comparatively little work of a qualitative nature with other microbial groups. However, a beginning has been made with fungi, and as mentioned earlier we have begun a systematic study of these organisms in the rhizosphere of normal, healthy plants. Some time ago we reported (Katznelson & Richardson, 1948) that in strawberry-bearing soils certain species of *Fusarium*, *Aspergillus*, and *Penicillium* were present, but not in the strawberry rhizospheres, which supported, on the other hand, species of *Cladosporium*, *Chaetomium*, *Rhizoctonia*, and certain unidentified types. Different soil treatments altered this picture considerably. During the past few years one of our staff, Dr. E. A. Peterson, working at Rothamsted, noted that *Penicillium* and certain species of *Mucorales* were relatively more abundant on the root surface of wheat and in the rhizosphere at the seedling stage than at later stages of growth. Species of *Fusarium* and of *Cylindrocarpon* and various sterile, dark fungi were predominant on the roots of healthy red clover and wheat, but were relatively rare in the rhizosphere and control soil. Peterson (1958) used a serial-wash treatment similar to that of Harley & Waid (1955) for the roots; the rhizosphere soil was obtained as described above. Dr. Peterson is now back in Ottawa and continuing this work, with emphasis on healthy plants.

TABLE 5

Oxygen uptake by rhizosphere and non-rhizosphere soils

Soil sample	Total oxygen uptake (μl) after 9 hr.
Wheat	250
Oats	165
Barley	325
Rye	310
Corn	375
Soybeans	425
Control	85

Leaving the strictly microbiological work, I wish to mention briefly some results of our manometric studies with the rhizosphere soil itself, by the method described previously (Katznelson & Rouatt, 1957b). As shown in Table 5, oxygen uptake by rhizosphere soil was distinctly greater than by control soil. Considerable difference between crops is also evident, the soil from corn and soybean roots being exceptionally active. The addition of substrates such as amino acids and carbohydrates caused even greater activity, in particular the former group of compounds. This particular observation is of interest because it supports the microbiological data obtained concerning the preferential effect of plant roots on amino acid requiring and ammonifying bacteria.

DISCUSSION

I have attempted to indicate the type of work that is being done on the rhizosphere problem in our laboratory. In part, it is a study in methodology, and I am not at all certain that we have found as yet the best method for studying this problem. However, it is amply clear that there is not only a marked increase in numbers of micro-organisms in the rhizosphere, but also a shift in, or selection of, types of bacteria favouring those with requirements for amino acids for growth, and of profusely growing and metabolically active species. It is to be expected, of course, that the microbiological equilibrium of the soil should be disturbed by the growing plant as a result of the increased food supply arising from sloughed-off dead and dying root fragments and through root excretions. Microbial activity is intensified, as are competitive and associative forces, and those soil organisms which grow most rapidly and are physiologically most active apparently establish themselves as the predominant forms in this zone, whereas others are inhibited or eliminated. A new equilibrium is therefore established which seems to retain its biotic characteristics as long as the plant is actively growing. In a study just completed (Rouatt & Katznelson, 1958a), it was shown that even on the very youngest roots (2 to 3 days old), this shift towards amino-acid requiring bacteria, and towards rapidly growing, actively metabolizing forms, had already begun. The establishment of this rhizosphere microflora occurs, then, almost as soon as the root influence is felt by the organism in the soil into which the root is penetrating. After that, the picture becomes more confused and more difficult to analyse, because there is superimposed on the root effect the associative and antagonistic reactions among the micro-organisms themselves— their ability to produce amino acids, growth factors, and inhibitory substances as shown by Lochhead and co-workers (Lochhead & Thexton, 1947; Lochhead, 1957; Lochhead & Burton, 1957), their competition for food, for oxygen, and even for space. Despite this, the prevalence of the bacterial types mentioned above in the root zone, and even more strikingly on the root itself (the rhizoplane), as shown also in recent studies by Rouatt and Katznelson (1958b), remains as one of the dominant and characteristic features of the rhizosphere population even in older plants.

I have purposely avoided discussing the rhizosphere effect in relation to root diseases, as this is an extensive field which deserves special consideration. Work along this line has been conducted in our laboratories on the Niagara Peninsula with strawberry-root rot and potato scab, and in the Province of Saskatchewan on root rot of wheat caused by *Helminthosporium sativum*. Significant changes in the soil rhizosphere populations can be induced by specific soil treatments (soybeans, dried blood, acetic acid) which appear to control the development of soil-borne root pathogens or semi-pathogens (Katznelson & Richardson, 1948; Rouatt & Atkinson, 1950; Zagallo & Katznelson, 1957). These treatments exert at best a temporary effect so far as the rhizosphere population is concerned; the essential features of the microbial equilibrium on the root with respect to actively growing organisms, ammonifying, and amino-acid requiring types being relatively unchanged.

I have also purposely avoided a consideration of the influence of the rhizosphere microflora on the plant, since this too is a very broad subject requiring special treatment. The transformation of organic and inorganic compounds by these organisms and how the plants benefit thereby is a complex problem requiring for its solution the application of the most recent techniques of chromatography, spectrophotometry, and tracer chemistry. Special effects, such as those induced by auxins and related compounds, also require clarification. There is little doubt that the microbial mantle on the root exerts a profound effect, be it positive or negative, on plant growth, but we are still far from knowing its nature and extent. The combined efforts of microbiologists and plant physiologists will be required to solve this basic problem.

REFERENCES

HARLEY, J. L., & WAID, J. S. (1955). A method of studying active mycelia on living roots and other surfaces in soil. *Trans. Brit. mycol. Soc.*, **38**, 104–18.

KATZNELSON, H. (1946). Rhizosphere effect of mangels on certain groups of soil micro-organisms. *Soil Sci.*, **62**, 343–54.

KATZNELSON, H. (1957). (In the Press.)

KATZNELSON, H., & BOSE, B. (1958). (In the Press.)

KATZNELSON, H., LOCHHEAD, A. G., & TIMONIN, M. I. (1948). Soil micro-organisms and the rhizosphere. *Bot. Rev.*, **14**, 543–87.

KATZNELSON, H., & RICHARDSON, L. T. (1948). Rhizosphere studies and associated microbiological phenomena in relation to strawberry-root rot. *Sci. Agric.*, **28**, 293–308.

KATZNELSON, H., & ROUATT, J. W. (1957*b*). Studies on the incidence of certain physiological groups of bacteria in the rhizosphere. *Can. J. Microbiol.*, 3, 265–9.

KATZNELSON, H., & ROUATT, J. W. (1957*a*). Manometric studies with rhizosphere and non-rhizosphere soil. *Can. J. Microbiol.*, 3, 673–8.

KATZNELSON, H., ROUATT, J. W., & PAYNE, T. M. B. (1956). Recent studies on the microflora of the rhizosphere. *Proc. VI Int. Congr. Soil Sci., Paris, III*, 25, 151–6.

LOCHHEAD, A. G. (1940). Qualitative studies on soil micro-organisms. III. Influence of plant growth on the character of the bacterial flora. *Can. J. Res. (C)*, 18, 42–53.

LOCHHEAD, A. G. (1957). Qualitative studies of soil micro-organisms. XI. Capability of the predominant bacterial flora for synthesis of various growth factors. *Soil Sci.*, 84, 395–403.

LOCHHEAD, A. G., & BURTON, M. O. (1957). Qualitative studies of soil micro-organisms. XIV. Specific vitamin requirements of the predominant bacterial flora. *Can. J. Microbiol.*, 3, 35–42.

LOCHHEAD, A. G., & CHASE, F. E. (1943). Qualitative studies on soil micro-organisms. V. Nutritional requirements of the predominant bacterial flora. *Soil Sci.*, 55, 185–95.

LOCHHEAD, A. G., & ROUATT, J. W. (1955). The 'rhizosphere effect' on the nutritional groups of soil bacteria. *Soil Sci. Soc. Amer. Proc.*, 19, 48–9.

LOCHHEAD, A. G., & THEXTON, R. H. (1947). Qualitative studies of soil micro-organisms. VII. The 'rhizosphere effect' in relation to the amino-acid nutrition of bacteria. *Can. J. Res. (C)*, 25, 20–6.

PETERSON, E. A. (1958). Observations on fungi associated with plant roots. *Can. J. Microbiol.*, 4, 257–65.

ROUATT, J. W., & ATKINSON, R. G. (1950). The effect of the incorporation of certain cover crops on the microbiological balance of potato-scab infested soil. *Can. J. Res. (C)*, 28, 140–52.

ROUATT, J. W., & KATZNELSON, H. (1957). The comparative growth of bacterial isolates from rhizosphere and non-rhizosphere soils. *Can. J. Microbiol.*, 3, 271–5.

ROUATT, J. W., & KATZNELSON, H. (1958*a*). Initiation of the rhizosphere effect. *Bact. Proc.*, 58, 9.

ROUATT, J. W., & KATZNELSON, H. (1958*b*). Unpublished data.

ROVIRA, A. D. (1956*a*). Plant-root excretions in relation to the rhizosphere effect. II. A study of the properties of root exudate and its effects on the growth of micro-organisms isolated from the rhizosphere and control soil. *Plant and Soil*, 7, 195–208.

ROVIRA, A. D. (1956*b*). A study of the development of the root-surface microflora during initial stages of plant growth. *J. Appl. Bact.*, 19, 72–9.

STARKEY, R. L. (1938). Some influences of the development of higher plants upon micro-organisms in the soil. VI. Microscopic examination of the rhizosphere. *Soil Sci.*, 45, 207–49.

ZAGALLO, A. C., & KATZNELSON, H. (1957). Metabolic activity of bacterial isolates from wheat rhizosphere and control soil. *J. Bacteriol.*, 73, 760–4.

THE FUNGAL FLORA OF TIDAL MUD-FLATS

G. J. F. PUGH

Department of Botany, University of Nottingham

The accretion of silt in various places around our coasts has led to the formation of tidal mud-flats which subsequently support a typical salt-marsh flora. Several workers have investigated the fungal flora of such salt marshes, but only Bayliss Elliott (1930) looked at the lower reaches of these mud-flats. She made a few isolations from the Salicornietum of the Dovey Salt Marshes, and drew up a list of the species which she isolated. The rest of her work, and that of Saitô (1952), describes the fungi isolated from the mature salt marsh. In the present work, the opposite approach has been taken, namely to find the fungal flora present in the mud-flats *before* they become colonized by higher plants and during colonization by *Salicornia stricta* agg. This is an annual plant, and is useful as a primary colonizer and also as a regular source of organic matter. It is a convenient plant to study because it grows alone in the lower regions of the salt marsh, and it is therefore easy to obtain samples from pure stands. It also occurs intermixed with other plants higher up the marsh, enabling comparisons to be made between the two types of habitat. This paper is intended to be a progress report giving some of the results so far obtained.

The mud-flats would appear to be a most unsuitable medium for fungal growth as they are regularly inundated by the sea, and consequently are badly aerated and water saturated. The pH varies between 7·2 and 7·8, and this reaction greatly encourages bacteria. The inevitable question in this type of work again has to be asked. Did the fungi isolated grow from hyphae or from spores? It is believed that they grew from hyphae chiefly for the following reasons:

(i) Direct examination of soils (Kubiena, 1938) usually shows conidiophores growing into air spaces between the soil crumbs. The nature of these muds precludes crumb structure and the presence of air spaces. It is known that most fungi will grow submerged in liquid cultures, and, under such conditions, they do not normally form spores. Further, direct microscopic examination of the mud has shown very occasional hyphae, but no fungal spores have been seen.

(ii) The majority of the species appear between 24–48 hr. after plating out. Those that develop later are usually slow-growing species, like *Stachybotrys atra*.

MATERIALS AND METHODS

Samples of uncolonized mud have been obtained from Bembridge Harbour, Isle of Wight, the Cleddau Estuary, Pembrokeshire, and Gibraltar Point, Lincolnshire, by pushing sterile tubes into the mud at random, and then sealing them. The cores were subsequently cut open longitudinally and the central portions plated out in Warcup soil plates. The results obtained must be viewed bearing in mind the limitations of the method.

Samples for investigating the fungal flora in the *Salicornia* zone were obtained from the Dee Estuary, Cheshire, Frieston, Lincolnshire, and Gibraltar Point. Blocks of mud containing the plants were dug up and transported to the laboratory, where they were broken open vertically and the roots removed from the fracture surfaces. The rhizosphere was investigated by plating out soil particles which were in contact with the roots. In this case the rhizosphere was studied, not primarily for itself but because it is a zone of increased activity, and therefore can be used as an indication of changes in the micro-population.

The root-surface flora was obtained by shaking roots in each of 5 changes of sterile water at 250–300 oscillations per min. The roots were then dried on sterile filter-paper and cut into 1-cm. lengths before plating out.

In all primary isolations 2% (w/v) plain agar was used. The colonies which developed were subsequently transferred to Potato Dextrose Agar for identification.

RESULTS

Species isolated from the uncolonized muds and from the rhizosphere

As would be expected, the species found in the mud have been isolated from the rhizosphere, with only one exception, together with a number of other species. These species are listed in Table 1. The most widespread species, which were isolated from all the different sites examined were amongst the most common in any particular habitat. Of these widespread species, the Mucors were the most frequently isolated both from the rhizosphere and from the mud. There were two prevalent species, *M. hiemalis* and *M. ? racemosus*, of which *M. ? racemosus* was some-

TABLE 1

Distribution and frequency of occurrence of the isolated species. Frequency of occurrence is given as a percentage of the total isolations from the rhizosphere and from the mud. Totals 360 and 320 respectively

Species	Distribution				Frequency as % of the totals	
	Gibraltar Point		Bem-bridge mud	Cleddau mud	Rhiz.	Mud
	Rhiz.	Mud				
Aspergillus fumigatus	+	+	+	+	9·0	11·6
A. terreus	+	+	+	+	0·5	4·0
Cephalosporium spp.	+	+	+	+	7·0	3·0
Fusarium culmorum	+	+	+	+	7·5	4·7
Mortierella alpina	+	+	+	+	4·0	1·3
Mucor spp.	+	+	+	+	14·0	23·2
Penicillium spp.	+	+	+	+	12·8	19·1
Trichoderma viride	+	+	+	+	7·0	16·6
Zygorrhynchus spp.	+	+	+	+	1·3	3·4
Sterile mycelia	+	+	+	+	5·0	7·8
Aspergillus niger	+		+	+	1·1	0·9
Cladosporium herbarum	+	+			0·3	0·3
Phoma sp.	+	+		+	0·8	0·9
Stachybotrys atra	+	+			2·5	1·3
Verticillium sp.	+	+		+	1·1	0·9
Cercospora salina	+				8·5	
Aspergillus glaucus	+				1·1	
A. nidulans	+				0·3	
Botrytis cinerea	+				2·5	
Chaetomium globosum	+				1·1	
C. ? spinosum	+				1·6	
Cylindrocarpon sp.	+				0·8	
Diplodina sp.	+				3·0	
Fusarium sp.	+				1·3	
Sterile white mycelium	+				5·5	
Actinomucor repens		+				0·3

what more common. Differences can be seen in the relative abundance of various species between the two regions, with *Cephalosporium*, *Fusarium*, and *Mortierella* appearing to prefer the rhizosphere, while the Mucors, species of *Penicillium* and *Trichoderma*, were much more frequently found away from the roots than near them.

Taking the habitats collectively, the Mucors, species of *Penicillium*, *Trichoderma viride*, *Aspergillus fumigatus*, *Fusarium culmorum*, and species of *Cephalosporum* were the most common fungi encountered in the muds.

Species which were not found in all the habitats were, in general, less common at a particular site than the widespread species. Some of these less common species are slow growing, and it may be that they were swamped on the isolation plates by those species with a faster growth rate.

The species found only in the rhizosphere were of sporadic occurrence, except for *Cercospora salina* and the sterile white mycelium. These two species were not found away from the roots, and, as will be seen, are frequently found on the root surfaces. While the presence of the other species in the rhizosphere and not in the mud may be due to the action of the rhizosphere or to unfortunate sampling, *C. salina* and the sterile white mycelium must, I think, be regarded as 'escapes' from the root surface. They almost certainly belong to Garrett's (1951) group of 'root-inhabiting' fungi, and as such must be separated from the other soil-inhabiting species.

Species isolated from the root surface of Salicornia stricta *agg.*

Altogether 240 roots have been sampled, but no fungi were isolated from 42 of these because of heavy bacterial contamination, and a further 14 were sterile. The species which were isolated are listed in Table 2, together with the number of roots on which they were found.

TABLE 2

Frequency of occurrence of species isolated from 240 roots

Sterile white mycelium	122
Cercospora salina	81
Sterile mycelia	26
Penicillium spp.	14
Botrytis cinerea	7
Cephalosporium sp.	4
Fusarium culmorum	2
Mortierella alpina	2
Mucor hiemalis	2
Phoma sp.	2
Stemphylium sp.	1

Apart from the sterile white mycelium which normally occurred towards the root tips, and *C. salina*, which was present on the older parts of the roots, the other species were infrequently found. *C. salina* occurred on only 6 roots by itself, the other isolations were all made from roots which yielded the sterile white mycelium. These species were isolated from all samples of *Salicornia*, regardless of where they were collected.

The very common occurrence of these species posed the question of how they arrived on the root surfaces. From the earlier results, it was seen that neither species was isolated from the uncolonized mud although both were present in the rhizosphere.

As *Salicornia* grows each year in some areas where it was not present the previous year, the possibility of seed infection was examined.

Seeds collected from living plants did not yield these species, whereas of 48 seeds collected from dead plants 24 were contaminated by *C. salina* and 20 with the sterile white mycelium. This was the only occasion when *C. salina* spores were seen on freshly collected *Salicornia*, as the loculi around the seeds, and some of the seeds, had sporing hyphae growing over them.

The penetration of these two and other species into the root tissues occurs after the death of the *Salicornia* plants in winter. The root cortex eventually breaks down, leaving the stele as a solid rod surrounded by a loosely fitting epidermis. These portions were separated and plated out independently, using a technique similar to that described by Waid (1956). It was found that of 37 roots examined in this way, the sterile mycelium was present on or in the epidermis of 16, and *C. salina* of 14, and both species were isolated from the steles of 5 plants. Other species present inside the dead roots were *Fusarium culmorum*, *Mucor hiemalis*, *Penicillium* sp., and sterile mycelia. The dead stems and inflorescence axes also yielded these species, while the living stems did not.

This led to a study of the seedlings, and, so far, only a small number have been examined.

The inflorescence axis may fall over and become buried by silt, and the seeds then germinate *in situ*. *C. salina* and biverticillate *Penicillium* sp. have been recovered from such seedlings.

In the case of the dispersed seeds, a range of seedlings has been sampled, from those with only the cotyledons open to those on which branches had started to develop.

C. salina has been isolated from seedlings with only their cotyledons open, and it and the sterile mycelium have been recovered from other seedlings on which the first pair of leaves had developed.

There was no great increase in colonization with advancing age, as was found by Stenton (1958) on pea roots, only one plant yielding a sterile dark mycelium, and another *Fusarium culmorum*, but these were isolated cases.

DISCUSSION

The presence of these common, soil-inhabiting species in newly formed marine muds will come as no surprise. The presence of *Trichoderma viride* calls for some comment as it is so often described as typically an acid-soil species, yet here it forms a large proportion of the fungal population.

In 1916, Waksman postulated a hypothetical soil flora, and with the exception of *Rhizopus* and *Scopulariopsis* they are all present in these muds. Bayliss Elliott suggested that salt-marsh fungi are introduced by drainage, by wind, or by birds and other animals, to which could be added the probability of continual invasion from the landward edge of the marsh, in which case any species could be present if it were able to grow under the prevailing conditions.

Twenty-seven species were isolated from the rhizosphere, as compared with 17 from the uncolonized mud, showing that the presence of a primary colonizer brings about an enrichment of the fungal flora. Work is now in hand to examine the relative abundance of these and other species in the more mature regions of salt marshes.

The colonization of the root surfaces of *Salicornia* was patchy, and the root-surface microflora was much sparser than that found on beech roots by Harley and Waid (1955). These results agree with theirs in the presence of sterile mycelia towards the root apices, but the widespread presence of *Cercospora salina* differs from their results.

Salt marshes are amongst the few natural areas where bare soil can be found, free even from weeds, for such studies in colonization, and where individual higher plants can be picked out, well separated from their neighbours and with no other species present. While there are disadvantages in working in such localities, there are advantages in using such a natural habitat for investigating changes in the fungal population during colonization of soil by higher plants.

REFERENCES

BAYLISS ELLIOTT, J. S. (1930). The soil fungi of the Dovey Salt Marshes. *Ann. Appl. Biol.*, **17**, 284–305.

GARRETT, S. D. (1951). Ecological groups of soil fungi: a survey of substrate relationships. *New Phytol.*, **50**, 149–66.

HARLEY, J. L., & WAID, J. S. (1955). A method of studying active mycelia on living roots and other surfaces in the soil. *Trans. Brit. mycol. Soc.*, **38**, 104–18.

KUBIENA, W. L. (1938). *Micropedology*. Ames, Iowa: Collegiate Press Inc.

Saitô, Toshi (1952). The soil fungi of a salt marsh and its neighbourhood. *Ecol. Rev.* (Japan), **13**, 2.

Stenton, H. (1958). Colonization of roots of *Pisum sativum* L. by fungi. *Trans. Brit. mycol. Soc.*, **41**, 74–80.

Waid, J. S. (1956). Root dissection: a method of studying the distribution of active mycelia within root tissues. *Nature, Lond.*, **178**, 1477–8.

Waksman, S. (1916). Soil fungi and their activities. *Soil Sci.*, **2**, 103–56.

A STUDY OF THE FUNGAL MICROFLORA IN THE RHIZOSPHERE OF FIR (*ABIES ALBA* MILL.)

W. MALISZEWSKA

I.U.N.G. Pulawy, Poland

AND

R. MOREAU

École Nationale de Medicine et de Pharmacie, Besançon, France

In the old fir plantations of the Jura, one often notices the more or less complete absence of regeneration: the fir induces 'fatigue' in the soil which bears it. In contrast, it regenerates well under the same crop when the population is still young (60–80 years), or under deciduous trees; moreover, it has been established that the seedlings spring up principally where the humus is acid (Schaeffer & Moreau, 1958).

Though various explanations have been given, which predicate the influence of either free growth (Roussel, 1956) or restriction (Ph. Duchaufour 1953) in the roots, none of these seems to be adequate. One should think rather of a complexity of causes, the ecological origins of which are diverse, and amongst which the compositions of both the humus and the microflora play an important role.

We were thus compelled to investigate the rhizosphere of the fir (*Abies alba* Mill.), as well as the microflora of different fir-growing soils. Preliminary results for the fungal microflora of the soils investigated are given here. This work requires elaboration; elsewhere we will give details of the dominant species, isolated and now under investigation.

Ecological characteristics of the forest studied

Our work related to the soils and plants found on a large *massif* upon which the villages of Adam-les-Vercel and Epenoy (Doubs, France) are sited. Situated at an altitude of about 750 m., the Epenoy forest grows in an 'evolved rendzina' type of soil made up by a tenuous layer of brown forest soil and 95% of calcareous substratum.

The soil is acid: pH of 4·5–5·0. Its C/N value is approximately 15; the ratio mineralN/ total N is about 1/110. The forest has a rainfall above 1400 mm. a year (average for the period 1952 to 1956: 1463 mm.). The average annual temperature is below 8° (average for the period 1952 to 1956, 7·6°). The De Martonne index is about 77.

The vegetation population is made up almost entirely by the fir; the principal species of the population are given below.

Aborescent stratum:
  Fagus silvatica L., abundant.
  Sorbus aucuparia L.
  Sambucus racemosa L.
  Lonicera nigra L., etc.
Herbaceous stratum:
  Athyrium filix femina (L.) Roth.
  Polystichum spinulosum Link and D.C.
  Polygonatum verticillatum (L.) All.
  Dentaria pinnata Link.
  Rubus sp.
  Oxalis acetosella L.
  Asperula odorata L.
  Prenanthes purpurea L.
  Senecio fuchsii Gmelin, etc.

These very briefly summarized observations show that the site examined is situated in conditions generally associated with the fir.

For comparison, samples collected in the neighbouring forest of Valdahon were examined. Situated at a slightly lower altitude, this forest falls just within the deciduous belt; also its soil is deeper. Scattered firs can be seen amongst the other type and, in ecological characteristics, the two forests are very similar. (For further details see Moreau & Schaeffer [1957], and the works cited therein.)

Methods of study[1]

Bacteria and Actinomycetes. We made our counts on the following medium:

Fertile soil extract	200 ml.
K_2HPO_4	0·5 g.
Tap water	800 ml.
Agar	14 g.

We inoculated 3–6 Petri dishes with 1 ml. per dish of a soil suspension. The medium was then poured over (20 ml. per dish). The colonies of

[1] The details of the techniques used are given in another publication (Marszewska-Ziemiecka, 1958).

Bacteria and of the Actinomycetes were counted separately on the same plates, the former after 5 days in the incubator at 28°.

Fungi (total number). In the absence of the determination of a 'mycelial mass' (Moreau, 1958), we counted the colonies after inoculating in the same medium as before but acidified with lactic acid (pH of 3–3 5). One could discuss the usefulness of these counts; at least they serve for comparisons between the soils studied.

In addition, we used a rose bengal medium (Wiltgen & Bonnier, 1952), modified by the addition of 5 g. of peptone per litre.

We generally inoculated each sample in 3–6 dishes, in the ratio of 1 ml. of a soil suspension at 1/1000, and 20 ml. of the medium was poured over; the dishes were then incubated for 4 days at 28°.

We concurrently used these two media for the following reasons:

(i) On the rose bengal medium, which is very rich, one virtually obtains a 'fungal image' significant of each soil studied (Wiltgen & Bonnier, 1952).

(ii) The acidified soil-extract medium, by contrast, is poor. The colonies develop only slowly in it and are less profuse. Furthermore, the bacteria are totally inhibited, which is not found with the other medium. The number of colonies is greater (Table 1) and, above all, more constant for a given soil amongst the various dishes.

TABLE 1

Number of fungal colonies

Samples of soil		1	2	3	4	5	A	B	C	D	E	F	G
Average number of colonies per dish diluted 1:3	Rose bengal mixture	42	30	45	16	16	17	68	39	186	31	84	130
	Extract of acidified soil medium	238	24	116	1·5	50	33	92	79	340	163	133	132

(iii) Cellulolytic fungi. We used the method of Winogradsky, modified by Felsz-Karnicka (1935). The medium consists of a solution of mineral salts and agar adjusted to a pH of 5·0–5·5. It is distributed to Petri dishes, then the agar is covered with a filter-paper. The plates are inoculated with grains of soil.

Results

These are summarized in Tables 2 and 3.

TABLE

First series of samples: specimen No. 8 from Adam-les-Vercel; firs at firs, overcrowded (No. 2): above the rotted stumps, good regeneration

Soil studied No. of samples	Regeneration	Total number of micro-organisms in 1 g. dry soil (in millions)		Percentage of fungi
		Flora, total Bacteria Actinomycetes	Fungi	
1 Rhizosphere of young fir seedlings (1–5 years)		381	0·30	0·07
2 Rhizosphere of over-crowded prime firs (15–20 years)	Mediocre	79	0·02	0·02
3 Rhizosphere of old firs (100 years)		127	0·08	0·06
5 Soil of the fir plantation	pH:4·5	14	0·065	0·46
4 Rhizosphere of the fir seedlings on stump-soil (2–5 years)	Good	100	0·005	0·005

The decomposition of the cellulose by the fungi was not determined.

2

least 100 *years old (sample No. 3); poor regeneration (No. 1); average
(No. 4), which was a common feature; the soil (No. 5) has a pH of* 4·5

Dominant types	Mycorrhiza
Mucorales, *Penicillium* sp.: fairly abundant *Trichoderma viride:* very abundant A good flora variety	All the radicles are mycorrhizal
Mucorales, *Penicillium* sp.: abundant *T. viride* represented A good flora variety	Transformed roots rare
Mucorales: abundant *Penicillium* sp. Poor flora	Transformed roots rare
Mucorales: abundant *Penicillium* sp. Poor flora	Abundant white mycelium of Basidiomycetes
Mucorales, *Aspergillus* sp., *Penicillium* sp. *T. viride* represented Flora scarce but varied	Abundant mycorrhiza

TABLE

Second series of samples (a) *specimen from Epenoy; 3 very old firs* (*200*
(b) *Specimen 9 from Adam-les-Vercel: fir 80 years old* (*D*), *in full growth.*
15 years, under

Soil studied No. of samples	Regeneration	pH of soil	Total number of micro-organisms in 1 g. dry soil (in millions)		Percentage of fungi
			Flora total Bact., Act. Fungi	Fungi	
B Rhizosphere of old firs (200 years)	Nil		377	0·05	0·02
A Soil of the fir plantation		5·5	39	0·05	0·1
E Rhizosphere of young fir seedlings (1–5 years)			251	0·1	0·04
D Members of the fir population (80 years)	Excellent		103·7	0·2	0·2
C Soil of the fir plantation		4·5	25	0·1	0·4
G Rhizosphere of firs of about 15 years (full growth)			958	0·1	0·01
F Soil under leaf mixtures	Excellent	6·5	39	0·2	0·5

3

years); thick layer of humus (A and B); no regeneration apparent.
Brushwood seedlings (E). (c) Valdahon: firs, very dense (G), about
deciduous trees

Dominant types	Decomposition of the cellulose	Mycorrhiza
Mucorales: represented *Penicillium* sp.: very abundant *T. viride:* trace Poor flora	Aspergillaceae	All the radicles are mycor-rhizal. White mycelium round many roots
Mucorales: very abundant *Penicillium* sp. Mycelium ster Poor flora	+++ *Chaetomium* Aspergillaceae	Abundant mauve mycelium of Basidiomycetes in thick humus
Mucorales: very abundant (not det.) *Zygorhynchus* sp. *Penicillium* sp.: scarce Very rich flora	++ Eurotiaceae Aspergillaceae	Abundant mycorrhiza
Mucorales not det.: abundant *Zygorhynchus* sp. *Penicillium* sp.: abundant Very rich flora	+++ Eurotiaceae Aspergillaceae	Mycorrhiza less abundant
Mucorales *Penicillium* sp.: abundant *Trichoderma viride* Flora not varied	+++ Aspergillaceae	
Mucorales numerous not det. *Mucor* sp. *Aspergillus* *Penicillium* sp. *T. viride.* Flora rich and varied	+++ Aspergillaceae	All the roots are mycor-rhizal
Mucorales, *Penicillium* sp.: abundant *T. viride:* represented Rich flora	+++ Aspergillaceae	

Examination of the results obtained using the plate method

One point emerges straightway: the fungi are present in more or less equal numbers in the soils and corresponding rhizospheres. Thus it seems that, generally, growth of the fungi is not, or only slightly, stimulated at the level of the fir roots, whatever the age and condition of the latter. The opposite effect is shown by the Bacteria and Actinomycetes.

Nevertheless, in this context we are ignoring mycorrhizal fungi for which, at present, no method of determining number is known. Moreover, in some samples we have noted the abundance of roots showing mycorrhiza.

The first finding was that the percentage of fungi is on average ten times greater in the soils than in the rhizospheres. It was further established that this percentage is constant for all the soils examined except sample B, collected under old firs, in which the proportion of colonies is appreciably lower.

Thus, the counts did not reveal differences characteristic of the diverse rhizospheres studied.

But, above all, it is the *qualitative* aspect which is interesting.

Though the Mucorales and Aspergillaceae are constant and fairly numerous, we have noticed in the rhizosphere of most of the seedlings and in the soils which exhibit good regeneration:

(i) a wider variety of species, (ii) the presence, and often abundance, of *Trichoderma viride*—the latter generally being an index of the soil's fertility.

In contrast, this fungus was absent, most of the time, from the rhizosphere of the old trees, also from soils in which regeneration was slow where, furthermore, the flora was much less varied.

The decomposition of the cellulose is effected essentially by the fungi (Eurotiaceae, *Chaetomium*, Aspergillaceae, etc.), and only to a small degree by the bacteria (as with Felsz-Karnicka, 1935, and Golebiowska, 1947, in the acid soils). Its intensity was ostensibly equal at the different sampling positions.

Conclusions

The main points of this first study seem to us to be the following:

(1) No stimulation of the fungi in the rhizosphere of the fir, but enrichment of the bacterial population in comparison with the corresponding soil.

(2) More varied flora in the soil and rhizosphere of young firs, both collected under deciduous trees (beech, etc.).

(3) Presence of *Trichoderma viride* around the roots of young firs, also in soils carrying a good regeneration.

In contrast, the absence of this species in soils offering only poor regeneration, or none, and in the rhizosphere of old trees.

Perhaps the presence or absence of this fungus can be interpreted as a first 'sign of response' with a composition determined by the excretions of the root system of the fir and with a certain state of the soil and of the humus? The work of Winter (1955) lends authority to this claim.

More precise work is in progress; but at this point one can begin to think of a modification of the microbial equilibrium of the soil and perhaps of a modification of the medium, through the influence of accumulation in the humus of excretions and decomposition products of organic material.

Several mechanisms could then operate:

(*a*) A direct toxic action by these substances on the young plants.

(*b*) An indirect action, by means of the microflora: a breakdown of equilibrium could induce a lifting of inhibition in favour of organisms pathogenic to the seedlings (at the extremities of the seedlings, for example).

(*c*) a combination of the two processes above.

In contrast, the humus of the deciduous trees seems to have a favourable effect, both on the bacterial and fungal microflora and on the regenerative capacity for firs.

In all events, one cannot dismiss the other ecological factors; dryness, for example, can result in a concentration of toxic substances in the superficial layers of the soil.

Light may be thrown on this question by the results of work now being carried out on the nutritional groups in the rhizosphere of the firs and the composition of the humus in the soils examined.

At the same time this work, taken in conjunction with the study of the fungi already begun, will enable us to discern relationships between the individual plants or populations, the types of soil which support them and the microflora of these soils. The preliminaty findings given above allow us to believe that this research will be fruitful.

REFERENCES

Duchaufour, Ph. (1953). Régénération de l'Epicea et pédologie. *Rev. For. Française*, **4**, 257–68.

Felsz-Karnicka, H. (1935). Rozklad celulozy w glebach kwas'nych. *Pamietnik P.I.U.N.G.*, **16**, 48.

GOLEBIWOSKA, J. (1947). Przyczynek do badan' nad rozktadem btonnika przez grzyby niższe wystepujace w glebie. *Ann. Univ. Mariae-Curie-Sktodowska, Lublin. Polonia*, **2**, 223–48.

MARSZEWSKA-ZIEMIECKA, J. (1958). *Mikrobiologia gleby i namozow organicznych.* Warszawa.

MOREAU, R., & SCHAEFFER, R. (1957). La descente du Sapin dans le département du Doubs: phénomène naturel ou provoqué par l'homme? *Bull. Soc. Hist. Nat. Doubs*, **59**, 149–69.

MOREAU, R. (1958). Les méthodes d'étude en microbiologie du sol: à propos du Symposium de Louvain, 1957. *Ann. Univ. de Besançon.* A paraitre.

ROUSSEL, L. (1956). À propos d'une nouvelle étude sur le phénomène de l'alternance. *Id.*, déc., pp. 3–8.

SCHAEFFER, R., & MOREAU, R. (1958). L'alternance des essences. I. *Bull. de la Soc. For. de Franche-Comté et des Prov. de l'Est.*, Mars, 3–12.

WILTGEN, N., & BONNIER, CH. (1952). À propos de l'examen mycologique du sol description d'une méthode. *Bull. de l'Inst. Agron. et des Stat. de Rech. de Gembloux.*, **20**, 391–6.

WINTER, A. G. (1955). Untersuchungen über vorkommen und bedeutung von antimikrobiellen und antiphytotischen substanzen in natürlichen böden. *Zeit. PH. Ernähr. Dürg.*, **69**, 224–33.

DISCUSSION

Dr. H. Katznelson. I was surprised to hear in Professor Burges' paper that the increases in numbers of fungi and bacteria were not particularly great during the decomposition of litter. This is quite different from the results we, and a number of other investigators, have obtained in similar studies which showed very marked increases in numbers of these organisms. These results were accompanied by a parallel increase in CO_2 output. Similar work with the incorporation of pine needles and yellow birch leaves which is going on now shows similar trends.

Prof. A. Burges. The increase is usually by a factor of times 5 for fungi, but the increase in CO_2 may be one-hundredfold.

Dr. H. Katznelson. Also I am curious as to the relative amounts of carbon lost as CO_2, fixed as microbial tissue or leached downward. It seems to me that the last is very important and should be considered.

Prof. A. Burges. We have not got a carbon 'balance sheet'; we do not know how much is leached downward.

Dr. G. Wallis. Does not the pH have a significant bearing on the breakdown on mull and mor humus sites? On the mull there would, I believe, be a larger population of bacteria, whereas on the mor there would be a predominance of fungi. As the mor humus builds up, there would be a corresponding build-up in fungi over the years. The mor would eventually reach such a thickness and the fungus population become great enough throughout that thick layer that breakdown would equal the annual fall.

Prof. A. Burges. I have not looked at bacterial populations. I was trying to make the point that I do not think the statement that there is a rapid turnover in mull and a slow turnover in mor is justifiable. Once mor is thick enough to make conditions favourable enough down below it can turn over carbon at the same rate as mull.

Dr. J. L. Harley. There are two points worth noting with respect to rates and kinds of litter breakdown:

(i) The leaf litter is subject to desiccation, and leaves are often readily reduced to as low a moisture content in dry air as they can be over $CaCl_2$. The accumulation of mor humus may well be due, in initial stages of growth of a pine plantation, to periodic desiccation. In later stages when litter has accumulated, the mean rate of breakdown increases because water is retained in the lower litter region.

(ii) Mull breakdown is partly due to animal activity. Animals drag organic matter into the surface soil. Here breakdown is at a fast rate, and one year's litter disappears within the current year. The direction of breakdown is also therefore different from that of mor.

Dr. M. Witkamp. In a mull type of soil the amount of CO_2 that can be drawn from this soil at a certain rate over a certain period of time has a peak in the autumn, a low during the winter, and a rise with temperature and fluctuating with moisture content of the soil during the spring and summer. In mor type of soil we get the same general result but less pronounced—a peak in the autumn, moderate fluctuations during the spring and summer.

The possible causes are readily available nutrients in the mull litter and quicker changes in the moisture content in mull than in more specially in spring and summer.

There is the influence of insects which minimize leaf particles by chewing and packing the resultant particles into faecal pellets that resist drying fairly well. This results in a prolonged increase in CO_2 evolution from these pellets as compared to the original leaves. After three weeks it is back to the same level. At the end of the period about 13 times as much CO_2 has been evolved from the pellets as from the leaves.

Mr. J. S. Waid. At the Nature Conservancy we obtained similar results to Witkamp by different methods. We found that when one follows the disappearance of ash leaves on mull and mor sites that the ash leaves disappear more quickly on mull sites, this being related to animal activity. There was no difference in the disappearance of bracken rachides or of oak leaves on the two sites. (Disappearance being estimated by dry-weight methods.) The physical condition of the material and the availability of nutrients may account for some of the results obtained by various workers.

Mr. D. V. Crawford. Was the 'peak' mentioned by Professor Burges in the organic matter corresponding to leaf fall and its subsequent dissipation a measure of the litter above the mineral surface, or did it represent the total organic matter in the soil above the *C* horizon? The latter would include undecomposed organic matter carried down in mull soils by the soil fauna.

Prof. A. Burges. The curve mentioned is by Blow, and it referred to material above the mineral soil. Data we obtained for *Casuarina* were almost identical except that the timing was different, this again referred to organic matter above the mineral soil.

Dr. H. Katznelson. We have found, in general, that the nature of the microflora is quite different, depending on the type of material being decomposed. In the mull-type of decomposition, with a pH about neutral, bacteria appear to predominate, though fungi are active also, whereas in the mor type of decomposition, at a somewhat lower pH, fungi appear to be the dominant forms involved and bacteria are not quite so important.

Dr. J. Webster. The results of Dr. Moreau are reminiscent of the work of Rishbeth working with *Fomes annosus*, a parasite of *Pinus* in East Anglia. In alkaline soils the disease is more severe than on acid soils. Rishbeth has shown that in acid soils *Trichoderma viride* is an important member of the root-surface population, and has presented evidence that antagonism between this fungus and *Fomes annosus* may prevent parasitic colonization by the latter.

Dr. R. Moreau. Il est possible que le *Trichoderma viride* (ou d'autres germes!) joue un role antagoniste envers certains micro-organismes pathogènes pour les jeunes semis (voir les conclusions de notre communication).

Dr. H. Katznelson. Dr. Iverson of our laboratory has been studying the rhizosphere problem of very young yellow birch seedlings from 3 to 6 months old, and has been finding it difficult to demonstrate a rhizosphere effect. It is felt that this may be due to the fact that the soil in which these roots are growing is so high in organic matter that a rhizosphere effect cannot be demonstrated. Since the rhizosphere effect is due in large measure to substances produced by roots, it would seem to me to be quite understandable that in a soil high in readily decomposable material there would not be a stimulation by the root because the substances used by both bacteria and fungi are already in the soil.

Dr. R. Moreau. Je suis d'accord sur le fait, que comme pour l'exemple cité par le Dr. Katznelson, la non-stimulation apparente des Champignons dans la rhizosphere des Abies fuisse étre dire à la tres grand richesse de l'humus. Je dois ajouter toutefois que les Bactéries et les Actinomycètes, eux, sont stimules.

Dr. L. G. Willoughby. In an investigation of submerged muds from fresh water, hyphae have not so far been found by direct examination. Has Dr. Pugh used special techniques to obtain hyphae he has observed, and have these hyphae been plated and identified?

Dr. G. J. F. Pugh. Very occasional hyphae have been seen, chiefly from near the roots of *Salicornia.* Warcup's technique was used, but it has not yet been possible to isolate viable hyphae.

Mr. J. S. Waid. Has Dr. Pugh seen algae in the muds?

Dr. G. J. F. Pugh. Rarely in newly collected muds.

Mrs. M. Turner. When the muds had been kept long enough there was algal development especially blue greens.

Dr. D. Parkinson. I should like to ask Dr. Pugh what methods were used for the rhizosphere infections, what was the age of the plants used, and was any attempt made of zonal isolations?

Dr. G. J. F. Pugh. Warcup plates of soil attached to or in contact with the roots of plants of various ages. All regions of the roots were sampled in an attempt to get an over-all picture.

Dr. D. Parkinson. In detailed studies on the distribution of fungi in the rhizosphere, I think it important to consider this zone as a group of micro-habitats and not a uniform micro-habitat.

PROBLEMS ASSOCIATED WITH
THE DECOMPOSITION OF ORGANIC MATTER
IN SOILS

CERTAIN PROBLEMS ASSOCIATED WITH THE DECOMPOSITION OF SOIL ORGANIC MATTER BY FUNGI

C. G. C. CHESTERS

Department of Botany, University of Nottingham

INTRODUCTION

While it is true that the organic matter of natural soils reaches its maximum value on and in the surface layers and decreases to a minimum value in the deeper layers, most mycologists interested in soil-inhabiting fungi neglect the surface detritus in favour of that apparently entrancing and most elusive quantity—'the soil'. A moment's thought should convince any biologist that the surface litter is of primary importance in the economy of natural soils. It is a layer of sheet compost contributing, by its microbiological decay, minerals and soluble organic compounds to the water descending from the surface into the soil. Physically it interposes a surface mulch between the A_1 horizon and the atmosphere—a not invaluable attribute. What contribution it makes to the solubles in the soil water results from its microbiological decomposition, a complex process involving not only fungi but also bacteria, actinomycetes, and a wide range of animal life. There lies the first problem for the mycologist—dare he work in isolation, can he afford to pursue his extraction of fungi from the litter, his study of their physiology and his tabulation of their numbers and kinds, disregarding the fact that they are an integral part, but only a part, of an ecological system of living organisms? While the absolute answer is negative, it is equally true that so very little is known even of the fungal flora of such surface debris that the time for a synthetic approach is not yet ripe, but it is important for the mycologist to present his facts bearing in mind that he is dealing with a part and not the whole. The necessity at the moment is that such facts should be forthcoming. Here is a field of exploitation which has scarcely been touched.

Within the soil the major contribution to the organic matter responsible for the return of essential minerals to the soil solution and for the organic plexus on which soil structure depends comes from the root systems of higher plants, from organic matter carried down into the soil by animals, soil movements and other physical phenomena, and from the bodies of micro-organisms, both plant, and animal which constitute the soil population. Most properly, attention has been directed to the pathogenic fungi attacking root systems, to the fungi occurring in the rhizosphere zone and on living root surfaces, to the fungi to be extracted from the total soil of different horizons in different soil series, to predaceous fungi, and to the fungi colonizing particular types of organic matter added to soil. However, the sequences of fungi occurring on the resident organic matter which can be extracted from soils have not received their due attention. While this aspect of the mycology of soils is beginning to interest investigators, particularly in the direction of the survival and 'saprophytic ability' of root pathogens, much remains to be done, much information of the fungi at work on organic débris within the soil awaits attention. Once more, it must be emphasized that the mycologist, concerned as he is with fungi, is working in a degree of isolation which he must recognize and acknowledge. This should not deter him so long as he realizes that he is working towards a time of synthesis, and so long as his work is supported by studies in the companion fields of bacteriology and 'soil zoology'. Such support is becoming an increasing necessity.

LINES OF INVESTIGATION

The decomposition of organic matter on and in soil can be approached along a wide variety of lines which may be conveniently grouped into chemical and biochemical investigations, and into floristic-ecological studies.

Chemical changes of organic matter in soils reflect the activities of the total soil population; specific changes brought about by individual fungi or groups of fungi must be studied in 'pure culture' or in sterile soil (which is only a crude approximation of actual soil). It is appropriate to consider how far results of such pure culture studies can be applied to pathways of decomposition in soils. It is arguable that what occurs in a test-tube on a chemically defined substrate is very different from what occurs in soil, but such work has the immense virtue of showing that certain changes are possible. Fungi take the path of least resistance if that is available; fungi which can decompose cellulose will grow on a simple carbohydrate, in fact there are very few fungi which cannot grow on such a carbohydrate as a source of carbon. This does not mean that, under the competitive conditions on soil organic matter, these fungi are able to establish themselves when soluble carbohydrates are still available. Relative growth rates, ability to associate with other fungi, and general competitive ability, all influence the direction of the growth and metabolism of soil fungi. But demonstrating that a fungus repeatedly isolated from soil, and thus to be accepted as a normal component of the fungal flora, can decompose cellulose, hemicellulose, the lignin complex, or any other carbon or carbon and nitrogen substrate in pure culture, does prove that the potential for growth on such substrates exists. Such chemical investigations could well be combined with elective cultures in which soil treated with the particular substrate is used as the basis for isolation of the fungi to be studied. Bacteriologists have made far more use of this technique than mycologists; the unicellular, colonial habit of growth of bacteria render them more ductile, but with experience much can be obtained from this technique when applied to filamentous fungi and specially to actinomycetes. The 'most probable number' method, for long a standard technique of bacteriologists examining particular populations of bacteria in soil, has been used recently for estimating populations of phytopathogens in soil (Maloy & Alexander, 1958). This technique could be more widely applied in soil mycology.

The enzyme production of a limited number of fungi has been studied intensively, as reference to any of the standard texts on the physiology of fungi will show, but very few soil-inhabiting fungi are included in those chosen. Much more intensive study of the enzyme potentials of soil-inhabiting fungi is required, and accumulation of such information, from pure culture studies, should lead to a clearer picture of the processes going on during decomposition of organic matter in soil.

Other lines, such as the trace element and vitamin requirements of soil-inhabiting fungi, are necessary to fill the many gaps in our knowledge. True, the fungi which have been used to study such requirements may occur in soil, but it would appear to be appropriate to start from the other end and select soil-inhabiting fungi as specific experimental material. Species of *Aspergillus* and of *Penicillium* have had a generous attention, there are a host of other soil-inhabiting fungi which have a claim to be 'put through the hoop'.

Considerable progress has been made with floristic-ecological investigations, and a review of certain methods which have been applied and suggestions for new approaches may not be out of place.

ISOLATION OF FUNGI FROM SOIL
ORGANIC MATTER

Direct observations

The very elegant techniques developed by Kubiena (1938) for the direct observation of fungi growing on organic materials of natural and experimental soils demonstrate conclusively that fungi growing in and fruiting on organic matter in soil can be isolated from their actual habitats, and some can even be identified *in situ* on their substrates in much the same way as higher fungi growing above ground. It is unfortunate that these techniques require considerable skill and are rather laborious. They represent perfection in the study of soil-inhabiting fungi, and the methods which Kubiena and his associates have developed might well be applied to particular ecological problems in soil microbiology. They allow observation of the fungi at work on substrates, and can be extended to follow changes in the flora with time and differences in the populations of different substrates.

In another sense the soil-sectioning techniques of Alexander & Jackson (1954) and of Hepple & Burges (1956) can be applied to studies of the growth of fungi *in situ* in soil, and with appropriate modifications may be used to follow progressive changes in the soil microflora. Neither method allows observation and isolation at one and the same time, but both could be combined with the removal of organic substrates in parallel isolation experiments to yield both visual and viable material. For surface litter and with soils containing mineral materials in a fine state of division, the agar impregnation technique of Haarløv & Weis-Fogh (1952) gives very clear details of the distribution of fungi and of small animals on organic substrates. Again, separate isolation methods must be applied to give cultures of specific fungi.

All these techniques, and especially that of Kubiena, are of considerable importance in answering charges that the precise origin of what ends up in a culture tube cannot be established in soil microbiological investigations. To see is to believe!

Direct isolation from organic matter

Some years ago I suggested a method by which organic debris in soil could be isolated by counter current washing with sterile water. By plating the washed débris, an estimate of the fungi growing in the substrates could be obtained (1948). The initial technique was cumbersome and required considerable time and attention during washing. However, it did provide fungi which were growing in the debris. More recently, Harley & Waid (1955) described a method of progressive washing of living root pieces which, when sufficiently prolonged, removed surface propagules and provided evidence of fungi growing over the surfaces of the roots. They suggested (1955) that the method of progressive washing could be applied to organic debris isolated from soil (Waid, 1957). This suggestion does much to remove one of the trials associated with the removal of debris from soil by washing. In the method at present in use debris is washed out of soil by a stream of distilled water passing through a series of graded screens in which the top screen holds the soil sample. The screens are graded so that a lower screen has a pore size exactly one half of the screen above. By selecting particular pore sizes, all but the finest debris and, in addition, water-stable aggregates are retained on screens, and can later be removed intact for final washing. The process takes time, but no longer than the time required to sample root surface fungi by the original Harley & Waid technique. At the final plating pure water agar is used, as experience has shown that sufficient nutrient exists in the organic debris to support enough hyphal growth to allow isolation. The nature of the debris isolated can be determined at least to the particular organ involved, thus giving a clearer picture of the distribution on particular substrates.

When natural vegetation is sampled, this method allows estimation of the rhizosphere fungi growing on living roots, as well as the fungi growing in dead organic materials and soil crumbs.

Presentation of substrates for colonization

Methods which fall within this category have much to recommend them. They have been used to follow direct colonization of a sterile or reasonably sterile substrate, or to follow competition between the soil microflora and a pure culture of a fungus introduced on an organic substrate. Sadasivan (1939) followed the colonization of pieces of wheat straw by *Fusarium culmorum* at progressive time intervals after burial, and by this method provided a new technique for the plant pathologist studying the ecology of root diseases. The importance of this method for the chemical and floristic investigation of particular substrates has not been exploited sufficiently by the soil microbiologist. Neither has the development of this method by Subramanian (1946) in which he used surface sterilized portions of roots of cotton to follow the colonization of *Fusarium vasinfectum* in Fusarium-infested soils. It is interesting to note that some two weeks elapsed before the cotton roots were colonized by fungi other than *F. vasinfectum*. The Madras

School has exploited this technique most successfully in studying soil-borne pathogenic fungi. Garrett and his colleagues have used inoculated straw buried in soil to follow persistence of soil-borne pathogens, and other workers have also made use of this type of technique for specific problems (Butler, 1953a, b, c). Much use could be made of the technique in general soil mycology, both in the field by exposure in a manner similar to Rossi-Cholodny slides using surface sterilized plant material enclosed in nylon gauze, and in experimental soils under laboratory conditions.

In another direction the film technique used by Tribe (1957, 1959) has much in its favour: it is simple, allows direct observation of colonizing fungi, and permits isolation of these fungi for subsequent experimentation. This excellent technique can be used with other materials which can be produced as films—e.g. alginate films.

Excised-root technique

The techniques of introducing sterile plant organs or pure chemicals into soil have normally been restricted to experimental soil which has been freshly disturbed and thus physically modified. This is inevitable and allows accurate control of the physical state of the soil.

Recently a technique has been developed at Nottingham which allows the study of the colonization of root tissues which have grown into soil and are then presented for colonization by excising the shoot system, leaving the roots to become moribund and to decay naturally. This work has been carried out by M. W. Assawah (1956), and the method appears to have much to recommend it.

Seed or 'sets' of the experimental plants are grown in pots of soil, and at appropriate stages the 'tops' are excised and the root system allowed to decompose *in situ*. By adjusting the numbers of experimental plants and the times of excision, it is possible to follow both the stages in colonization of the excised roots and the decomposition stages with ageing of the root system.

The type of results which may be obtained are illustrated in Table 1.

Iris pseudacorus 'sets' were grown in pots of screened soil. At the time of commencing the experiment, lengths of autoclaved sterilized and propylene oxide sterilized roots were buried in pots of similar soil, and all pots were incubated under similar temperature régimes and moisture contents. At intervals, roots were excised from the rhizomes of the living material, and were allowed to remain in the soil for varying lengths of time, from 1 to 60 days, before isolations were made. In the same way the buried root pieces were exposed for different time periods.

In these experiments, Assawah combined the excised-root technique with the techniques employed by Sadasivan and Subramanian. On removal from soil both excised roots and sterilized root pieces were washed in changes of sterile water, and planted in plain water agar for isolation of the colonizing fungi. Early isolations were made at 18 hr., thus obtaining rapidly growing mycelia, and final isolations at three weeks when a representative population was considered to have developed.

Table 1 demonstrates that the sterilized root pieces are colonized by a slightly larger number of individuals than are the 'excised roots', whether the fungi are those mainly isolated during the first 20 days of colonization (Group 2) or those isolated throughout the period of colonization (Group 1). The types of fungi colonizing the three substrates vary to a certain extent, but further comparative experience of the techniques will be required to prove the true extent of quantitative and qualitative differences.

The fungi which occur on the root surfaces of *Iris germanica* are indicated in the left-hand column. When those which are isolated during the first 18 hr. of incubation are compared with the fast-growing mycelia on incubated, colonized roots (bold face in Table 1), it is apparent that the same fungi are involved in this process, and that the majority of them can be isolated throughout the 60 days of colonization.

This technique has several obvious applications in relation to the age of the root system being studied and in relation to the nutrient status of the roots at the time of excision. Combined with the technique suggested by Waid (1956, 1957) for differentiating cortical from subcortical infections in grass roots, it could be used to obtain a very clear picture of the ecological phases in the decomposition of the most characteristic organic matter of the true soil layers.

It is widely recognized that fungal mycelium occurs over the surfaces of living roots, and that certain areas of the individual roots bear the mycelia of several species while other areas are less well populated. The questions may be asked: are these fungi entirely superficial in habit; do they live on root excretions and on organic débris sloughed off from the root surfaces? Is any of their nutrition obtained from organic material not of root origin but adjacent to living roots? Do some of the root-surface fungi live in minute lesions of the surface tissues of roots? These are very pertinent questions.

During certain other investigations at Nottingham, Acheson (1951) studied the fungi occurring in minute superficial lesions of roots of a number of grasses. The lesions were only visible microscopically, and

TABLE 1

Comparison of 'root surface fungi', fungi colonizing 'excised roots', and 'buried root pieces'. Numbers represent the percentage of the total isolations in each treatment (Assawah, 1956).

Root surface fungi	Excised roots	Propylene oxide	Autoclave
		sterilized roots	
Group 1: Present throughout 60 days			
Arthrobotrys cylindrospora — 9·5*	15·5	8·5	7·0
Pythium spp. — 3·0 (2)	7·0	**9·0**	**11·5**
*Mucor spp. — 5·5	6·5	**9·5**	7·5
Volutella ciliata — 13·0*	14·0	3·5	
Fusarium oxysporum — 1·5 (0·5)	9·0		
Zygorrhynchus moelleri — 4·0 (1)	3·5		
*Fusarium culmorum		**8·0**	6·5
Monotospora daleae — 9·5 (7·5)*		7·5	8·0
Septonema horniscium — 6·0*		4·5	11·5
Sterile (hyaline) — 4·0 (1·5)		**10·0**	**11·5**
*Rhizoctonia solani		7·5	
Mortierella spp. — 1·5 (1)*		1·0	
Phoma spp.			7·0
*Trichoderma viride			**5·5**
Group 2: Present mainly during initial 20 days			
Gliocladium roseum — 20·0	10·0	9·5	
Penicillium spp. — 2·0	1·0	0·5	
Cylindrocarpon spp. — 9·5 (0·5)*	3·0	7·5	2·0

Species				
Fusarium spp.	1·0	2·5	2·0	
*Sterile (hyaline)		**6·0**		
Monotospora daleae	0·5	1·0		
Septonema hormiscium		1·0		
Dicoccum asperum			1·5	3·0
Trichoderma viride			0·5	1·0
*Zygorrhynchus moelleri			**2·5**	**2·5**
*Rhizoctonia solani				**2·0**
Volutella ciliata				2·5
Mucor spp.				0·5
Group 3: *Present mainly during last 40 days*				
*Sterile (brown)		5·5	4·0	4·0
*Rhizoctonia solani		**8·5**		
*Fusarium culmorum		**5·0**		
Acrotheca spp.			2·0	5·0
Phoma spp.			2·5	
Other species				
	9·5 (3·5)*			

* Fungi isolated during first 18 hours of incubation; those in brackets represent the proportion of 'root-surface fungi' isolated during this time. Fast-growing mycelia are indicated in bold.

when found were excised with a portion of the clean root, were washed, blotted dry, and plated on agar. Fungi developing were identified as far as possible, and were scored as a percentage of the isolations occurring during each month between January and May. The results obtained are set out in Table 2.

TABLE 2

Isolations from minute superficial lesions of grass roots, expressed as a percentage of total isolations in each month (Acheson, 1951).

	Jan.	Feb.	Mar.	Apr.	May
Fusarium spp.	24	19	—	15	10
Trichoderma spp.	4	12	24	7	14
Mucor spp.	9	—	10	11	16
Mortierella spp.	9	5	5	7	12
Absidia spp.	—	5	—	22	8
Cladosporium spp.	—	1	19	2	2
Pythium spp.	12	6	2	—	3
Zygorrhynchus spp.	—	2	14	—	6
Cephalosporium spp.	3	3	—	2	7
Gliocladium spp.	2	2	—	—	—
Botrytis sp.	1	—	—	—	—
Ascochyta sp.	1	—	—	—	—
Sclerotium sp.	—	1	—	—	—
Unidentified species	35	44	24	34	22

The lesions examined were in extremely early stages of development, but the fungi isolated fall within genera normally accepted as those containing 'root-surface fungi'. The writer considers that much more attention should be given to visual examination of washed-root surfaces, and that the whole position of the root-surface fungal flora requires careful re-examination. There is every reason to believe that at least some of the 'root-surface fungi' exploit minute lesions as a food base.

SURFACE DEBRIS

As has been pointed out above and as was emphasized some years ago (1949), few microbiological investigations of soil pay any attention to the surface litter; it is thrust aside in an effort to get at the 'soil'. Is this logical or wise? In all natural vegetation there is an accumulation of plant and animal materials at the soil surface which undergo decomposition just as much as do organic materials within the soil. The amount of organic matter is higher at the surface than within the soil, and its decomposition resembles that which occurs in artificial compost heaps—in fact, it is natural sheet composting. The release of minerals from the decomposition of tree-leaf litter has been examined by Burges (1956), and has been shown to reach impressive proportions. The fauna of litter layers has been examined by Murphy (1953) and Haarløv & Weis-Fogh (1953), and the associations of fungi occurring in coniferous litter have been explored by Ward (1952) and by Kendrick (1958).

The techniques applicable to litter material more closely resemble those in use for isolating pathogenic fungi, because the organic matter can be collected in recognizable fractions, at least in the upper layers, and can be surface sterilized for the isolation of fungi within the material. Ward found the silver nitrate-sodium chloride method employed by

TABLE 3

Distribution of fungi isolated from layers of Corsican pine leaf litter (Ward, 1952).

	Litter zones		
	L	F	H
Total fungi isolated = 1220			
Total fungi isolated in each layer	399	399	422
Fungi expressed as % total fungi:			
Total Mucorales	1·6	3·4	6·3
Total Ascomycetes	1·2	0·6	0·3
Total basidiomycete mycelia	2·4	1·2	—
Total Fungi Imperfecti	27·6	27·5	28·0
Species expressed as % Mucorales (138):			
Mortierella isabellina	4·4	10·2	8·7
Mortierella hygrophila	2·9	3·6	13·8
Mucor rammanianus	0·7	5·1	5·8
Other Mucorales	5·8	11·6	27·5
Species expressed as % Fungi Imperfecti (1014):			
Phoma spp.	4·0	0·4	—
Geotrichum spp.	1·3	0·4	—
Cephalosporium spp.	3·5	3·9	0·9
Hormiactis spp.	1·9	1·0	0·1
Pullularia pullulans	1·5	0·2	0·1
Dark sterile mycelium	4·4	1·4	0·5
Hyaline sterile mycelium	2·2	1·5	1·0
Trichoderma viride	8·1	14·8	16·8
Penicillium spp.	2·9	8·1	13·3

Davies (1935) to give the best results, and using it she obtained the following pattern of distribution of fungi in the several layers of coniferous needle litter.

The total fungi isolated from each litter zone show no significant differences, but the distribution of the kinds of fungi within these zones shows considerable variation. Ascomycetes and mycelium of Basidiomycetes are more abundant in the fresh (L) and partly decomposed (F) zones whereas the Mucorales are more frequently isolated from very decomposed litter (H). The Fungi Imperfecti appear to be evenly distributed throughout each of the three zones, but when the flora of each zone is inspected the distribution pattern of individual Fungi Imperfecti is seen to change. *Trichoderma viride* and species of *Penicillium* make up the major part of the population of the F and H layers. A somewhat similar pattern has been described by Pugh (1958) for the vertical masses of leaf débris accumulated round plants of *Carex paniculata*.

With leaf litter it is possible to obtain débris which bears sporophores of the colonizing fungi, thus providing a check to the isolation data. Equally, surface sterilized, entire needles can be incubated on sterile sand, and frequently bear species which either fail to appear on isolation plates or appear as sterile mycelium. As is demonstrated in Table 4, Ward found that certain fungi occurring on surface sterilized coniferous needles were confined to individual zones in the litter, while others were more frequent in certain zones although present throughout the litter layers.

Similar results have been obtained by Kendrick (1958) using washed and incubated needles (Table 5).

Such examples show that the examination of the fungal flora of decomposing leaf litter can be accomplished by well-tried experimental techniques which yield reasonably accurate pictures of the fungi involved in the decomposition of superficial detritus. But the results will gain in significance if they are combined with a study of the release, and return, of mineral elements to the soil during the process. In this the whole microbial population is involved, and the investigation becomes chemical and biochemical rather than mycological. Even so, very little is known of the physiology of the litter-inhabiting fungi.

Forest leaf litter is an obvious locus of investigation, but equally the turf layer of natural grasslands requires attention and can be rewarding. The time has passed when 'soil' samples should merit the entire attention of the mycologist. Just as there is a renewed emphasis on fundamentals in science, so there should be a renewed appeal to the soil

TABLE 4

Fungi developing on whole needles of Corsican pine after surface steriliza-tion and incubation: expressed as percentages of identifications in each layer (Ward, 1952).

	L	F	H
Mycena sp.	4·8	—	—
Coprinus sp.	4·8	—	—
Mollisia sp.	4·8	—	—
Mucrosporium sphaerocephalum	4·8	—	—
Torula (*herbarum*)	4·8	—	—
Mortierella hygrophila	—	5·5	—
Cladosporium herbarum	—	5·5	—
Tomentella ferruginea	—	5·5	—
Lophodermium pinastri	14·2	11·1	—
Mucor sp.	4·8	5·5	—
Verticicladium trifidum	4·8	5·5	—
Corticium sp.	4·8	—	6·3
Poria sp.	—	5·5	6·3
Phoma sp.	—	5·5	6·3
Septocylindrium sp.	—	5·5	6·3
Piptocephalis perispora	—	—	6·3
Basidiomycete mycelium	19·0	5·5	6·3
Dark sterile mycelium	14·2	5·5	6·3
Hymenochaete cinnamomea	9·5	27·2	43·7
Hormiactis sp.	4·8	5·5	12·5

microbiologist to examine the whole of the soil profile; of this the litter layers represent the crust, whether natural or cultivated soils are under consideration. Too little attention has been paid to this very significant horizon of natural soils.

In this review most attention has been paid to certain methods of obtaining active fungi from the soil profile. The excuse for this is that the soil mycologist still requires to develop new methods of attack to expand and clarify his outlook on the active soil fungal flora. The time has arrived when not only the ecological systems involved in the growth of fungi on and in plant materials in soil deserve attention, but also the physiological potentials of soil fungi require intensive examination (Henderson, 1959). The search for antibiotic-producing micro-organisms focused attention on one aspect of the physiology of soil fungi, as did the work on textile spoilage on another, but these represented isolated and very specialized aspects of the potentials of soil fungi. It is time that attention was paid to the less exciting but equally vital general physiology of the fungal population of soil.

TABLE 5

From Kendrick (1958)

	L		F$_1$		F$_2$	
Direct	Lophodermium pinastri	35	Helicoma sp.	92	Basidiomycete mycelium	55
			Verticicladium trifidum	89		
			Lophodermium pinastri	40		
			Basidiomycete mycelium	12		
Washing	Antennularia spp.	75	Trichoderma viride	75	Trichoderma viride	100
	Fusicoccum bacillare	35	Antennularia spp.	40	Penicillium spp.	45
	Trichoderma viride	35	Penicillium spp.	25	Antennularia spp.	5
			Fusicoccum bacillare	10		

Numbers = percentage of total number of needles on which each fungus observed.

Each mycologist, as in fact each scientist, has his own particular field of interest, and scientists would scarcely be human if they did not regard such specialities as of paramount importance. The writer is human enough to consider that too little attention has been paid to the superficial layer of débris constituting the protective surface of soils at large and representing at least a major source of the return of nutrients to the soil proper. He also feels that much more attention should be paid to particular habitats of fungi in soil; rhizospheres have had a good 'innings' and have given rise to much controversy and diversity of fact and interpretation. It is time that other organic substrates in soil had a similar detailed investigation.

REFERENCES

ACHESON, M. E. (1951). *Studies in aquatic phycomycetes and their occurrence in pasture soils with a high water table.* Ph.D Thesis, University of Nottingham.

ALEXANDER, F. E. S., & JACKSON, R. M. (1954). Examination of soil micro-organisms in their natural environment. *Nature, Lond.,* **174,** 750.

ASSAWAH, M. W. (1956). *Root region fungi of Iris and other plants.* Ph.D. Thesis, University of Nottingham.

BURGES, N. A. (1956). The release of cations during decomposition of forest litter. *Sixieme Cong. de la Sci. du Sol.,* II, **48,** 741–5.

BUTLER, F. C. (1953a). Saprophytic behaviour of some cereal root-rot fungi. I. Saprophytic colonization of wheat straw. *Ann. appl. Biol.,* **40,** 284–97.

BUTLER, F. C. (1953b). Saprophytic behaviour of some cereal root-rot fungi. II. Factors influencing saprophytic colonization of wheat straw. *Ann. appl. Biol.,* **40,** 298–304.

BUTLER, F. C. (1953c). Saprophytic behaviour of some creal root-rot fungi. III. Saprophytic survival of wheat straw buried in soil. *Ann. appl. Biol.,* **40,** 305–11.

CHESTERS, C. G. C. (1948). A contribution to the study of fungi in the soil. *Trans. Brit. mycol. Soc.,* **30,** 100–17.

CHESTERS, C. G. C. (1949). Concerning fungi inhabiting soil. *Trans. Brit. mycol. Soc.,* **32,** 197–216.

DAVIES, F. R. (1935). Superiority of silver nitrate over mercuric chloride for surface sterilization in the isolation of *Ophiobolus graminis* Sacc. *Canad. J. Res. C.,* **13,** 168–73.

HAARLØV, N. (1955). Vertical distribution of Mites and Collembola in relation to soil structure. In *Soil Zoology,* 167–79. London: Butterworth Scientific Publications.

HAARLØV, N., & WEIS-FOGH, T. (1953). A microscopical technique for studying the undisturbed texture of soils. *Oikos,* **4,** 44–57.

HARLEY, J. L., & WAID, J. S. (1955). A method of studying active mycelia on living roots and other surfaces in the soil. *Trans. Brit. mycol. Soc.,* **38,** 104–18.

HENDERSON, M. E. K. (1959). Studies on the physiology of lignin decomposition by soil fungi. *Symposium Ecology of Soil Fungi.* Liverpool, 1958.

HEPPLE, S., & BURGES, A. (1956). Sectioning of soil. *Nature, Lond.,* **177,** 1186.

KENDRICK, W. B. (1958). Microfungi in pine litter. *Nature, Lond.,* **181,** 432.

KUBIENA, W. L. (1938). *Micropedology.* Ames, Iowa: Collegiate Press Inc.

MALOY, O. C., & ALEXANDER, M. (1958). The most probable number method for estimating populations of plant pathogenic organisms in soil. *Phytopath.*, **48**, 126–8.

MURPHY, P. W. (1953). The biology of forest soils with special reference to the mesofauna and meiofauna. *J. Soil Sci.*, **4**, 155–87.

PUGH, G. J. F. (1958). Leaf-litter fungi found on *Carex paniculata* L. *Trans. Brit. mycol. Soc.*, **41**, 185–95.

SADASIVAN, T. S. (1939). Succession of fungi decomposing wheat straw in different soils, with special reference to *Fusarium culmorum*. *Ann. appl. Biol.*, **26**, 297–508.

SUBRAMANIAN, C. V. (1946). The saprophytic activity of *Fusarium vasinfectum*, the Cotton Wilt pathogen in the soil. I. Colonization of cotton roots buried in soil. *J. Indian. Bot. Soc.*, 1946, 209–13.

TRIBE, H. T. (1957). Ecology of micro-organisms in soils as observed during their development upon buried cellulose film. *Microbial Ecology Seventh Symposium Soc. gen. Microbiol.*, Cambridge University Press, 287–98.

TRIBE, H. T. (1959). Decomposition of buried cellulose film with special reference to the ecology of certain soil fungi. *Symposium Ecology of soil fungi*, Liverpool, 1958.

WAID, J. S. (1956). Root dissection: a method of studying the distribution of active mycelia within root tissue. *Nature, Lond.*, **178**, 1477–8.

WAID, J. S. (1957). Distribution of fungi within the decomposing tissues of rye-grass roots. *Trans. Brit. mycol. Soc.*, **40**, 391–406.

WARD, G. M. (1952). *Studies in the succession of fungi in the decomposing litter of coniferous forest soils*. Ph.D. Thesis, University of Nottingham.

MICROBIOLOGICAL PROBLEMS ASSOCIATED WITH THE DECOMPOSITION OF HUMIC ACID

N. A. BURGES AND P. M. LATTER

Department of Botany, The University of Liverpool

The organic matter in soil can be divided into organic debris, in which there is still clear evidence of the original structure of the leaves, etc., and humus, which is generally described as the black amorphous organic material remaining after primary decomposition has taken place. From early work it is clear that humus can be separated into a number of fractions. One of these is humic acid, which is usually obtained by extracting soil with alkalies and precipitating the crude humic acid by the addition of mineral acid. Extraction of the precipitate with alcohol removes hymatomelanic acid. The humic acid can be further purified by removing fatty material with ether, and mineral matter by dialysing against dilute hydrochloric acid. Using such methods, samples of humic acid can be obtained from most soils. Little is known at present regarding the formation, chemical structure, and decomposition of this material, nor of the other fractions present in humus. With our present knowledge of the chemistry of humic acid, it is not possible to say whether the products obtained by different extractants represent a single chemical substance, or even whether the extracts obtained from different soil types represent the same material. It is because of these doubts that the present investigation has been restricted to humic acid prepared from a single horizon of the podzol at Delamere Forest, and using a single extractant, the view being taken that because of the possibility of there being a number of different forms of humic acid, work should initially be confined to one form of humic acid. The B_1 horizon was used because it represents a relatively pure natural accumulation of humic acid. Although the present methods have worked well in this investigation, they are not necessarily applicable to all other soil types.

Method of extraction. In order to obtain consistent material for the microbiological work, humic acid has been extracted as follows:

Lactic acid is used as the extractant, as Dr. S. Hepple working in this department has shown that it provided an excellent extractant for humic acid from the B_1 horizon of a podzol. Extractants such as NaOH were avoided, since it is known that humic acid absorbs oxygen under alkaline conditions, and also the use of acetyl bromide and other such drastic treatments were considered undesirable. 50% (w/v) lactic acid is allowed to percolate through a column of the soil sample which is mixed with cleaned coarse quartz sand to assist drainage. The resulting clear brown solution is filtered through No. 3 Whatman filter-paper, and then passed through an ion-exchange column, containing amberlite resin I.R.120 to remove cations, principally iron. The solution is then diluted with about 4 parts distilled water, and concentrated hydrochloric acid is added until precipitation occurs. The precipitate is allowed to settle, the supernatant decanted off, and is then centrifuged and placed in vinyl dialysis tubing. It is dialysed against 20% (v/v) HCL until iron can no longer be detected. The tubes are then transferred to water, and dialysed until no further chlorine ions are present. The humic acid is dried in a vacuum oven at 40°. 1000 g. of fresh soil gives a yield of approximately 20 g. of dried humic acid. The dried product is dark brown in colour, and is an amorphous powder.

Chemical analyses have shown that the product obtained has an approximate composition as follows: C 50; H 3·9; O 38; N 0·3–0·4; OMe 1; ash, 1–2%.

The ash consists of 25% Si, 18% Fe_2O_3, 16% TiO_2, as well as more than 5% of Ca and of Na and traces of K, Mg, Cu, V, and Sr.

Enrichment experiments

In an attempt to obtain organisms capable of utilizing humic acid, a series of enrichment experiments have been carried out, using shake cultures in flasks, vermiculite in Petri dishes, and soil-perfusion techniques. The soil-perfusion apparatus used is that designed by G. Metcalfe (Naguib, 1957).

At intervals the culture vessels have been sampled and a comparison made between the organisms present in the controls and those in which humic acid had been added. In all these experiments there was an increase in the number of species of fungi and in their abundance when humic acid was present, but no particular organism or organisms have persistently dominated in the humic-acid cultures when compared with the controls, with the possible exception of *Trichoderma viride*.

Table 1 summarizes the information so far available from these enrichment experiments. The results shown under heading A in Table 1 are those from 4 soil perfusion experiments. Separate perfusion columns were prepared containing the 3 substrates used—soil, sterile sand, and sterile vermiculite, in each experiment, making a total of 12 columns with humic acid and 12 controls.

The four experiments were as follows:

(1) 8/11/56. Perfusion with Knop's solution, no carbohydrate, room temperature, inoculated with garden soil.

(2) 28/8/57. Perfusion with Czapek's solution, 0·5% (w/v) sucrose,

room temperature, inoculated with soil from mixed broad-leaf forest.

(3) 15/12/57. Perfusion with Czapek's solution, no carbohydrate, room temperature, inoculated with garden soil.

(4) 15/12/57. As in (3), but at 25°.

The humic acid was dissolved in 1% (w/v) K_3PO_4 and added to the perfusate to make a concentration of 0·1%, while K_3PO_4 alone was added to a similar series of controls.

TABLE 1

Frequency of stimulation or inhibition of fungi in presence of humic acid. Arranged in a decreasing sequence of stimulation

	Name of fungus	A Soil perfusion experiments			B Flask culture and vermiculite-plate experiments		
		Stimulation	No change	Inhibition	Stimulation	No change	Inhibition
Stimulated	Candida sp.	7	3	2	6	1	0
	Cephalosporium sp.	5	5	2	—	Absent	—
	Trichoderma viride	5	5	2	7	1	1
	Penicillium spp. monoverticilliate	4	4	2	6	2	0
	Other Penicillia	4	4	2	0	5	0
	Scopulariopsis spp.	2	1	0	—	Absent	—
	Fusarium spp.	1	2	1	9	1	0
	Mucor spp.	3	7	2	1	0	0
No change	Dematiaceae	2	9	1	—	Absent	—
	Verticillium sp.	2	8	2	—	Absent	—
	Actinomycetes	3	8	1	1	0	1
	Zygorrhynchus spp.	0	10	2	2	1	0
	Aspergillus spp.	1	8	3	—	Absent	—

The results from the flask-culture and vermiculite-plate experiments are shown under heading B in Table 1. 150-ml. flasks were used each containing 25 ml. 0·06% (v/v) Knop's solution, and were inoculated in one series with greenhouse soil and in the other with soil from a vegetable plot. There were three replications in each experiment, and each flask was subcultured by transferring a loopful to a similar fresh solution on 5 successive occasions at intervals of 2 weeks.

Another two series were inoculated with garden soil. In one series 0·06% of Knop's solution was used; in the other a medium containing:

S.E.S.F.—16

$$(NH_4)_2 SO_4 \quad 0.1\% \text{ (w/v)}$$
$$K_2 HPO_4 \quad 0.1\% \text{ (w/v)}$$
$$CaCO_3 \quad 1.0\% \text{ (w/v)}$$

Tap water pH   6.4

The vermiculite plates were kept moist with these same two solutions in the two series, and were inoculated with 4 different garden soils. There were 5 replications in each experiment. In both the flasks and the plates humic acid was added to one set and the other run as a control set as in the perfusion experiment.

The results indicate the number of experiments in which the frequency of the particular organism was increased or decreased as compared with the control, which did not contain humic acid. Determination of frequency was by means of soil-crumb and dilution plates.

Growth of fungi on humic-acid media

Certain of the fungi which appear to be most frequently associated with the humic-acid cultures were selected for detailed study. The organisms chosen were *Paecilomyces* sp., *Penicillium spinulosum*, *Penicillium* sp., *Fusarium solani*, *Trichoderma viride*, *Scopulariopsis* sp., *Geotrichum candidans*, and *Candida* sp. These were tested on Czapek's mineral medium, omitting the sucrose, and with humic acid as the sole source of carbon. No satisfactory evidence of utilization of this substrate has been obtained. On plate cultures, growth is very sparse on both controls and those with humic acid. An increased linear spread was shown by some species, notably a *Paecilomyces* sp., and the results of an experiment with this organism are shown in Fig. 1. A similar sparse growth occurs in flask culture, and the dry weight of the mycelium of any of these fungi after 10 days never exceeded 5 mg. per 25 ml. medium in either control or test flasks. Although *Paecilomyces* showed an increased linear spread it gave no increased growth in flask culture.

In many experiments a supplement of sugar was added, and in some cases there appeared to be evidence of utilization, but careful investigation showed that these apparently successful results could be interpreted differently. Plates containing 0.1% (w/v) humic acid which were inoculated with *Penicillia* spp., *Scopulariopsis* spp., or with *Streptomyces* spp., showed a colourless zone around the growing colony where the dark brown colour of the humic acid had disappeared. This suggested a utilization of the humic acid. Similarly, if these fungi were grown in shake cultures in flasks containing variants of Czapek's medium and 0.1% (w/v) humic acid, the medium which was initially dark brown in colour gradually became paler, and in the case of experiments with *Penicillium* (?) *oxalicum* in a medium with ammonia nitrogen replacing nitrate nitrogen, the colour completely disappeared after 6 days, again suggesting some breakdown and utilization of the humic acid.

Microscopical observation of the mycelium from such plate or flask cultures showed that they were stained a reddish-brown colour. Frequently this took the form of a thick sheath coating the cell wall and in media which develop a low pH, as with ammonia nitrogen, this sheath

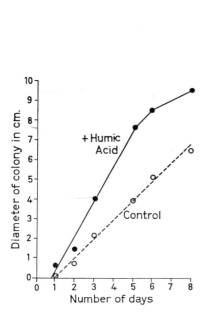

Fig. 1. Linear growth of Paecilomyces sp. on Czapeks Agar Plates.

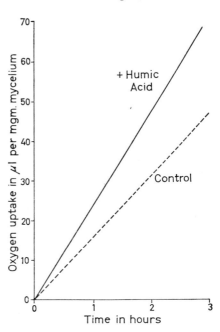

Fig. 2. Effect of Humic acid on the respiration of Paecilomyces sp.

may appear granular due to precipitation of humic acid on the mycelial walls. This unusual appearance of a sheath in humic-acid media has previously been described by Flaig & Schmidt, (1957). Stained mycelium was removed from the flasks and the pellets extracted with warm 1% (w/v) K_3PO_4 solution and this led to the recovery of the humic acid apparently unchanged. After precipitation and washing, the dry weight obtained showed that up to 93% could be re-extracted from the mycelium and the culture solution. The 7% loss could well be due to experimental error, since it is difficult to remove completely all traces of colour from the mycelium.

However, these results must be interpreted with reservation, since it has also been shown that the nitrogen content of humic acid extracted from media and mycelium is increased from about 0·4% to 4·2%, presumably due to chemical combination of the humic acid with nitrogen compounds which is well known.

If this nitrogen is present as amino acids or protein, calculation shows that up to 24% of the original low-nitrogen humic acid could have been utilized. This confusion is greatly increased in media with organic nitrogen, and makes any quantative determination of humic acid after growth very difficult.

In parallel experiments, the disappearance of humic acid was checked by using a spectrophotometer, and this again indicated that the re-extracted humic acid was almost identical in amount and nature to that originally present before growth.

In further experiments to test whether there was an increase in dry weight of mycelium in the presence of humic acid compared with the control medium, a number of dry-weight experiments were undertaken and sucrose was added in varying amounts as a carbon supplement. The dry weight was determined on weighed sinter funnels. Allowance was made for the adhering humic acid, either by washing the harvested mycelium with potassium phosphate or by recovering the humic acid from the culture solution and obtaining, by calculation, the amount which could have been absorbed. No experiment has given unequivocable evidence of an increase in growth due to humic acid when supplied as the sole carbon source, nor when sucrose is provided as an initial carbon substrate.

Respiration of fungi in humic-acid media

Experiments in which humic acid was added to washed mycelial pellets in Warburg flasks and the resulting oxygen uptake measured have shown a marked effect of humic acid on some of the soil organisms. A typical experiment with *Paecilomyces* sp. gives approximately 30% increase of oxygen uptake in the presence of humic acid, as shown in Fig. 2. Other fungi which gave a similar result include *Scopulariopsis* sp. and *Asteromyces cruciatus*. A detailed consideration of these results, coupled with those from the growth rate experiments, leads us to conclude that the oxygen uptake recorded does not necessarily represent increased respiration due to utilization of the humic acid, but is more akin to the decoupling effect as obtained with dinitro-phenol.

The above experiments are recorded in detail because they illustrate the difficulties and problems associated with the microbiological investigations of the utilization of humic acid, and also suggest that in many of the experiments previously recorded in the literature, the evidence is not sufficiently conclusive to warrant the claim that the substrates tested have been utilized by the fungi under investigation.

The work described in this paper was carried out as part of a project for the chemical and microbiological investigation of humus in soil made possible by a grant from the Nuffield Foundation.

REFERENCES

FLAIG, W., & SCHMIDT, H. L. (1957). Einwirkung von Huminsäuren auf das Wachstum einiger Penicilliumarten. *Archiv für Mikrobiologia.*, **27**, 1–32.

NAGUIB, ADMAD IBRAHIM (1957). On the co-existence of nitrate-reducing bacteria with the nitrifying organisms. *Proc. Egyptian Acad. Sci.*, **12**, 47–53.

DECOMPOSITION OF BURIED CELLULOSE FILM, WITH SPECIAL REFERENCE TO THE ECOLOGY OF CERTAIN SOIL FUNGI

H. T. TRIBE

School of Agriculture, Cambridge

In a discussion on decomposition of organic matter in soil, consideration of the break-down of cellulose is of some importance, since cellulose in a number of forms is continually being added to soils. For example, plant residues containing structural cellulose become incorporated into arable soils during agricultural operations, and cellulose is also
incorporated into these soils in farmyard manure. In the form of leaf
litter, cellulose is added to forest soils, though here the conditions for
decomposition differ in that successive layers of leaves are deposited
one upon the other on the soil surface, whilst in the former examples the
cellulose is intimately mixed with the soil. Cellulose in these forms is
associated with many other materials of, for example, lignin, cutin, or
protein nature. A microflora may be already present on these cellulose-
containing substrates before they reach the soil. The analysis of the
natural decomposition process is therefore very complicated. In the
work on which this paper is based (Tribe, 1957), cellulose film, washed
and sterilized before burial, was used as a substrate on which to follow
microbial development. Grade PT 300 'Cellophane', kindly supplied
by the British Cellophane Company, Bridgwater, Somerset, is a pure
form of cellulose and its transparency renders it a perfect substrate
on which to observe soil organisms under the microscope. The absence
of encrusting materials from the film may result in a poorer fungus
flora than is normally found on cellulosic plant residues. A number of
fungi however developed readily on cellulose film. The mineral nutrients
and perhaps growth factors were presumably supplied from the soils in
which the film was buried.

The technique of study of buried cellulose film is simple. Pieces of washed 'Cellophane' of *c.* 0.5×1.0 cm. were damped in sterile water and placed singly on
$\frac{7}{8}$ in. cover slips, to which they adhered, and the cover slips buried vertically in
soil. On recovery, the microbial material colonizing the cellulose was stained in
picronigrosin in lactophenol (Smith, 1954), which did not stain the cellulose.
Permanent preparations were made in lactophenol. Certain isolations of fungi were

made from cellulose immediately after its removal from soil. Where isolations were made from mycelium, care was taken in every case to observe microscopically that the fungal colony resulting from the isolation grew directly from mycelium established on the cellulose. The soil samples in which cover slips were buried were kept at laboratory temperatures, and moisture content fluctuated between about 40–60% of moisture-holding capacity.

The localities and the soils in which some study has been made were as follows:

(1) Black fen peat, pH 7·0, arable, Stretham, Cambridgeshire.
(2) Calcareous loam, pH 7·2, arable, Cambridge.
(3) Loamy sand, pH 6·8, arable, University Farm, Cambridge.
(4) Weathered chalk, pH 7·6, side of a quarry, Cambridge.
(5) Leaf litter, pH about 5·2, under conifers and acid sandy soil (pH about 4·4) underlying litter, Santon Downham in the Breckland, Suffolk.
(6) Gault clay, arable, University Farm, Cambridge.
(7a) Sandy loam, pH 7·5, arable, Hildersham, Cambridgeshire.
(7b) Sandy loam, under grass, Hildersham, Cambridgeshire.
(8) Mull, pH 7·0, under mixed-leaf litter, North Gower, Ottawa, Canada.

These soil samples were put through a 3-mm. sieve before use (No. 5 was not sieved, and No. 8 was coarsely sieved).

Before discussing individual fungi, a brief description of the course of decomposition of cellulose film as it related to broad groups of soil organisms will be given. In general, the process is as follows: Shortly after burial in soil, fungi develop on the film. Chytrids are frequent early colonists, but owing to their mode of growth, with limited spread of rhizoids, they are not of much importance in cellulose breakdown unless present in large numbers. Filamentous fungi appear at the same time. Most of these grow over the surface of the film, and put down numerous 'rooting' or 'nutritional' branches into the thickness of the cellulose sheet. Sometimes these 'rooting' branches obviously secrete a cellulase enzyme, dissolving out visible cavities around the branches, but more usually enzymic action is restricted and no such cavities can be seen. Later the branches extend considerably. Other filamentous fungi may grow over the surface of the film without development of 'roots'. Visible zones denoting solution of cellulose may occasionally be noted surrounding these hyphae, but more usually they are not visible. After a variable period of time, of the order of a few weeks, mycelium becomes moribund and bacteria develop over it, and over apparently undecomposed cellulose in large numbers. Whether these include true cellulose-decomposing bacteria is uncertain. Bacteria which directly decompose the cellulose contribute little to its breakdown during the early stages before fungal action. The bacteria invariably support a population of nematodes and sometimes patches of amoebae. The nematodes are often parasitized by predacious fungi. These appear to be the only fungi developing over the bacterial debris;

no fungi seem to live on moribund bacterial cells. If no larger soil fauna appear, this condition persists indefinitely up to at least six months. Frequently, however, microbial tissue and cellulose are consumed by soil animals. So far, mites, collembolans, and enchytraeid worms have been found. The first two produce well-defined excremental pellets consisting of microbial tissue and (presumably) undecomposed cellulose. Mites were found to predominate in the litter and acid sand soil studied, eventually converting the cellulose into masses of pellets. Enchytraeid worms mix up the residues with a large proportion of soil, and their excreta is difficult to distinguish from small soil particles (Kubiena, 1955). They will remove all traces of cellulose from the cover slip on which it is mounted, and since they may be 1 cm. or more in length will deposit the excreta away from the cover slip into the soil. Enchytraeid worms have so far been found in one sample of fen soil, in both samples of sandy loam, and in the mull. They can often be seen in the soil from the time of burial of the cellulose film, but do not attack it until microbial tissue has replaced part of the cellulose, perhaps after 5–8 weeks. Sometimes young enchytraeids have been found which have probably originated on the film. Further decomposition of residual cellulose in excremental pellets has not been studied. Earthworms have not been found so far—possibly because of sieving the soil samples before use.

Thus the fungi are of importance in the early stages of decomposition, as has often been surmised, and become moribund after perhaps 2–6 weeks, or longer in the chalk or litter soils. It should be noted, however, that cellulose film is quite thin (about 55μ), and differs in this respect from some forms of natural cellulose. Fungi would certainly persist longer in thicker substrates.

Having outlined the general manner in which cellulose film is decomposed under aerobic conditions, I shall now consider some of the fungi found in relation to the decomposition process. A few fungi which were not found but which one may have expected to find will also be considered, since their absence may have ecological significance.

Chytrids were frequently observed on cellulose film, particularly when it was buried in soils No. 1, 3, and 7. No attempt was made to study chytrids in any detail. 'Cellophane' has often been used as a bait for isolation of these fungi, from ponds and ditches (Haskins, 1946) and from soil (Sparrow, 1957).

Filamentous fungi occurring most frequently on cellulose film buried in the arable soils were those which put the characteristic 'rooting' branches into the film. Isolates consisted of *Botryotrichum piluliferum* Sacc. and Marsh. (soil samples No. 1, 2, 3, and 6), *Humicola grisea*

Traaen (soils No. 2, 3, and 6), and one resembling *B. piluliferum* (soils No. 7 and 8).

B. piluliferum has been fully redescribed as a strong cellulose-decomposing fungus, several strains of which are maintained in the Quartermaster Collection of micro-organisms (White & Downing, 1951). This is a collection of micro-organisms believed to be of importance in spoilage of stored materials. It has rarely been recorded from soil. It was found in Manitoba soils by Bisby, James, & Timonin (1933), and from filter-paper from certain neutral soils by Jensen (1931) as *Coccospora agricola*. Downing (1953) proved that *Coccospora agricola* Goddard was the same fungus as *B. piluliferum*, whose essential characteristics were hyaline globose spores of 10–25μ diam. and rough olivaceous hairs. She further discovered the presence of microconidia, borne on simple phialides, which had not been recorded in the original description of *B. piluliferum*. In culture, aleuriospores are typically borne in raceme-like clusters or on short side branches; on cellulose in soil they usually appear quite late as isolated spores, probably abstricted from the sides of hyphae on tiny evanescent papillae. Sometimes they are produced in this way in slide cultures, and then are not, by definition, aleuriospores. It is not possible to identify this species with certainty on cellulose film with the microscope.

Humicola grisea Traaen is characterized by production of dark, typically globose aleuriospores 12–17μ diam. It also has recently been described by White & Downing (1953). It is recorded as a powerful cellulose-decomposing fungus, and is known only from soils, decaying wood, and other coniferous and hardwood débris in or on the soil. Like *B. piluliferum*, it is not known to form a perfect stage. *H. grisea* (Traaen) is synonymous with *Monotospora dalae* Mason, *Mycogone nigra* (Morgan) Jensen, *Basisporium gallorum* Moll., and *Melanogone puccinioides* Wollenweber & Richter. Microconidia, similar to those found in *B. piluliferum* were recorded, but only in one of seven isolates studied by White & Downing. When growing on cellulose in soil, it sometimes spreads over the surface of the supporting glass cover slip on which it produces large numbers of its spherical brown spores. It can then be identified microscopically from the slide.

The isolates resembling *B. piluliferum* obtained from soils No. 7 and 8 often bore chlamydospores on the 'rooting' branches in the cellulose film. The aerial mycelium was bright orange and a red 'plum-juice' coloured pigment was produced in Czapek-Dox agar. The isolate from soil No. 7 produced some olivaceous hairs, but that from soil No. 8 was less deeply pigmented and did not produce hairs.

I must add here that none of my isolates of the above-mentioned species have ever produced microconidia. Another fungus, isolated from soils No. 1, 2, 4, 6, and 7 would, however, produce no aleuriospores, but only microconidia on tiny phialides as described for *B. piluliferum* and *H. grisea*. Some isolates of this fungus formed imperfect perithecia on potato dextrose agar. Both phialides and imperfect perithicia have occasionally been found on cellulose film *in situ*, and on one slide made from cellulose film buried in weathered chalk these were associated with a *Chaetomium* perithecium. There is evidence that this isolate is an imperfect *Chaetomium*, because similar colonies were obtained from ascospores from a perithecium of *C. elatum* Kunze, a number of which had developed on filter-paper laid on top of the chalk. Twenty-one spores from this perithecium were picked out on to Czapek-Dox agar. Only two of these spores germinated, close together, and the resulting colony was indistinguishable from the microconidial isolates in form, pigmentation, microconidial production, and in eventual formation of imperfect perithecia. Various media including those with added paper or straw failed to induce proper perithecial formation in any isolate, nor were they formed at the edges of various isolates when grown together. Neither Chivers' monograph (1915), nor Skolko and Groves' treatments of *Chaetomium* species (1948, 1953) mention microconidia as being present, but Mason (1933) figures an illustration from Zopf for *C. globosum* showing these, and Bainier (1909) figures them for *C. elatum*, and states they were present in large numbers when *C. elatum* was grown on any of three substrates. Although perithecia of *Chaetomium* have only twice been seen on slides of buried 'Cellophane', it thus appears likely that a species of this genus is present in an imperfect form. There appears to be a similarity between at least two species of *Chaetomium* and the aleurispore-forming genera. *C. seminudum* (Ames, 1949) produces chlamydospore-like bodies, 10–15μ diam., usually on the ends of short, slender stalks. Hair-like structures which resemble the perithicial hairs may be scattered on the agar surface. *C. homopilatum* (Omvik, 1955) also produces aleurio-spores, of rather smaller size, in beer-wort agar, together with intercalary chlamydo-spores. Omvik's species, with another new *Chaetomium* and a new species of *Humicola*, were isolated from filter-paper from a Norwegian soil.

I think that all these isolates from 'Cellophane' form a natural group, at least having greater similarities among themselves than with the other fungi to be described.

An entirely different fungus which produced typical 'roots' occurred in the weathered chalk only (No. 4). This was a species of *Stysanus*, found co-dominant with the microconidial isolate mentioned above on cellulose in the chalk. Typical coremia and an *Echinobotryum* stage (Mason, 1933) were developed on the cellulose film. It was once isolated from fen soil, but not seen sporing on 'Cellophane'.

Stachybotrys atra Corda was found, rather sporadically, in soils No. 1, 2, and 3. It is readily identified microscopically (Bisby, 1943), and cannot be missed on examination of a slide. It differs from the fungi mentioned above in morphology of the 'rooting branches', the fungus growing through the cellulose as single hyphae and dissolving out long narrow cavities. Smith (1954) notes this species to decompose cellulose rapidly in the presence of small amounts of mineral nutrients. It has been frequently isolated from exposed cotton fabrics (Siu, 1951, p. 336), and has been frequently isolated from soils.

The closely related *Memnoniella echinata* (Rivolta) Galloway, also a destructive fungus and unlikely to be missed, has not been seen on 'Cellophane'. Its ecology has been thoroughly discussed by White *et al.* (1949), who concluded that it was a tropical species whose preference was for the purer forms of cellulose. On the basis of direct examination, it was seen on paper and fabrics in the tropics more frequently than any other single species. Fungi mostly associated were *Gliomastix convoluta* and *Stachybotrys atra*, and perithecia of *Ascotricha* and *Chaetomium*. White *et al.* also showed that it acted upon cotton fibres by growing over the surface, and at intervals sending down short sucker-like branches which were seen extending into dissolved-out pockets. They stated *Myrothecium verrucaria* and *Humicola* sp. gave similar results, which shows their action and growth form is not dissimilar from that of *Humicola* sp., at least on cellulose film.

Myrothecium verrucaria (Alb. and Schw.) Ditm. ex Fr. (= *Metarrhizium glutinosum* Pope (White & Downing, 1947)) is another cellulose-decomposing fungus not found so far on cellulose film. It is considered by Siu (1951) to be about the most powerful cellulose-destroying fungus known in the laboratory, but is practically never observed fruiting or growing on cotton fabrics in the field, although it has been isolated quite a few times, probably as surface contaminants (p. 159). Species of *Myrothecium* are not infrequently recorded in lists of soil fungi.

A number of *mycelia sterilia* have been isolated from time to time, especially from soils No. 2, 3, 7, and 8. One of these from soil No. 3 was powerfully active on cellulose in the soil, putting coarse 'rooting' branches into the film. These branches tended to autolyse, leaving large cavities. The fungus grew quite sparsely in culture on Czapek-Dox agar, but would not attack cellulose film if the latter were placed on the agar surface. This was in contrast to the behaviour of the aleuriospore and microconidial isolates, which put down the usual 'rooting' branches into 'Cellophane' laid on agars.

From soils 7a and 8, mycelium identified as *Rhizoctonia solani* Kühn was found to be dominant. It grew vigorously over the film, acting upon it directly without 'roots'. A mixture of equal parts of soils No. 3 which contained no *Rhizoctonia* with No. 7a resulted in 100% colonization of added cellulose by *Rhizoctonia*. The 'rooting' forms present in soil No. 3 were active, but *Rhizoctonia* was much more vigorous, having larger hyphae and a faster growth rate, and overgrew them. Occurrence of this fungus on cellulose film was unexpected.

Blair (1943) showed that his isolates of *Rhizoctonia* had only weak cellulose-decomposing activity as measured on agar plates containing precipitated cellulose. Species of *Penicillium, Trichoderma, Helminthosporium,* and *Fusarium* were used for comparison. None of his isolates grew over filter-paper laid on water agar and saturated with a mineral nutrient solution. It is possible, however, that like the sterile isolate from soil No. 3 mentioned above, it may be active on cellulose only under certain conditions. Blair found that his strains of *Rhizoctonia* grew through soils at a rate of about 1 cm. per day, and that removal of the agar inoculum after 2 days had practically no effect on this growth rate. He found that addition of 1% (w/w) ground wheat straw, lucerne meal, or grass meal depressed spread to about one-third, attributing this to poor cellulose-decomposing ability, and also partially to nitrogen starvation and to fungistatic carbon dioxide produced by micro-organisms decomposing the organic matter. Again, it is conceivable that *Rhizoctonia* hyphae were investing this material in preference to spreading through the soil.

Isolation to culture from cellulose film from soil No. 8 proved to be difficult. Pieces of 'Cellophane' seen to be extensively colonized were plated on to Czapek-Dox agar. Often the hyphae autolysed completely. If they survived, they grew very slowly on to the agar. In some platings, spores of a species of *Mucor* were present, and in every case had germinated and formed colonies 1·5 cm. in diameter, while the *Rhizoctonia* had just grown off the film. Experiences of this kind demonstrate the need of microscopic observation. The isolates grew rather better on soil extract agar, and certain transfers to this medium grew away, and when inoculated into sterilized soil containing 'Cellophane' pieces grew rapidly over these, entirely destroying the strength of the pieces in 2–3 weeks. Growth and appearance were exactly as on 'Cellophane' in the original unsterile soil. It is obvious that this fungus, though its hyphae were morphologically very similar to those of *R. solani*, possessed physiological properties quite dissimilar from normal isolates of *R. solani*.

Rhizoctonia comes into contact with 'Cellophane' in these soils by means of hyphae travelling through the soil, probably originating from sclerotia or resistant hyphae. Warcup (1957) obtained *Rhizoctonia* from a wheat-field soil from both these sources, and illustrates resistant hyphae showing new growth in agar. He noticed that both *Rhizoctonia solani* and a sterile fungus appeared most abundantly during the period of decomposition of straw in the soil he was studying, but he was uncertain whether these fungi played any part in the decomposition. Until quite recently *R. solani* has rarely been isolated from soil by dilution- and soil-plate techniques, but by methods favouring hyphal isolation it can readily be obtained (Thornton, 1956; Warcup, 1957).

It is a matter of interest that *R. solani* developing vigorously on cellulose film was not attacked by *Trichoderma viride* Pers. ex Fries, nor indeed was the cellulose film. Certain isolates of this fungus have cellulose-decomposing activity in the laboratory; as, for example, on cotton sheeting (Reese *et al.*, 1950). White states, however, that direct examination of hundreds of cotton fabric samples in various stages of decay from nearly all parts of the world did not reveal any fruiting structures of *T. viride* on the fabric. *T. viride* was considered to exist on the samples much like other spores which had been deposited with the dust of the atmosphere (White, in Siu, 1955, p. 159). *T. viride* was isolated from cellulose film in the acid litter, but not from any other soil studied. Even on 'Cellophane' in litter it was not dominant. It is known that *T. viride* is more active against other fungi in environments of low pH, against for example *R. solani* (Weindling & Fawcett, 1936) and *Fomes annosus* (Rishbeth, in Garrett, 1956), and that it grows well in soils which have been sterilized (Warcup, 1951; Mollison, 1953). In ordinary neutral soils, however, from which it is usually readily isolated, its ecological niche remains a mystery. The perfect stage is *Hypocrea rufa*, in which form it appears on dead wood and stems, often accompanied by the *Trichoderma* stage (Bisby, 1939).

Sporotrichum (or *Aleurisma*) species were commonly associated with 'rooting' forms in soils No. 1, 3, and 6. They were not primary cellulose-decomposing fungi, but appeared when the other had become established.

Gliomastix convoluta was found occasionally.

Penicillium spp. have never been seen sporing on cellulose film (except in soil No. 5), but some were once isolated from thinly developing mycelium on 'Cellophane' from fen soil.

In the coniferous litter and the underlying acid sand (No. 5), the microflora developing on buried cellulose film was entirely different from that on the arable soils or the mull. None of these species were found; instead, species of *Oidiodendron* Robak and *Geomyces* Traaen were dominant, and a species of *Penicillium* was seen sporing on the film. *Trichoderma* was isolated occasionally from 'Cellophane' in litter. The combination of *Oidiodendron* spp. and mites resulted in total disintegration of the cellulose film in some 12 weeks. *Oidiodendron* spp. were first described on wood pulp (Robak, 1932). They are increasingly being reported in soil lists, probably as they become better known. Further study is necessary on cellulose in a litter environment. There are probably numbers of Basidiomycetes to be found (Lindeberg, 1946).

Returning to arable soils, mention must be made of predacious fungi found parasitizing nematodes. These fungi have recently been reviewed by Duddington (1957), together with a discussion on their ecology. Species producing mycelial networks (soils No. 3 and 8), constricting rings (soil No. 6), adhesive knobs (soil No. 8), and in soil No. 6 an obligate parasite, *Harposporium* sp. (kindly identified by Mr. D. C. Twinn, The Nature Conservancy, Grange-over-Sands, Lancs.), have been seen on cellulose film. Occasionally spores have been associated with these, probably belonging to the genera *Arthrobotrys* and *Dactylella*. The species producing constricting rings was abundant in the clay soil sample after 12–18 weeks burial of the 'Cellophane'. Although these are in no sense cellulose-decomposing fungi, they have been caused to develop through addition of pure cellulose to the soils. In his review Duddington says that 'it is a little surprising, when we consider the richness of the soil predacious fungus flora, that they do not play a larger part in published lists of soil fungi'. He suggests this is partly due to their failure to appear on isolation plates in absence of suitable prey, when they cannot compete with the more vigorously growing moulds, and partly to the unsuitably low pH of many isolation media.

By way of summary it is of interest to briefly examine the dominant filamentous fungi which developed in the different soils studied. A number of pieces of cellulose film buried in a soil sample mean that the cellulose is virtually offered to the whole variety of population of that sample. In the nearly neutral arable soils (No. 1, 2, 3, 6, and 7), though very diverse in texture and composition, the fungi which were normally dominant belonged to the 'rooting' group, viz. *Botryotrichum*, *Humicola*, and the microconidial isolates. The different species of this group were able to co-exist on the same piece of cellulose. If, however, *Rhizoctonia* were present in a soil, together with species of the 'rooting' group, as in soils 7a, 8 and the mixture of 7a and 3, it usually overgrew these. It had greater *competitive saprophytic ability* than the 'rooting' species—this expression is defined as the summation of physiological characteristics (possessed by a fungus) that make for success in competitive colonization of dead organic substrates (Garrett, 1956). On account of its larger hyphae and faster growth rate, it rapidly colonized the cellulose film, rendering the film in condition for development of the bacterial stage. This was presumably through excretion from the hyphae, autolysis, and enzymic softening of the substrate. In soil No. 8, certain pieces of 'Cellophane' remained untouched for a period of several weeks, by which time those originally attacked by *Rhizoctonia* or by a 'rooting' fungus were extensively colonized. Presumably, therefore, neither of these fungi happened to be near to the untouched pieces, and none of the other fungi in contact were able to develop on the cellulose.

Stachybotrys had the capacity to become dominant or co-dominant with the 'rooting' fungi, which it occasionally was in soils No. 1 and 3. Its occurrence was, however, sporadic; presumably it was not abundant in the soils.

In weathered chalk (soil No. 4) *Stysanus* was co-dominant with a 'rooting' fungus. *Stysanus* was either not present in the other soils or required relative freedom from competition. It was noteworthy that few bacteria developed on cellulose film in this soil, despite the high pH, probably because there was little organic matter present. Development of the bacterial stage did not occur to its usual extent, even by 10 weeks they were quite few, and this may have allowed the big coremia of *Stysanus* to develop fully on the 'Cellophane'.

In the litter sample, and also in the acid sand (which was practically devoid of organic matter and hence probably received its microflora from the litter layer above it), the fungi found were quite different. Species of *Oidiodendron* and the closely related *Geomyces* were dominant. A species of *Penicillium* was present, and was seen sporing on some pieces of 'Cellophane'. It is probable that the dominants recorded from the arable soils were absent, though it is conceivable that they were present and inactive. Conversely, were *Oidiodendron* spp. present in the other soils? I should doubt whether *Oidiodendron* spp. would compete successfully with the dominants in the arable soils, as the former were comparatively slow to develop.

As far as the arable soils are concerned, these results are in agreement with those of Jensen (1931), concerning the fungus flora of straw buried in neutral soils. He did not record *Rhizoctonia*, but this would not have been revealed by his plating method had it been present. Certain fungi commonly recorded on straw by other workers have not been seen on cellulose film, species of *Fusarium* (especially *F. culmorum*), *Aspergillus*, *Penicillium*, and *Trichoderma*. *F. culmorum* definitely colonizes straw from soil (Butler, 1953). *Penicillium* and *Trichoderma* have been recorded from straws after thorough washing and surface sterilization procedures by Sadasivan (1939) and Walker (1941). Species of all these moulds possess cellulose-destroying power (Norman, 1930; Reese *et al.*, 1950; Siu, 1951). Perhaps *Penicillium* and *Aspergillus* species are more characteristic of growth on cellulose in damp environments which are better aerated than the average soil—it is possible they may grow on cellulose film exposed under such conditions above ground. On the other hand, the presence of encrusting substances along with the cellulose may be expected to stimulate a richer microflora than would arise on pure cellulose.

To conclude, methods combining the techniques of microscopic observation and isolation of the fungi seen to be present on particular substrates buried in soils seem to me to show promise in furtherance of knowledge of fungal ecology. All substrates are not as favourable for this purpose as 'Cellophane', but with a certain experimental ingenuity these techniques should be capable of extension to numbers of other substrates.

REFERENCES

AMES, L. M. (1949). New cellulose-destroying fungi isolated from military material and equipment. *Mycologia*, **41**, 637–48.

BAINIER, M. G. (1909). Mycothèque de l'École de Pharmacie, XXX. Monographie des *Chaetomidium* et des *Chaetomium*. *Bull. trim. Soc. Mycol. de France*, **25**, 191–237.

BISBY, G. R. (1939). *Trichoderma viride* Pers. ex Fries, and notes on *Hypocrea*. *Trans. Brit. mycol. Soc.*, **23**, 149–68.

BISBY, G. R. (1943). *Stachybotrys*. *Trans. Brit. mycol. Soc.*, **26**, 133–43.

BISBY, G. R., JAMES, N., & TIMONIN, M. (1933). Fungi isolated from Manitoba soil by the plate method. *Canad. J. Res. Set. C*, **8**, 253–75.

BLAIR, I. D. (1943). Behaviour of the fungus *Rhizoctonia solani* Kühn in the soil. *Ann. appl. Biol.*, **30**, 118–27.

BUTLER, F. C. (1953). Saprophytic behaviour of some cereal root-rot fungi. I. Saprophytic colonization of wheat straw. *Ann. appl. Biol.*, **40**, 284–97.

CHIVERS, A. H. (1915). A monograph of the genera *Chaetomium* and *Ascotricha*. *Mem. Torrey Bot. Club*, **14**, 155–240.

DOWNING, MARY H. (1953). *Botryotrichum* and *Coccospora*. *Mycologia*, **45**, 934–40.

DUDDINGTON, C. L. (1957). The predacious fungi and their place in microbial ecology. *Microbial Ecology. Seventh Symp. Soc. gen. Microbiol.*, 218–37. Cambridge University Press.

GARRETT, S. D. (1956). *Biology of Root-infecting Fungi*, Cambridge University Press.

HASKINS, R. H. (1946). New chytridiaceous fungi from Cambridge. *Trans. Brit. mycol. Soc.*, **29**, 135–40.

JENSEN, H. L. (1931). The microbiology of farmyard manure decomposition in soil. II. Decomposition of cellulose. *J. agric. Sci.*, **21**, 81–100.

KUBIENA, W. L. (1955) in *Soil Zoology* ed. Kevan, D. K. McE, London: Butterworth.

LINDEBERG, G. (1946). On the decomposition of lignin and cellulose in litter caused by soil-inhabiting Hymenomycetes. *Arkiv. f. Bot.*, **33A**, 1–16.

MASON, E. W. (1933). Annotated account of fungi received at the Imperial Myco-logical Institute, List II (Fascicle 2). I.M.I. Mycological Papers, No. 3.

MOLLISON, JANET E. (1953). Effect of partial sterilization and acidification of soil on the fungal population. *Trans. Brit. mycol. Soc.*, **36**, 215–28.

NORMAN, A. G. (1930). The biological decomposition of plant materials. III. Physiological studies on some cellulose-decomposing fungi. *Ann. appl. Biol.*, **17**, 575–613.

OMVIK, AASA. (1955). Two new species of *Chaetomium* and one new *Humicola* species. *Mycologia*, **47**, 748–57.

REESE, E. T., LEVINSON, H. S., DOWNING, MARY H., & WHITE, W. L. (1950). Quartermaster culture collection. *Farlowia*, **4**, 45–86.

ROBAK, H. (1932). Investigations regarding fungi on Norwegian wood-pulp and fungal infection at wood-pulp mills. *Nyt. Mag. f. Naturv.*, **71**, 185–330.

SADASIVAN, T. S. (1939). Succession of fungi decomposing wheat straw in different soils, with special reference to *Fusarium culmorum*. *Ann. appl. Biol.*, **26**, 497–508.

⋆ SIU, R. G. H. (1951). *Microbial Decomposition of Cellulose.* New York: Reinhold.

SKOLKO, A. J., & GROVES, J. W. (1948). Notes on seed-borne fungi. V. *Chaetomium* species with dichotomously branched hairs. *Canad. J. Res. Sect. C.*, **26**, 269–80.

SKOLKO, A. J., & GROVES, J. W. (1953). Notes on seed-borne fungi. VII. *Chaetomium.* *Canad. J. Bot.*, **31**, 779–809.

SMITH, G. (1954). *An Introduction to Industrial Mycology.* London: Arnold.

SPARROW, F. K. (1957). A further contribution to the Phycomycete flora of Great Britain. *Trans. Brit. mycol. Soc.*, **40**, 523–35.

THORNTON, R. H. (1956). *Rhizoctonia* in natural grassland soils. *Nature, Lond.*, **177**, 230–1.

TRIBE, H. T. (1957). Ecology of micro-organisms in soils as observed during their development upon buried cellulose film. *Microbial Ecology. Seventh Symposium Soc. gen. Microbiol*, 287–98. Cambridge University Press.

WALKER, A. G. (1941). The colonization of buried wheat straw by soil fungi, with special reference to *Fusarium culmorum*. *Ann. appl. Biol.*, **28**, 333–50.

WARCUP, J. H. (1951). Effect of partial sterilization by steam or formalin on the fungus flora of an old forest nursery soil. *Trans. Brit. mycol. Soc.*, **34**, 519–32.

WARCUP, J. H. (1955). On the origin of colonies of fungi developing on soil-dilution plates. *Trans. Brit. mycol. Soc.*, **38**, 298–301.

WARCUP, J. H. (1957). Studies on the occurrence and activity of fungi in a wheat-field soil. *Trans. Brit. mycol. Soc.*, **40**, 237–62.

WEINDLING, R., & FAWCETT, H. S. (1936). Experiments in the control of *Rhizoctonia* damping-off of citrus seedlings. *Hilgardia*, **10**, 1–16.

WHITE, W. L., & DOWNING, MARY H. (1947). The identity of '*Metarrhizium glutinosum*'. *Mycologia*, **39**, 546–55.

WHITE, W. L., & DOWNING, MARY H. (1951). *Coccospora agricola* Goddard, its specific status, relationships and cellulolytic activity. *Mycologia*, **43**, 645–57.

WHITE, W. L., & DOWNING, MARY H. (1953). *Humicola grisea*, a soil inhabiting, cellulolytic Hyphomycete. *Mycologia*, **45**, 951–63.

WHITE, W. L., YEAGER, C. C., & SHOTTS, HELEN (1949). History, distribution and economic significance of the cellulose-destroying fungus *Memnoniella echinata*. *Farlowia*, **3**, 399–423.

DECOMPOSITION OF CELLULOSE C¹⁴
AND LIGNIN C¹⁴ IN THE SOIL

JAQUES MAYAUDON AND PAUL SIMONART

Centre de Microbiologie du Sol, Universite de Louvain, Belgium

By means of radioactive carbon an investigation has been made of the decomposition in soil of the cellulose fraction which, in monocotyledons, is composed of about 80% cellulose and 20% lignin.

Two types of radioactive cellulose fractions were prepared from leaves of rice. First, by photosynthesis in the presence of $C^{14}O_2$ (Simonart & Mayaudon, 1958), we obtained a cellulose fraction 10% of the radioactivity of which rested in the lignin (cellulose fraction $C^{14}O_2$). Then, after immersing the leaves of rice in a solution of phenylalanine C^{14} (Brown and Neish, 1956) we isolated a cellulose fraction in which the lignin represented 38% of the radioactivity (cellulose fraction PhaC¹⁴). It should be mentioned that these two cellulose fractions have the same chemical composition and differ only in the distribution of radioactivity in their constituents. Subjecting the $C^{14}O_2$ cellulose fraction successively to the Klason (1923) and Freudenberg (1940) procedures, nominally pure cellulose C^{14} and lignin C^{14} were obtained, though the purity of both may have been affected by the extraction processes. In addition, the principal constituents of lignin were extracted from the $C^{14}O_2$ cellulose fraction: vanillin C^{14}, syringaldehyde C^{14}, and p-hydroxy-benzaldehyde C^{14}.

The decomposition of biologically synthesized radioactive substances was investigated, each of them being mixed with a quantity of meadow soil corresponding to 4 g. dry weight, and kept at a humidity of 35% and temperature of 25° (Simonart & Mayaudon, 1956). After 30 days, by which time the release of $C^{14}O_2$ was negligible, a classical procedure was used to separate the humic components of the soil into three fractions: (1) fulvic acids, the soluble fraction; (2) humic acids, the precipitated fraction; and (3) a residue, humin. In their turn the humic acids were broken down by hydrolysis in a nitrogen atmosphere into two sub-fractions: a soluble fraction (HS) and an insoluble fraction (HR). Each of these humic fractions was later heated by the Van Slyke-Folch method, and the $C^{14}O_2$ released quantitatively from the reaction was collected as $BaC^{14}O_3$, the radioactivity of which was measured by a flow-counter (Mayaudon & Simonart, 1959).

The values obtained indicate that the cellulosic fraction ($C^{14}O_2$) loses 28% of its radioactivity to the humic fractions of the soil, whilst the cellulose fraction (PhaC^{14}) relinquishes 44·5%. One must assume that, in the cellulose fraction $C^{14}O_2$ the cellulose and lignin constituents are dispersed at different rates. This is also shown by the decomposition of the cellulose C^{14}, where it has been established that 20% of the initial radioactivity remains in the humic fractions, whilst for lignin C^{14} the value is 70%. The percentage of the radioactivity of the fulvic acids, of the humic acids and of the humin were respectively 25, 30, and 45 for cellulose C^{14}, compared with 10, 49, and 41 for lignin C^{14}. Based on the initial radioactivity of cellulose C^{14} and lignin C^{14} respectively, 5·9% and 34·2% related to the humic acids. The distributions of the radioactivity amongst the hydrolysable (HS) and non-hydrolysable (HR) fractions of the humic acids also differ for cellulose and lignin: in effect, after decomposition, 82% of cellulose C^{14} radioactivity is found in the HS, whereas 73% of the lignin C^{14} passes to the HR. A distribution of radioactivity similar to that for lignin is shown after decomposition of vanillin C^{14}, syringaldehyde C^{14}, and p-hydroxybenzaldehyde C^{14}.

Knowing, on the one hand, that in the humic acids the HS fraction is made up for the most part by amino acids (Bremner, 1955), whilst the HR fraction is composed of phenolic acids and aldehydes found also in the lignin, the results obtained suggest that the quaternary substances found in the HS fraction arise from microbial proteins formed at the expense of carbohydrates, whilst the non-hydrolysable HR would be formed principally at the expense of the lignin or its phenolic substances.

REFERENCES

BRAUNS, F. E. (1952). Sulfuric acid or Klason lignin. In *The chemistry of lignin*, New York, N.Y.: Academic Press, Inc.

BREMNER, J. M. (1955). Nitrogen distribution and amino-acid composition of fractions humic acid from a chernozem soil. *Zeit PH. Ernähr. Dürg.*, **71**, 63–6.

BROWN, S. A., & NEISH, A. C. (1956). Studies of lignin biosynthesis using isotopic carbon. *Can. J. Biochem. Phys.*, **34**, 769–78.

FREUDENBERG, K., LAUTSCH, W., & EUGLER, K. (1940). Die Bildung von Vanillin aus Fichtenlignin. *Ber. Dtsch. Chem. Ges.*, **73**, 167–71.

MAYAUDON, J., & SIMONART, P. (1959). Etude de la décomposition de la matière organique dans le sol au moyen de carbone radioactif V. Décomposition de cellulose et de lignine. *Plant and Soil*, **11**, 181–92.

MAYAUDON, J., & SIMONART, P. (1959). Étude de la décomposition de la matière organique dans le sol au moyen de carbone radioactif III. Décomposition des

substances solubles, des protéines et des hemicelluloses. *Plant and Soil*. **11**, 170–75.
SIMONART, P., & BATISTIC, L. Etude chromatographique des fractions humiques. (In preparation.)
SIMONART, P., & MAYAUDON, J. (1958). Étude de la décomposition de la matière organique dans le sol au moyen de carbone radioactif. I Cinétique de l'oxydation en CO_2 de divers substrats radioactifs. *Plant and Soil*, **9**, 367–75.

DISCUSSION

Prof. C. G. C. Chesters. If the rhizosphere is taken as a habitat within the soil, what part are the root surface fungi playing in the biology of the rhizosphere? Are they contributing anything to the plant, are they merely selfish and looking out for themselves on the root surface, or are they pathogenic fungi which have been stopped from going any farther because of the chemical makeup and physical conditions of the particular root on which they are growing? What is their biological status within this zone of marked microbial activity round the root? I feel that probably they are not as important as the bacterial complement of that rhizosphere zone. I think the position is different in the soil immediately round the root, but it is the root surface fungi about which I am rather troubled.

Dr. J. L. Harley. With regard to Professor Chesters' question as to the activity, or otherwise, of root-surface fungi, I should like to make two points. Firstly, many of the organisms isolated from the rhizosphere and root surface of healthy plants are potentially pathogenic. This has been shown particularly in some of the work on cereal crop plants. Secondly, we must not assume that fungal and plant walls are biologically inert. Enzymes have recently been shown to be attached on these surfaces so that they must not be considered as inert but part of the living system. Hence fungi which appear to be resting in the root surface, in fact may be absorbing nutrients from the root cells.

Prof. C. G. C. Chesters. Far more of root-surface fungi are getting into superficial tissues of the root than most papers dealing with rhizospheres have suggested. I have never seriously considered the cell wall of fungi to be inert; I think that it has to be regarded as a surface on which vigorous chemical reactions are taking place.

Dr. H. Katznelson. Professor Chesters' question as to the role of organisms, especially fungi, on the root surface has raised a vital point. As I tried to point out in my lecture to the Symposium, there are two broad lines of investigation of the rhizosphere phenomenon. One concerns the influence of the plant on the microflora of the soil, the other concerns the influence of the microflora of the rhizosphere on the plant. As microbiologists, we have naturally inclined to the study of the former problem—a study of the nature of the organisms developing on or near the root, their relationships to each other, and so on. Their effect on the plant requires nutritional and physiological studies, which should certainly be done but which have so far lagged behind the purely microbiological studies.

Prof. A. Burges. Tribe's work showed quite a large sheet of cellulose with hyphae quite capable of dissolving cellulose and utilizing the products, and yet the great bulk of the cellulose had not been destroyed by the fungus. There was no problem of competition for space because there were quite big gaps on the cellulose. This seems a general problem, that there is available food material, plenty of space for hyphae or bacteria, and yet only a portion of the food material seems to be utilized. One suggestion is that perhaps there was so much cellulose there that the fungus could not utilize it because it had utilized all the available nitrogen or some other substance. Another possibility is that a fungistasis has developed, and the fungus has got as far as it can and then this slowing down occurs. What do others think about this apparently general problem?

Dr. H. Katznelson. As regards Professor Burges' question concerning the inhibition of fungal development on cellulose, I might suggest that it is either a matter of direct competition for nutrients by bacteria which follow the initial colonization of the cellulose by fungi such as *Rhizoctonia solani*, or the production of antagonistic substances. The fact that Dr. Tribe found it extremely difficult to grow this strain of *R. solani* in pure culture may be due to its requirements for substances such as vitamins or minute amounts of essential elements which are depleted through extensive proliferation of bacteria.

Dr. J. G. Savory. With reference to Professor Burges' remarks, cellulose-destroying microfungi attack wood at localized points along their hyphae, and give rise to discrete cavities within the wood cell wall at those points. Furthermore, decay of wood *by Chaetomium globosum* in pure culture has been shown to be proportional to the amounts of mineral nutrients available to the fungus.

Prof. A. Burges. I think some explanation like this is so, but if it is it means that when we are looking at cellulose decomposition we must realize that very soon cellulose ceases to be the critical thing we are studying, and we have to look at other things, sources of vitamins, nitrogen, etc., and that a great deal of the decomposition is controlled not by the substrate in which you are interested beyond the very earliest stage of attack.

Dr. D. A. Griffiths. Professor Chesters made the point that water agar is suitable to allow isolation as nutrients in the soil solution are sufficient to allow germination. He has stated in a previous discussion that spores in soil may be coated with colloidal materials which effect fungistasis. Would not the incorporation of glucose in soil give a better picture of soil fungi in a particular horizon (i.e. overcome fungistasis)? That such stimulation of inactive spores in the organic débris might occur, due to intermediates of other decomposition reactions, would therefore affect the further decomposition of the organic débris.

Prof. C. G. C. Chesters. I have tried to get rid of spores, and I attempt to isolate only from hyphal fragments in the organic débris.

Prof. J. Ziemiecka. Did Professor Burges and Miss Latter study the decomposition of humic acid only in pure cultures or in mixed cultures as well, so as to find out the role of each of them in the process in following their metabolisms? Did you not find Actinomycetes able to decompose humic acid?

Prof. A. Burges. We did find evidence of Actinomycetes being increased in the presence of humic acid, but nowhere near as much as we had expected. As regards the sequence of fungi, it seemed that the fast-growing fungi were there a few days ahead of the others (e.g. *Trichoderma, Paecilomyces*), but I think it is difficult to get any evidence of sequential colonization where soil is put on a humic-acid medium.

Dr. R. H. Estey. Australian and American workers report 3% nitrogen in humic acid from soils, whereas you find less than half of 1%; yet after the fungi have worked on your extracts, you are finding that the humic acid now has 3% nitrogen. Can you explain this?

Prof. A. Burges. We are guessing a lot on this, but what we think to be the basic chemical structure is that there is probably an aromatic linking giving a long molecule, that there are phenolic OH's, there are carbonyls, and that either in the main chain or side chains there are quinone groupings. Similarly we think this the basic one, and some polyphenolic substances are linked either to the side chains or to the main chain. The reason we dislike acid treatment is that we suspect these phenolic units are being hydrolysed by the acid. Dr. Steelink carried out prolonged acid hydrolysis, and examined the products chromatographically and obtained evidence of various polyphenols. In a highly leached soil where nitrogen is very scarce and is fairly rigorously tied up in the litter layer, we think that the material which comes down to the B horizon is very poor in nitrogen, and that therefore the quinone groups are not saturated with amino acids; but if the humic molecule is synthesized in the presence of amino acids from micro-organisms then we think that you get the normal amino-acid combination with quinone groupings. Now, in a chernozem or similar situation, where there are abundant amino acids, it may be that when the synthesis occurs there is at the same time a coupling with amino acids, so that the humic-acid molecule, as it occurs in the soil under those conditions, does contain the amino group linked in. It is just that this rather unique situation in our podzol means that it has been synthesized in the absence of very much amino acid. Now, when we put the molecule with the free quinone groups into our culture media, the fungi are taking up nitrogen and also allowing nitrogen to leak out. Dr. Morton, I think showed that if you grow fungi giving them 1·0 g. of NO_4 they take it up and push back about 0·3 g. of the nitrogen in the form of complex amino compounds into the medium. Perhaps the re-synthesized nitrogen materials produced by the fungi coupling with the quinone groups are again giving us an amino-humic complex having something like 4% nitrogen. Perhaps somewhere about 4% nitrogen represents the level at which all these quinone groups are saturated by amino acids. Dr. Taylor has shown that the figure for quinone oxygen is quite low, so that one could block all quinone oxygens with a relatively small amount of amino acid.

Dr. H. Katznelson. Was an attempt made to extract humic acid from the A or surface horizons to compare it with that obtained from the B horizon? I am curious if this material is produced by microbial action or is liberated by microbial action from the organic combination in undecomposed material.

Prof. A. Burges. The amounts of lactic-acid soluble humic acid differ very much; in the B horizon once could take out about 70% of the total carbon with lactic acid, but for the H horizon of litter only about 10% is lactic-acid soluble. It is difficult to interpret these results, because the amount of mineral material in the humic acid seems to determine the solubility. Whether the humic acid in the B horizon is something that has been left behind and then becomes soluble, or whether it is something which is synthesized and is washed down or is a fragment from the decomposition which is washed down, we have no evidence.

Dr. S. Hepple. It may be that extracts from the surface litter do contain compounds similar to the amorphous humus of the B_1 horizon because, during fungal growth on litter extracts a brown deposit collected on the mycelium similar in appearance to that on mycelium grown in B_1 extract.

Mr. D. V. Crawford. The relatively large proportion of lactic acid soluble humic acid in the podzol B_1 horizon described by Professor Burges, compared with the amounts in the A horizons, may be due to the abundance of other, more easily decomposed, organic matter in the A horizons, and do not indicate synthesis in the B_1 horizon. This material is colloidal and susceptible to dispersion and flocculation by various agencies—sesquioxides in the B_1 horizon can be shown to absorb such material originating from upper horizons.

Prof. A. Burges. I hope I did not give the impression that we thought that this material was made in the B_1 horizon. Our feeling is quite the opposite, we feel that it is made up above, and this is a chromotogram taking it down, nature doing a separation for us.

262 DISCUSSIONDISCUSSION

Dr. C. G. Dobbs. Regarding the non-utilization of cellulose in Tribe's work, it seems to me that both a mycostatic factor and a limiting shortage of nutrients is concerned. We have found that nearly all soils need the addition of a certain threshold amount of carbohydrate before germination or growth will occur. In this connexion it is worth noticing that Hinson found that the mycostasis returned earlier when salts were added with glucose than when glucose was added alone. This suggests that the shortage of other nutrients may have acted more strongly upon the mycostatic organisms than upon the fungi being studied.

Dr. R. Moreau. On a signale des associations entre *Clostridium*, fixateurs d'azote et des champignons cellulotiques. Avez vous deja observe des faits indentique?

Dr. S. Hepple. I do not think Dr. Tribe has considered the association of cellulose-destroying fungi with bacteria. He has concentrated almost entirely on the fungi.

PHYSIOLOGY OF SOIL FUNGI

THE PHYSIOLOGY OF SOIL FUNGI

J. L. HARLEY

Department of Agriculture, University of Oxford

The term *soil fungi* has no very precise meaning. It is applied to the heterogeneous collection of fungi which may be isolated from soil or which have been observed to exist in some form in soil. It is impossible, therefore, to generalize about the physiological activities of this group, except in so far as one can generalize about the physiology of all fungi. In this paper, some of the main physiological attributes of fungi will be considered with respect to their relevance to the life of fungi in the soil.

The fungi and other soil organisms bear, in a sense, a similar relation to the chemical processes of the soil as do enzyme systems to the metabolism of an organism. If we extract either kind of system into artificial surroundings—that is, into pure culture or *in vitrum*—in order to study its activity there, we can only conclude from our experiments that the system will act in a certain way or ways. We may speculate that it does act in these ways in the natural state, we cannot conclude that it does so act or even that it acts at all. The results of cultural studies on the physiology of soil fungi must be reassessed by experiments with soil systems before they become of value in interpreting soil ecological processes.

One of the most striking features of the fungi is the apparent structural simplicity of their vegetative bodies which contrasts with the relative complexity of their reproductive structure. The majority have some kind of filamentous mycelium simple in morphology and complex in physiological activity which exists immersed in its substrate and is difficult to observe.

The mycelium presents a large surface of contact to the substrate, and through this surface a ready interchange of substances takes place. The individual hyphal filaments grow apically by an extension zone restricted to a few microns at the hyphal tips, and the whole hyphal surface is therefore able to remain in close contact with the substrate throughout life. Substances are absorbed and lost through the whole surface as a result of metabolic processes which are often most active in the youngest regions.

It is imagined that the food substances enter directly into metabolic sequences in which various intermediate reactive substances are formed. From these a part goes into the building of the stabler parts of the living system. Another portion is eventually broken down to CO_2 in the respiratory and fermentative sequences, yielding energy utilizable in the various sorts of endergonic processes. A third portion may be converted into substances often of high molecular weight which when they remain in the mycelium are called 'storage products'. Other usually simpler substances are released into the medium and are often called 'metabolites'.

The first two sequences are essential to the life of the organism in a direct sense. The others may be viewed as the resultants of a temporary or permanent inefficient use of materials or as resultants of a lack of balance in the processes of absorption and utilization (see Table 1). The

TABLE 1

Fumaric acid production by Rhizopus nigricans
(Foster & Waksman, 1939, Recalculated)

Glucose concentration g./100 ml. medium	Consumed in 7 days	Mycelium weight g.	Fumaric acid mg.
2·5	2·07	0·828	5·0
5·0	3·895	0·83	90·36
10·0	6·485	0·810	141·52

storage substances and the substances released into the medium are the products of side reactions to the main metabolic sequences which lead to subsidiary reaction sequences or shunts. These substances may be utilized by the organism in conditions where there is a deficit of a primary food substance, and both the soluble substances secreted into the medium as well as the storage substances may re-enter the main metabolic pathways.

There are two further activities which are of great importance. Firstly, amongst the substances secreted into the medium may be enzymes capable of causing hydrolysis of complex substances such as cellulose, lignin, starch, pectin, or protein, or capable of catalysing other reactions such as oxidation of polyphenols. Secondly, enzymes are also attached to the hyphal walls or membranes. These may bring about a considerable variety of reactions, such as cleavage of disaccharides and phosphate esters, or the oxidation of ascorbic acid, etc.

Although active fungal mycelia can be pictured in this way, they do not, of course, all exhibit all the processes described in equal measure, nor does any one fungus behave in this regard similarly in all conditions. It is, however, a general feature that they bring about changes in their environment by a multiplicity of mechanisms which are relevant to a consideration of their life and activity in the soil. Some further consideration of these changes may therefore be made under two headings; those caused by absorption of substances and those caused by the release of substances.

Changes caused by absorption

The absorption of substances from solution results, of course, in a local deficit of them in the immediate environs of the hyphae which tends to be made good by movement, particularly along diffusion gradients, towards the hyphal surface. Hence, except in artificially shaken conditions, the local concentration of nutrients and oxygen tends to be lower in the immediate vicinity of active hyphae. Such an occurrence will, of course, be of lesser importance in culture, where high concentrations of nutrients are usually supplied, than in natural conditions, for the local fall in concentration about the hyphae may be relatively slight or the diffusion gradient relatively steep. But the effects will be of importance when the concentrations are at a low level as may occur in soil. Indeed, one can envisage the condition in natural surroundings where absorption rates are dependent most nearly upon rates of movement of substances towards the hyphae or upon the rate at which hyphae exploit new surroundings. In substrates containing low concentrations of essential nutrients, it is possible that the rate of spread of any fungus for a given absorption rate may be a factor affecting its ability to dominate or otherwise influence the fungal population.

Apart from the straightforward effects of absorption affecting the concentration of nutrients, there are also subsidiary effects arising out of differential absorption of components of the substrate. Perhaps the most important is the differential absorption of ion species. The absorption of nitrogenous substances provides a good example. Ions such as ammonium and nitrate are absorbed by most fungi with greater rapidity than others. Hence in cultures, even in those culture media with considerable buffer capacity, considerable changes of pH occur, nitrate media tending to alkalinity and ammonium containing media tending to acidity. The changes in pH may have various far-reaching effects of a secondary nature. Firstly, they may affect the solubility of essential substances, such as the precipitation of double salts of alkali metals and magnesium with phosphate at neutrality or above. Secondly, they may alter the degree of ionization of weak acids and weak bases, or alter the equilibrium of the various species of ions of such salts as phosphates. Such changes alter very greatly the availability of constituents of the medium to fungi. For instance, phosphate is commonly most readily absorbed in the form $^-H_2PO_4$, and less readily so as the ion species $^=HPO_4$ or $^≡PO_4$. Hence changes of pH to alkaline values may not only decrease the availability for the reason of precipitation as a double salt, but also small changes in pH above about 4·5 will decrease the concentration of the most readily absorbed ion. A discussion of the effect of pH upon the biological activity of weak acids and bases was made by Simon & Beevers (1952). Thirdly, pH affects the activities of surface and secreted enzymes. Indeed, the sensitivity of insoluble enzymes to external pH values which do not greatly affect intracellular pH values is one of the strong arguments suggesting that the position of many carbohydrases, phosphatases, ascorbic oxidase, and other enzymes is on the cell surface (Rothstein, 1954).

Changes due to release of substances

The release of metabolic end-products into the medium also brings about significant changes in the substrate, which may alter the conditions for the growth of fungi.

Carbon dioxide is an inevitable product, and its concentration around an active fungal hypha exceeds that at some distance. The pH of the medium will greatly affect its solubility, and CO_2 production may to some extent buffer the medium against extreme pH changes in an alkaline direction. CO_2 may act in at least two ways on fungal growth. For many it is an essential metabolite, and dark fixation reactions have been observed to be widely present in fungi. The effect of high external CO_2 concentration may therefore result in a change of the nature or quantity of end-products, especially where these are organic acids and in a change in the carbohydrate consumed for a given weight of mycelium produced (Foster, 1949). In addition, many fungi show increased growth rate in the presence of carbon dioxide at higher partial pressures than that in the atmosphere. A good example is given by Rippel and Heilmann (1930), who showed an increase of dry-weight production by *Botrytis cinerea* in atmospheres containing CO_2 up to 1·2% (v/v).

It has been claimed that the depth distribution of soil fungi may be more affected by CO_2 concentration in the soil atmosphere than by oxygen supply. Estimates of the oxygen and carbon dioxide in soil have been made by Penningsfeld (1950) and by Brierley (1955), which do indicate that O_2 concentrations differ relatively less from that of the atmosphere than do those of CO_2 in various soil horizons. Even so the rises of CO_2 concentrations recorded do not seem large enough to offer a general explanation, for they often seem to lie within the range in which CO_2 may stimulate germination and growth of some fungi in cultural conditions.

The secretion of metabolic end-products is so common a feature of fungal metabolism, and the kinds of product so various, that any detailed account cannot be attempted here. The kinds of product vary from simple alcohols and fatty acids to complex organic substances. We may consider, however, two aspects of their production. Firstly, the effects that they have on fungal growth and secondly, the factors which affect their production.

Their effects may be inhibiting due to direct poisoning as by excessive alcohol production or by virtue of fungistatic or bacteriostatic activity. Secondly, they may, by precipitation of inorganic ions such as metals or by change of pH with the consequent effects mentioned above, alter the availability of essential nutrients. In addition, the chelating activity of some of them, even though slight, may as Steinberg has suggested also alter the availability of trace metals.

Other substances may be stimulating to neighbouring organisms. Vitamins or vitamin precursors may be secreted for instance, in certain conditions. Tatum & Bell (1946) give examples of *Neurospora* mutants which, when given a minimal supply of thiamine, secrete pyramidine and thiazole into the medium, and again the behaviour of *Mucor ramannianus* is very familiar. This fungus secretes excess pyrimidine if adequate thiazole is provided.

Finally, substances may be produced by aged mycelium. Important examples are nitrogenous compounds, such as amino acids and organic phosphate compounds. Both these categories of substances appear particularly in cultures as the supply of sugars diminishes, and may often be products of autolysis. Mann working with *Aspergillus niger* (1944) records the release of organic phosphate compounds after the disappearance of glucose from the culture fluid. Hawker (1948) and Buston *et al.* (1953, 1956) have recorded not only the presence of sugar phosphates but also their importance as a factor in stimulating growth in *Chaetomium* species.

In assessing the importance of these results in the context of the activities of fungi in the soil, we need to know something of the factors which affect the processes of absorption of substances by fungal hyphae and the processes which result in the release of metabolites.

The process of absorption

Although the movement of materials up to and away from the surface of the mycelium has been described as a diffusional movement in still cultures, it must not be assumed that the processes of absorption and release of substances are necessarily rate-limited by diffusion. Fungal cells, like the cells of other plants, exert a selective effect in absorption processes, and are often affected in their absorption rates by factors affecting metabolic processes. Table 2 gives an example of selection of

TABLE 2

Selection of glucose from mixtures of glucose and fructose by
Chaetomium
(*Unpublished results of J. H. Walsh*)
(*Replicate samples of mycelium 123 mg. dry weight in 50 ml. medium containing 5 mg./ml. fructose with glucose added as stated*)
Time 18 hr. at 25°

Glucose added, mg/ml.	0	0·25	0·5	1·0	2·5	5·0
Fructose absorbed, mg.	27·0	8·0	0	0	0	0
Glucose absorbed, mg.		12·5	24·0	28·0	29·0	33·0

glucose from mixtures of glucose and fructose by *Chaetomium globosum* studied by J. H. Walsh. Similar selection between hexoses is not an uncommon phenomenon (Harley & Smith, 1956; Harley & Jennings, 1957). Moreover, the rate of absorption of sugars is very sensitive to oxygen supply, to temperature, and to the presence of metabolic inhibitors (Table 3), so that one concludes that a pace-making step in the absorption process is chemical, i.e. metabolic. The absorption of other substances is also rate-dependent upon vital processes. Mann (1944) showed that phosphate absorption by *Aspergillus niger* was sensitive to oxygen supply, and inhibited by cyanide, azide and other poisons. Rothstein has emphasized that yeast cells, although impermeable to ions in the resting condition, may absorb them rapidly when metabolizing actively. Using *Torulopsis utilis*, Yemm (1954) showed that ammonium absorption is linked with respiratory turnover and synthesis of amino compounds, and this now appears to be of general occurrence in fungi.

There is no need to labour this point further, for it is clear that in respect of absorption fungi do not differ in principle from other organisms. It is, however, of interest to note that where surface-attached or free-hydrolytic enzymes are produced by the mycelium, these may not be equally sensitive to factors affecting metabolic rates as is the rate of absorption. Table 3a shows the effect of sodium fluoride, and Table 3b the effect of lack of oxygen upon hydrolysis of sucrose by the surface carbohydrase and sugar absorption by the hyphae of *Chaetomium*. In each case the hydrolytic process is not inhibited; indeed, it appears to be somewhat stimulated by the operation of the factor which inhibits absorption.

TABLE 3

Effect of sodium fluoride and lack of oxygen upon sucrose hydrolysis and hexose absorption by Chaetomium globosum. *Medium contains 5 mg./ml.*
sucrose
(*Unpublished results of J. H. Walsh*)
Time 18 *hr. at* 25°

(A)

	Control no addition	+ NaCl		+ NaF	
		50 mM	10 mM	50 mM	10 mM
Hydrolysis	116 mg.	134 mg.	117 mg.	175 mg.	162 mg.
Uptake	43·5 mg.	50 mg.	47 mg.	Nil	31 mg.

(B)

Atmosphere	N₂	Air
Hydrolysis	204	171
Uptake	Nil	96

A final point about absorption is that water uptake is not related in any direct sense to other processes of absorption. A fungal mycelium will clearly loose water to the air by evaporation when it is exposed, but mycelium immersed in water or in contact with moist air in the soil remains in a state of turgidity. Although we must assume that in the processes of initiation and development of fruit-bodies, rhizomorphs, and sclerotia, translocation occurs within the hyphae of the mycelium, it cannot be associated with a mass flow of water. The recent discussion of fungal translocation by Schütte (1956), in which conclusions were reached that some fungi do not appear to translocate materials, seems to me to be more valuable for the fact that it emphasized our ignorance of the movement of materials within hyphae than for its results.

Factors affecting the rates of processes

The most potent factors affecting the quantity and quality of the substances released from any fungal mycelium during its growth are those which affect the rates of enzyme reactions relative to one another and relative to the supply of substrates. In Table 1 it has already been shown how an increase of one compound alone, the glucose, in an artificial medium results in an increased production of fumaric acid by *Rhizopus* without significant change in the production of mycelial dry matter. This and similar observations on many fungi may be interpreted as resulting from the fact that an increased substrate supply so increases absorption of carbohydrate that the metabolic sequences are overladen and shunt products or their derivatives are greatly increased and released into the medium. It is not necessary that they should be released, this will depend upon the species or strain of fungus and the nature of the product.

TABLE 4

Fat synthesis and glucose concentration in Aspergillus
(*Pril* et al., 1935. Biochem. J., **29**, 21)

Glucose g. /100 ml.	Fat as % of dry weight
1	10·4
5	10·8
10	13·1
15	15·6
30	23·3

Table 4 gives an example of internal fat accumulation in *Aspergillus* grown in increasing concentrations of glucose. Again, the amount of the side or storage product increases with excess glucose supplied. This type of reaction to excess substrate is well known, especially in the study of mould products and their production on a commercial scale. The distortion of the metabolism may be decreased by balanced nutrient supply at high level, and increased by treatments which further diminish the activities of the pacemaking enzyme systems. For many of the latter metallic elements such as copper, zinc, and molybdenum are essential, so that deficiency of any of these in the medium may stimulate the production or increase the production of shunt products. Although much is known of the functions of metals as components of enzyme systems, the detail of the ways in which specific end-products arise is far from clear. Many metals are components or more than one enzyme system, and some seem to be mutually interchangeable and some even antagonistic to others. This aspect of the effect of metals has been emphasized by Chesters & Rolinson (1951), from whose paper Table 5 is taken.

As can be seen, the deficiency of each of the three metals increases acid production, although it seems at the moment unlikely that they all act in enzymic processes affecting the same metabolic phase.

TABLE 5

The effect of deficiencies of iron, copper and manganese during incubation for 50 hr. of a strain of Aspergillus niger
(*From Chesters & Rolinson, 1951*)

Metal	Conc. ppM	ml. 0·1N acid produced/g. glucose
Iron	0·05	340
	0·5	17·2
Copper	0·01	37·8
	0·5	25·4
Manganese	0·0	35·0
	0·05	27·8

Another powerful set of factors may influence the kinds of metabolite formed and their rates of formation. These are internal factors arising out of the genetic constitution of the organisms. Nuclear mutants are of peculiar importance because the nuclei of fungi are with minor exceptions haploid. In those which are homocaryotic the effects of mutation are immediately apparent in modified activity. Amongst heterocaryotic forms the presence of relative proportions of nuclei of different genetic kinds may partly confer properties usually associated with diploidy deficiency mutations being compensated by normals in other nuclei. At the same time the elasticity in nuclear complement itself allows for considerable variation of behaviour. It is only in the Basidiomycetes and yeasts amongst common soil fungi that an approach to diploidy or true diploidy occurs. In the Basidiomycetes the dicaryon pair may well confer a similar genetical potential to the true diploid where recessive mutants can be stored while at the same time something of the elasticity of heterocaryosis is preserved.

Because of these peculiarities, biochemical mutants are commonly encountered in natural environments such as the soil. They are often characterized by deficiencies of enzyme systems which result in the ready development of shunt or side reactions leading to the production of metabolites and their release into the medium.

For our present purposes only, we may classify these genetic variants into two kinds. Those in which a pacemaking stage in metabolism is such that a new metabolic product is produced or a familiar product produced in excessive quantities. Secondly, those in which a particular enzyme stage is so deficient that the organism fails to grow without suitable organic supplementation of its medium. Both these kinds of variant are found in fungi isolated from soil. The first may lead to a variability in the behaviour of isolates, and may, if not treated carefully, lead to false conclusions with regard to their activity in soil. Clearly if explanations of antagonistic effect of isolates upon other organisms are based upon their study in culture, a considerable survey of genetic variability is essential before they can be given full credence.

The second kind of variation—absolute demand for a particular factor for full development—may provide explanation of ecological site-preference. For instance, many root-inhabiting fungi, especially those associated with mycorrhizal infection of trees, are vitamin dependent. The considerable researches of Professor Melin and his associates (1954a, b) have shown this to be true. Care must be taken to see such observations in their true prospective. In this case the defective metabolism associated with vitamin requirement is not necessarily a positive factor fitting the fungi for their habit as mycorrhiza formers. Rather is it the result perhaps of this habit, a site of growth which does not select against vitamin demanding forms, and so will be inhabited by a population in which many such forms occur. Before leaving the subject of genetical variation and its impact upon physiology of soil fungi, it is of interest to consider the growth habit of the fungi in the soil. There seems to be two extreme types. The ephemeral Phycomycetes on the one hand and the perennial, long-lived Basidiomycetes on the other. These are contrasted also by being haploid and dicaryotic. It is attractive to relate the ephemeral habit with haploidy and the inability to store recessive genes and to relate the dicaryotic state with persistence, i.e. with ability of the species to remain permanently adapted. Between these two there are the many Ascomycetes and Fungi Imperfecti which have perhaps the best of both worlds. Heterocaryosis and some potential to store recessive variants and elasticity of variation in respect of their multinucleate condition.

If we are to attempt to put these ideas in their proper context, we must

consider the soil as a source of essentials for fungal growth. It is immediately apparent that the usual methods in use for studying the growth
of fungi in culture depend upon the provision of essential nutrients at
what may be termed luxury levels. At the beginning of the growth period
essential substances are present in the culture in quantities which may
well lead to excessive rates of absorption over efficient utilization. We
cannot, therefore, directly apply the results of such studies to interpretation of activities in the soil. Analyses of the available substances in
the soil gives the impression that nutrients are present in much lower
quantities. It may be that this is again itself due to faulty sampling. For
we have to remember the lack of uniformity is very great, and that small
restricted sites of high nutrient content may be present. Indeed, a very
important problem in the study of activities of soil micro-organisms is
the consideration of small soil discontinuities of a magnitude measured
in microns which may afford special habitats for fungi or bacteria. The
surfaces of living roots constitute one example of such habitats, which
do select peculiar populations of fungi and bacteria. Certain analyses of
the quantities of soluble substances, especially nitrogenous substances,
have been made of the root region of some plants. Although these may
show a much higher concentration of amino acids to be present than in
the surrounding soil, the analyses themselves are not above reproach.
This is because the extraction methods used will inevitably kill the
micro-organisms of each habitat, and the soluble materials of their
bodies will be released and be recorded as available substances.

We have to conclude that the study of the physiology of fungi in
culture has outlined the kinds of variability in requirements for essential
materials and the kinds of reaction they can bring about, but as yet it has
afforded little in explaining in detail their ecological distribution except
in a few cases.

REFERENCES

BOULTER, D., & BURGES, A. (1955). Oxidases of *Polystictus versicolor. Experientia.*,
    11, 188–9.
BRIERLEY, J. K. (1955). Seasonal fluctuations in the oxygen and carbon-dioxide
    concentrations in beech litter, with special reference to the salt uptake of beech
    mycorrhizas. *J. Ecol.*, **43**, 404–8.
BUSTON, H. W., JABBAR, A., & ETHERIDGE, D. F. (1953). The influence of hexose
    phosphates, calcium and jute extract on the formation of perithecia by *Chaeto-
    mium globosum. J. gen. Microbiol.*, **8**, 302–6.
BUSTON, H. W., & KHAN, A. N. (1956). The influence of certain micro-organisms
    on the formation of perithecia by *Chaetomium globosum. J. gen. Microbiol.*,
    14, 655–60.

CHESTERS, C. G. C., & ROLINSON, J. L. (1951). Zinc in the metabolism of a strain of
  Aspergillus niger. J. gen. Microbiol., **5**, 553–8.
FOSTER, F. W., & WAKSMAN, S. A. (1939). The specific effect of zinc and other
  heavy metals on growth and fumaric-acid production by *Rhizopus. J. Bact.*,
  37, 599–617.
FOSTER, F. W. (1949). *Chemical activities of fungi.* New York: Academic Press.
HARLEY, J. L., & JENNINGS, D. H. (1957). The effect of sugars on the respiratory
  response of beech mycorrhizas to salts. *Proc. Roy. Soc. B.*, **148**, 403–18.
HARLEY, J. L., & SMITH, D. C. (1956). Sugar absorption and surface carbohydrase
  activity of *Peltigera polydactyla* (Neck.) Hoffm. *Ann. Bot. N.S.*, **20**, 513–43.
HAWKER, L. E. (1948). Stimulation of the formation of perithecia of *Melanospora
  destruens* Shear. by small quantities of certain phosphoric esters of glucose and
  fructose. *Ann. Bot. N.S.*, **12**, 77–9.
MANN, T. (1944). Studies in the metabolism of mould fungi, I. Phosphorus meta-
  bolism in moulds. *Biochem. J.*, **38**, 339–45.
MELIN, E. (1954). Growth-factor requirements of mycorrhizal fungi of forest trees.
  Svensk. Bot. Tidsk., **48**, 86–94.
MELIN, E., & DAS, V. S. R. (1954). Influence of root metabolites on the growth of
  tree mycorrhizal fungi. *Physiol. Plantarum.*, **7**, 851–8.
PENNINGSFELD, F. (1950). Investigations on the respiration of some soil profiles.
  Z. PflErnähr. Düng., **50**, 135–64.
RIPPEL, A., & HEILMANN, F. (1930). Action of carbon dioxide on heterotrophs.
  Arch. Mikrobiol., **1**, 119–36.
ROTHSTEIN, A. (1954). The enzymology of the cell surface. *Protoplasmologica.
  Handbuch der Protoplasma-forschung.* Vienna: Springer-Verlag.
SIMON, E. W., & BEEVERS, H. (1952). The effects of pH on the biological activities
  of weak acids and bases. *New. Phytol.*, **51**, 163–97.
SCHÜTTE, K. H. (1956). Translocation in the fungi. *New Phytol.*, **55**, 164–82.
STEINBERG, R. A. (1942). Effects of trace elements on growth of *Aspergillus niger*
  with amino acids. *J. Agr. Res.*, **64**, 455–75.
TATUM, E. L., & BELL, T. T. (1946). Neurospora. III. Biosynthesis of thiamin.
  Amer. J. Bot., **33**, 15–20.
YEMM, E. W., & FOLKES, B. F. (1954). The regulation of respiration during the
  assimilation of nitrogen in *Torulopsis utilis. Biochem. J.*, **57**, 495–508.

THE USE OF VARIOUS TISSUE PREPARATIONS IN THE STUDY OF THE OXIDATIVE METABOLISM OF SOME FUNGI

D. BOULTER AND H. M. HURST

Department of Botany, The University of Liverpool

VARIOUS types of tissue preparation have been used to investigate the intermediary metabolism of plants. Of these the thin tissue slice bears the closest resemblance physiologically to the intact organism or tissue. These slices, however, have the disadvantage that added substances may not penetrate membranes, and this has led to the development of various types of homogenates in which the cellular structure is disorganized and permeability barriers reduced. Methods have also been developed for the separation of particulate components of homogenates by differential centrifugation. This paper describes the results of the application of these methods of investigation into the oxidative metabolism of *Neurospora crassa* and *Polystictus versicolor*.

In higher plants, oxidative metabolism is mediated in a large measure via a Krebs Cycle coupling with a cytochrome system (Hackett, 1955). In order to show that the oxygen uptake of an organism may be in part due to the operation of a Krebs cycle, it is necessary not only to demonstrate the presence of the individual enzymes of the cycle by oxidation of added cycle acids, but also that small concentrations of these acids catalyse (or 'spark') the oxidation of pyruvate. If the Krebs Cycle couples with a cytochrome system, then the overall oxygen uptake will be inhibited by CO, and this inhibition reversed by light.

METHODS

Culture media. Neurospora crassa, and *Polystictus versicolor* were grown in 2% (w/v) malt extract liquid medium. In those instances where Krebs Cycle acids were fed to the mycelium of *N. crassa*, this fungus had been grown in Fries' minimal medium (Beadle & Tatum, 1941) modified in that 0·1% (w/v) glucose was used instead of 2% (w/v) sucrose as a source of carbon.

Inoculum. Mycelial suspensions of *P. versicolor*, prepared by blending

72-hr. cultures as described in Boulter (1957), were used for inoculations. Spore suspensions of *N. crassa* of known concentrations in water
containing a drop of 'Tween 80' were used for inoculations. These were
prepared by filtering a concentrated spore suspension through glass
wool, centrifuging at a low speed, and adjusting the supernatant spore
suspension to a known turbidity.

Culture conditions. Cultures were incubated at 25° on a Vibro shaker
(Towers).

Preparation of homogenates and particulate fractions. The mycelium
was harvested by filtering through muslin and allowed to stand for
$1\frac{1}{2}$ hr. with 3 changes of 500 ml. of ice-cold distilled water. 5–10 g.
washed tissue was ground in a mortar for 15 min. with twice its volume
of 40-mesh reagent-grade quartz sand and 80 ml. 0·5 M-sucrose solution
containing 0·03 M-phosphate buffer (pH 7·3) and neutralized 0·01
M-ethylenediaminetetraacetic acid (Versene). During the grinding, ice
was added to keep the temperature at 0·5° and Na_2HPO_4 solution to
keep the pH just above neutral. The slurry was filtered through muslin
and centrifuged at 500 g. for 5 min. to remove cell débris and quartz
sand, and the supernatant fluid then centrifuged at 15,000 **g** for 15 min.
This supernatant fluid was discarded and the residual brown pellet
re-suspended with a small glass homogenizer in 10 ml. of 0·03 M-
phosphate buffer containing 0·5 M-sucrose. 1·0 ml. of the re-suspended
particulate fraction (equivalent to 0·5 to 1·0 g. of the original tissue) was
used in each Warburg flask.

All operations were performed in a cold room at 2°, and all vessels
and materials were pre-cooled to this temperature before use.

Measurement of enzyme activity of particulate fraction. The activity
of the enzymes of the Krebs Cycle was measured as the rate of oxygen
uptake in Warburg manometers at 30°. The flasks contained particulate
suspension; 0·02 M-substrate acid; 0·001 $M-MgSO_4$; 0·001 M-ATP;[1]
0·001 M-DPN in a total volume of 3·0 ml. and 0·2 ml. 15% (w/v) KOH
on filter-paper in the centre well. DPN was omitted from the reaction
mixture when succinate was used. In 'sparking reactions', where the
oxidation of pyruvate was catalysed by various Krebs Cycle substrates,
the concentration of the sparker substrate was 0·002 M; 0·0005 M-DPT
was always added in these reactions. The flasks were equilibrated for
10 min. and readings were taken at 5-min. intervals.

Respiration measurements on intact mycelium. The respiration was

---

[1] The following abbreviations will be used: ATP, adenosine triphosphate; DPN, di-
phosphopyridine nucleotide; TPN, triphosphopyridine nucleotide; DPT, diphospho-
thiamine.

measured at 25° by determining the O_2 uptake in Warburg manometers by the direct method (Dixon, 1943). The application of CO and the calculation of the percentage inhibition were as described by Boulter (1957).

RESULTS

Added glucose or intermediates of the Krebs Cycle did not affect the O_2 uptake of the washed mycelium of *Neurospora crassa* when the fungus had been grown in 2% (w/v) malt extract liquid medium. Growing the fungus in a medium with a low C/N ratio (see Methods) reduced the endogenous respiration, and the O_2 uptake of the washed mycelium was then stimulated by the addition of Krebs Cycle acids when these were added at a value of pH 3·3.

The results of Table 1 show that the endogenous O_2 uptake of both *Polystictus versicolor* and *Neurospora crassa* was largely inhibited by CO and that this inhibition was reversed by light.

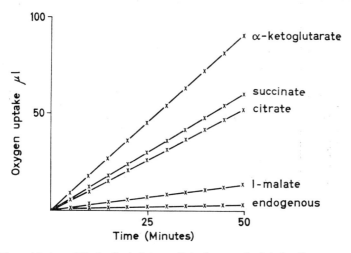

Fig. 1. The oxidation of Krebs Cycle intermediates by a particulate fraction prepared from a 3-day-old culture of *Polystictus versicolor*. Each Warburg vessel contained 0·02 M-substrate; 0·5 M-sucrose; 0·03 M-phosphate buffer pH 7·3; 0·001 M-MgSO₄; 0·001 M-ATP; 0·001 M-DPN in a total volume of 3·0 ml. and 0·2 ml. 15% (w/v) KOH in the centre well. DPN was omitted when succinate was used.

Particulate preparations of *Polystictus versicolor* and *Neurospora crassa* had a low endogenous O_2 uptake, but rapidly oxidized added Krebs Cycle intermediates under suitable conditions (Figs. 1 and 2).

The fast rates of O_2 uptake of mitochondria from *Polystictus versicolor* were maintained for several hours, whereas the O_2 uptake of mito-

TABLE 1

Inhibition of the respiration of intact mycelia of N. crassa and P. vesi-color in 19:1 (v/v) CO:O_2 mixtures in the light and in the dark.

Organism	% inhibition	
	dark	light
P. versicolor	54	0
N. crassa	60	0

chondria from *Neurospora crassa* fell rapidly. Fig. 2 shows that this decrease in rate was most marked with the enzymes requiring DPN, and although the rates of O_2 uptake were increased by adding DPN, the

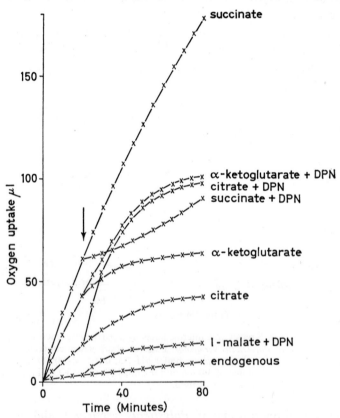

Fig. 2. The oxidation of Krebs Cycle intermediates by a particulate fraction from a 48-hr.-old culture of *Neurospora crassa*. Each Warburg vessel contained 0·02 M-substrate; 0·05 M-sucrose; 0·03 M-phosphate buffer pH 7·3; 0·001 M-MgSO$_4$; 0·001 M-ATP; 0·001 M-DPN in a total volume of 3·0 ml. and 0·2 ml. 15% (w/v) KOH in the centre well. Additional DPN was added after 20 min. DPN was omitted from the initial reaction mixture when succinate was used.

effect was short lived. The oxidation of succinate was maintained at an almost constant rate for an hour; addition of DPN inhibited the rate. Fig. 3 shows that 0·02 M-pyruvate alone was not oxidized by mitochondria from *P. versicolor*. When 0·002 M-malate or succinate were added to this concentration of pyruvate, the oxygen uptake was considerably greater than when these sparker concentrations of succinate or malate were added alone. The same type of result was obtained with *N. crassa* mitochondria (Figs. 4A and 4B).

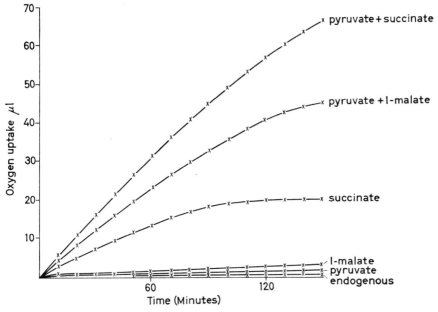

Fig. 3. The effect of 'sparker' concentrations of malate and succinate on the oxidation of pyruvate by a particulate fraction from 3-day-old culture of *Polystictus versicolor*. Each Warburg vessel contained 0·02 M-pyruvate; 0·002 M-'sparker' acid; 0·05 M-sucrose; 0·03 M-phosphate buffer pH 7·3; 0·001 M-MgSO₄; 0·001 M-ATP; 0·001 M-DPN; 0·0005 M-DPT in a total volume of 3·0 ml. and 0·2 ml. 15% (w/v) KOH in the centre well.

DISCUSSION

Mycelial felts grown on solid medium or on unshaken liquid medium are of limited value in physiological and biochemical studies, since the environmental conditions in different parts of the colony are very different, giving rise to physiologically heterogeneous material. For the work reported in this paper, it was necessary to grow the fungi in submerged cultures, which were shaken vigorously to ensure that the nutrients and metabolic products were evenly distributed throughout the medium. With the conditions of inoculation and culture described

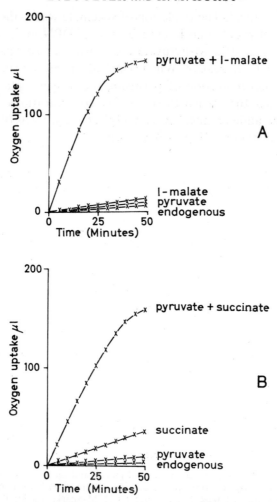

Figs. 4A and B. The effect of sparker concentrations of malate and succinate on the oxidation of pyruvate by a particulate fraction from 48-hr.-old culture of *Neurospora crassa*. Each Warburg vessel contained 0·02 M-pyruvate; 0·002 M-'sparker' acid; 0·05 M-sucrose; 0·03 M-phosphate buffer pH 7·3; 0·001 M-MgSO₄; 0·001 M-ATP; 0·001 M-DPN; 0·0005 M-DPT in a total volume of 3·0 ml. and 0·2 ml. 15 % (w/v) KOH in the centre well.

in the Methods section, *Polystictus versicolor* grew as small pellets and *Neurospora crassa* as small strands of mycelia; both pellets and strands could be pipetted to give aliquots containing the same amount of mycelium.

To obtain reproducible results, it was necessary to standardize some steps of the experimental procedure more rigorously than is usual for physiological experiments with higher plants. Thus, it was important that the previous growth history of the inoculum was kept constant, and that the liquid volume to flask volume ratio and the rate and way flasks were shaken was carefully controlled.

Washed mycelial preparations correspond to the thin tissue slices of higher plants, and are useful in feeding experiments and where selective inhibitors of steps of a metabolic process may be applied. Such tissue preparations of *Neurospora crassa* showed the presence of the Krebs Cycle enzymes in that when intermediates were added to the mycelial preparation the O_2 uptake was stimulated. The results of Table 1 show that a large part of the O_2 uptake of this organism and of *Polystictus versicolor* were mediated via a cytochrome system, since the major part of the O_2 uptake was inhibited by CO, and this inhibition was reversed by light.

Whilst these experiments with intact mycelia indicate the presence of the Krebs Cycle enzymes within the organisms, they do not show whether pyruvate can couple with oxaloacetate to initiate the Krebs Cycle. To show this it was necessary to demonstrate the catalysis of pyruvate oxidation by sparker amounts of Krebs Cycle intermediates. As these intermediates were already present in the mycelium and there was no way of reducing their concentration sufficiently, it was necessary to prepare homogenates in which the intermediates were effectively removed by dilution. As the Krebs Cycle in higher plants has been shown to be associated with particles (Hackett, 1955) particulate preparations were prepared from the homogenates. These preparations had the advantage that the enzymes were rapidly removed from contaminating cell components, some of which may have been inhibitory. They were prepared by grinding the mycelium with fine quartz sand, as it had been found that this method gave a higher cytochrome oxidase activity when used with *Gelasinospora tetrasperma* than homogenization with a glass homogenizer, the use of an Atomix Blendor or hand grinding with other abrasives (Boulter, 1957). The particles were separated by high-speed centrifugation, and probably correspond to the 'mitochondrial' fraction of higher plants. They contained enzyme systems for the oxidation of citrate, *a*-ketoglutarate, succinate, fumarate, and *l*-malate; pyruvate was not oxidized. When, however, low concentrations of succinate or malate were added to the mitochondrial preparations in the presence of pyruvate, the O_2 uptake was in excess of that due to the added sparker alone, indicating that these had supplied oxaloacetate which then condensed with the pyruvate and thus initiated the Krebs Cycle. Thus, not only were the enzymes of the Krebs Cycle present, but also the mitochondria incorporated and oxidized added pyruvate. DPN was a co-factor requirement for the oxidation of citrate, a-ketoglutarate and malate. The stimulation of citrate oxidation by DPN suggests that the oxidation of this substrate is via iso-citric acid dehydrogenase which may be DPN specific as is a similar enzyme in yeast (Kornberg & Pricer, 1951) or, alternatively, DPN may give rise to TPN as suggested by Green (1951).

Fig. 2 shows the effect of adding DPN on the oxidation of citrate, a-ketoglutarate, malate and succinate by *N. crassa* mitochondria. The stimulation due to this compound was short-lived owing to the presence of a DPN-ase enzyme in *N. crassa* (Nason, Kaplan & Colowick, 1951). Similarly in Fig. 4A and 4B the rate of pyruvate oxidation fell rapidly, and was only restored for a short period by adding DPN, due again to the activity of this enzyme. The inhibition of succinate oxidation by the addition of DPN was probably due to the production of oxalacetate formed from malate since DPN promotes the formation of oxalacetate from malate and oxalacetate is a potent inhibitor of succinic dehydrogenase (Pardee & Potter, 1948).

The possession by these fungi of the enzymes of the Krebs Cycle does not necessarily mean that the cycle is active in the intact organism. Abelson & Vogel (1955), however, in an isotopic dilution study of amino-acid biosynthesis in *Neurospora crassa*, have concluded that their results showed a Krebs Cycle operating in the intact organism. These results showed the importance of the Krebs Cycle in synthesis, but did not show whether this was a major route of oxidation.

Although there is much indirect evidence that a Krebs Cycle operates in moulds in general (Foster, 1949), the presence of the necessary enzymes has been demonstrated hitherto in only a few instances (Moses, 1957; Bonner & Machlis, 1957).

REFERENCES

ABELSON, P. H., & VOGEL, H. J. (1955). Amino acid biosynthesis in *Torulopsis utilis* and *Neurospora crassa*. *J. Biol. Chem.*, 213, 355–64.

BEADLE, G. W., & TATUM, E. L. (1941). Genetic control of biochemical reactions in *Neurospora*. *Proc. Nat. Acad. Sci.*, 27, 499–506.

BONNER, B. A., & MACHLIS, L. (1957). Respiration of the mycelia and mitochondria of the filamentous watermold *Allomyces macrogynus*. *Plant Physiol.*, 32, 291–301.

BOULTER, D. (1957). The oxidases of *Gelasinospora tetrasperma* in relation to the endonegous respiration. *J. gen. Microbiol.*, 16, 305–316.

DIXON, M. (1943). *Manometric methods*. Cambridge University Press.

FOSTER, J. W. (1949). *Chemical activities of fungi*. New York, Academic Press Inc.

GREEN, D. E. (1951). The cyclophorase complex of enzymes. *Biol. Revs. Cambridge Phil. Soc.*, 26, 410–55.

HACKETT, D. P. (1955). Recent studies on plant mitochondria. *Int. Rev. Cytology*, 4, 143–96.

KORNBERG, A., & PRICER, W. E. (1951). Di- and triphosphopyridine nucleotide isocitric dehydrogenase in yeast. *J. Biol. Chem.*, **189**, 123–36.

MOSES, V. (1957). The metabolic significance of the citric acid in the growth of the fungus *Zygorrhynchus moelleri*. *J. gen. Microbiol.*, **16**, 534–49.

NASON, A., KAPLAN, N. O., & COLOWICK, S. P. (1951). Changes in enzymatic constitution in zinc-deficient *Neurospora*. *J. Biol. Chem.*, **188**, 397–406.

PARDEE, A. B., & POTTER, V. R. (1948). Inhibition of succinic dehydrogenase by oxaloacetate. *J. Biol. Chem.*, **176**, 1085–94.

STUDIES ON THE PHYSIOLOGY OF
LIGNIN DECOMPOSITION BY SOIL FUNGI

MOIRA E. K. HENDERSON

Microbiology Section, The Macaulay Institute for Soil Research,
Aberdeen

ONE of the most important problems in the decomposition of organic matter under natural conditions is the question of the breakdown of lignin. However, investigations concerning lignin are beset with difficulties, the principal one being that we do not know, from the chemical point of view, exactly what lignin is. Brauns, in his excellent book (1952) remarks, 'we do not even know the exact structure of the building stones (of lignin), which was known for cellulose 100 years before its structure was finally established'.

Chemistry of lignin and its occurrence in plant materials and in soils

Present-day indications are that lignin is a complex polymer built up from certain basic units. Also it is recognized that different kinds of lignin vary in their basic units. Lignin is known to contain carbon, hydrogen, and oxygen (Brauns, 1954). It is also known to contain methoxyl and hydroxyl groups, to have an aromatic structure, and probably a propyl side chain on at least some of the aromatic rings. Several theories for lignin structure are based on a phenyl-propane building unit with methoxyl and hydroxyl groups attached to it, e.g. the guaiacyl-propane unit (Fig. 1), but it is not yet certain how the units are

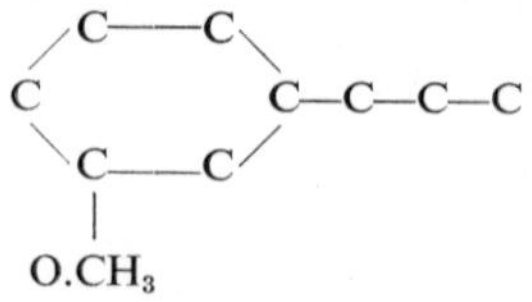

Fig. 1. Guaiacyl-propane unit.

attached to one another. According to Freudenberg (Brauns, 1954), the units condense with the formation of benzofuran and benzopyran rings which are linked in chains, while Erdtman (1949) states that the units are linked in chains with carbon-carbon and carbon-oxygen-carbon linkages. Certain units can be released on alkaline nitrobenzene oxidation of lignin—thus vanillin is derived from softwood lignins, syringaldehyde and vanillin from hardwood lignins, and *p*-hydroxybenzal-dehyde from monocotyledon lignins (Creighton *et al.*, 1944). More recently, Leopold (1952) has shown that coniferous lignins may, in fact, also yield *p*-hydroxybenzaldehyde and syringaldehyde, in addition to vanillin which is the principal product.

Nor is it known how lignin occurs in plants, whether it is present in a mixture with the other constitutents or whether it is chemically combined with them. Lignin cannot be isolated from plant material in any great quantity. The only method by which unaltered lignin may be extracted is that of Brauns (1939) using alcohol. However, since this method yields only 8–10% of the total lignin content of wood, it would seem that the product is not representative of the lignin content of the plant as a whole. Other methods of extraction using acid and alkali give higher yields but are rather drastic, and the lignin is considerably altered during the extraction process.

Furthermore, it is not known in what form lignin occurs in the soil. Since it is one of the principal plant constituents, it is obvious that large amounts of it must be added to soil on the decay of plant material and, since it is much more resistant to biological decomposition than are the other plant constituents, it must accumulate in quantity and become a major component of soil organic matter. Evidence that lignin-like material does accumulate has been obtained by using the methoxy content of soil and its solubility in 72% (v/v) H_2SO_4 as a measurement. The presence of typical lignin constituents in humic acid has been demonstrated, but according to Gottlieb & Hendricks (1945), it would seem that considerable alteration in the ratio of the different groups and their arrangement occurs. Waksman & Iyer (1932) believe that in soil lignin forms a complex with protein, and Hobson & Page (1932) claim that the nitrogen of artificial ligno-protein complexes acted similarly to humus nitrogen, while others refute this idea. However, work recently carried out by Dr. R. I. Morrison (1958) in the Biochemistry Dept. at the Macaulay Institute provides strong evidence for the occurrence in humus of a fraction derived directly from plant residues. On the alkaline nitrobenzene oxidation of soils and peats, the presence of syringyl, guaiacyl, and *p*-hydroxyphenyl residues was demonstrated, and the relative proportions of these groups were similar to those in the parent plant material, where this was known.

Microbiological decomposition of lignin

Attempts to study lignin decomposition by micro-organisms have been made using plant materials and preparations isolated by various methods. However, little or no conclusive evidence has been obtained, partly due to the fact that pure, unaltered lignin cannot be isolated and partly to the absence of a reliable method for lignin estimation. Using plant materials, the indication from proximate methods of analysis, e.g. Waksman's (1926), is that lignin is decomposed by some fungi and bacteria, generally more slowly than are other plant constituents. Wood-rotting fungi have been divided into white-rots and brown-rots— the former attack lignin, but will also decompose cellulose; while the latter attack cellulose exclusively. Various isolated lignins have also been used, such as alkali, sulphuric acid, and phenol lignins; but results obtained with them are inconclusive—partly on account of their altered structure and partly on the presence as impurities of substances which can be utilized for growth by bacteria and fungi. In a few instances compounds related to lignin have been used. Konetzka et al. (1952) showed that a-conidendrin, which is structurally related to lignin, being composed of two guaiacyl-propane units, was attacked by *Flavobacterium* sp. Extracellular enzymes from *Polystictus versicolor* formed coloured products from conidendrin, syringaldehyde, vanillin, and ferulic acid. Dion (1952) attributed this to quinone formation by phenoloxidase activity which did not involve decomposition of the molecules.

The investigations of the author on lignin decomposition have been based on studies of the metabolism by fungi of some of the lignin-related molecules which are known to be released chemically from lignin and which are obtainable in pure form, e.g. vanillin, syringaldehyde, and p-hydroxybenzaldehyde. They were supplemented by the study of the release of such units by fungi from untreated, naturally occurring material in the form of wood saw-dusts.

Isolation of possible lignin-decomposing fungi from soils

The fungi employed were isolated by Waksman's (1916) dilution-plate technique. The different areas selected for collection of soil samples were chosen on account of the plant community they supported, and isolates were obtained from broad-leaved and coniferous forests, a pasture, garden, heath, moor, peat moss, and sand dunes. Since the primary aim of the work was the collection of fungi concerned in the decomposition of lignin, a method selective for the isolation of such fungi was sought. Bavendamm (1928) and Davidson, Campbell & Blaisdell (1938) showed that wood-rotting fungi could be differentiated by their reaction with tannic acid. They found that white-rots, which are most active in decreasing the lignin content of wood, could oxidize tannic acid to a brown product, and when the acid was incorporated in the medium the oxidation product was visible as a halo surrounding the fungal colony. It was hoped that lignin decomposers in soil might be selected in a similar manner, and 0·1% (w/v) tannic acid was always added to the modified form of Waksman's medium used for the dilutions. The medium was modified by the replacement of peptone by $(NH_4)_2SO_4$ to reduce the rate of growth of rapidly spreading fungi. Representative isolates from colonies not producing a brown halo as well as from those which did were cultured. A large number of species was obtained, but those which were identified all belonged to the Fungi Imperfecti.

Growth of soil micro-fungi on lignin-related molecules

The lignin-related compounds used in the initial stages of the work (Henderson & Farmer, 1955) were vanillin, syringaldehyde, *p*-hydroxybenzaldehyde and ferulic acid (Fig. 2). The three former were selected since they are obtained on

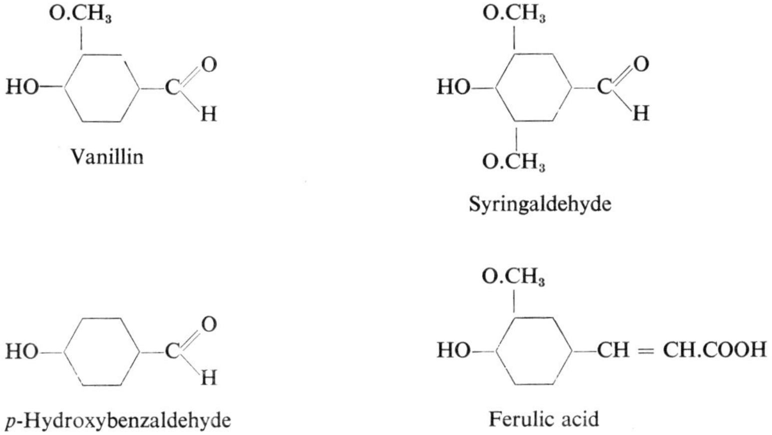

Fig. 2.

alkaline nitrobenzene oxidation of various lignins, the latter as it contains the phenyl-propane unit regarded as being the basal unit of the lignin molecule. It has also been isolated from lignin (Smith, 1955). These compounds were added to 10 ml. of a mineral salts medium in a petri dish as sole source of carbon. The medium was Czapek's with sucrose omitted and since $FeSO_4$ reacts with phenols to form coloured compounds it was also omitted. The phenolic compounds are toxic to the fungi at about 0·04% (w/v), and to keep below this level the three aldehydes were present in a final concentration of 0·01% (w/v) and

S.E.S.F.—19

ferulic acid at 0·006% (w/v). In this preliminary work about 60 different fungi were used. After 24 days incubation, the amounts of growth were noted, and although these were small there was definitely an indication that the phenols were supporting growth. The culture solutions were analysed by U.V. spectrometry, and the disappearance of the original phenols was estimated and in some cases intermediate metabolic products were identified. A close correlation was found to exist between the increased growth supported by the phenols and their disappearance as revealed by the spectrochemical analyses of the culture media at the end of the growth period. Certain fungi, e.g. *Alternaria* sp., *Hormodendrum* spp., *Penicillium* sp., and *Torula* spp. were more active than the others and caused complete disappearance of the ring structure of all four compounds, while other fungi attacked different compounds to different extents. As might be expected, the simplest substance, *p*-hydroxybenzaldehyde, was most readily decomposed. Vanillin was more quickly broken down than syringaldehyde. Generally decomposition of ferulic acid was similar to that of vanillin.

Intermediates identified in the decomposition of the phenols were vanillic acid, formed from vanillin and ferulic acid, and syringic acid, formed from syringaldehyde (Fig. 3). Some fungi seemed to be unable to metabolize the acids further and they accumulated in the media, but in many cultures no acid could be identified at all, indicating that it had been metabolized, while in others only small amounts or traces of acid were present. No further phenolic intermediates could be identified, from which it was concluded that if they were formed they were metabolized very rapidly, or that the ring was being ruptured at this stage. The spectrochemical method of analysis gave no information about products formed after breaking of the ring. Two fungi (*H. cladosporioides* and *Penicillium* sp.) grew on α-conidendrin and decomposed it, but it was not possible to identify any intermediates or end-products.

The results obtained by the spectrochemical analyses were augmented by others from paper chromatography. For this 100-ml. lots of medium were used and extracted with ether, the extractions being made after periods of a few days. In this way it was possible to confirm the formation of acid intermediates by those fungi which removed all traces of phenolic compounds during the 24-day incubation period.

Metabolism of lignin-related molecules by soil fungi

Warburg technique using spore suspensions. To support the results obtained from the growth experiments, respiration experiments were carried out in the Warburg apparatus. In an attempt to surmount the well-known difficulties encountered when carrying out respiration experiments with fungi (the high endogenous respiration and the preparation of uniform suspensions), spore suspensions were used (Henderson, 1956). These were prepared by placing strips of cellophane bearing sporing growths of fungi in a solution of 0·1% (v/v) 'Tween 80' in a boiling tube. The spores were readily obtained in suspension by shak-

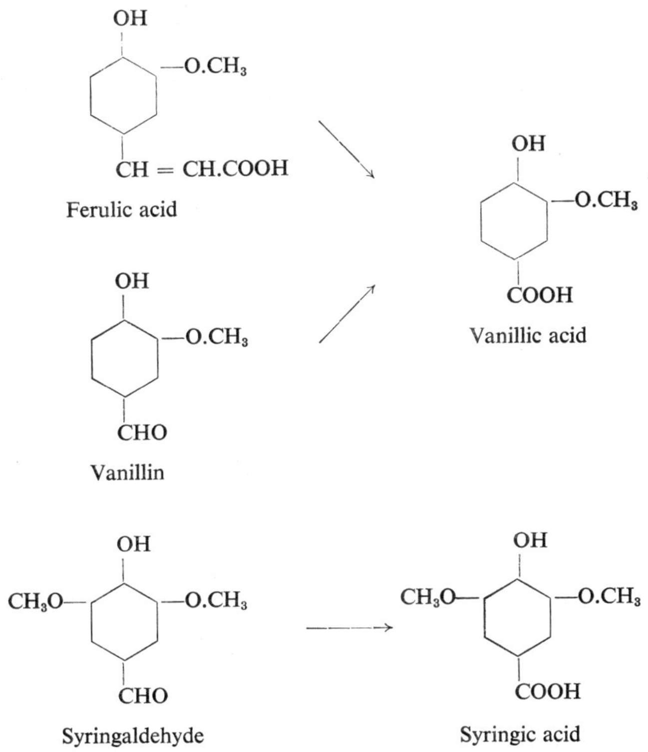

OH

—O.CH₃

CH = CH.COOH

Ferulic acid

OH

—O.CH₃

COOH

Vanillic acid

OH

—O.CH₃

CHO

Vanillin

CH₃O—

OH

—O.CH₃

CHO

Syringaldehyde

CH₃O—

OH

—O.CH₃

COOH

Syringic acid

Fig. 3.

ing, and could be poured off, leaving the mycelium adhering to the cellophane. The spores were centrifuged down, washed twice with distilled water, and finally suspended in distilled water, a very uniform suspension being obtained, which could readily be pipetted into the Warburg flasks. In order to obtain sufficient activity, the suspension was incubated overnight in a mineral salts solution containing yeast extract. By morning germination had occurred and the added substrates had been utilized, so that the basal respiration rate was very low and marked increases in oxygen consumption were obtained on the addition of substrates. This method is necessarily restricted to fungi producing abundant spores, but it was successfully used with species of *Hormodendrum*, *Haplographium*, *Penicillium*, and *Spicaria*. Since each experiment was continued over a period of about 24 hrs. altogether, it was essential to carry out all steps under aseptic conditions.

The oxygen uptakes obtained when the substrates were *p*-hydroxybenzaldehyde, ferulic acid, syringaldehyde, and vanillin could be correlated with the results obtained from the spectrochemical analyses of the culture solutions. *p*-hydroxybenzaldehyde, which was most readily utilized in the growth experiments, gave the most rapid oxygen uptakes. Syringaldehyde which was most slowly utilized gave the lowest oxygen uptakes, while ferulic acid and vanillin gave uptakes intermediate between the other two. The oxygen uptakes with the corresponding acids were also studied. In general, they were more slowly oxidized than were the aldehydes, which probably explains the tendency for them to accumulate in culture solutions. It was interesting to note that *p*-hydroxybenzoic acid was usually more rapidly oxidized than were the other two acids. It is the expected product from *p*-hydroxybenzaldehyde, but it was never traced in culture solutions, the indication being that it was further metabolized too rapidly for it to accumulate.

Kluyver experiments using preformed mats. Another technique was sought whereby conditions might be developed under which intermediates would accumulate in quantities sufficient for identification. For this purpose a modification of Kluyver & van Zijp's (1951) technique was used in which solutions of the experimental substances were poured under pre-grown fungal mats and incubated for various lengths of time. In this way it was possible to work with more concentrated solutions than could be used in the growth experiments. The culture solutions were extracted with ether as before, and the extracts were run on paper chromatograms. By this method *p*-hydroxybenzoic acid was readily obtained from *p*-hydroxybenzaldehyde, and protocatechuic acid was also identified. This indicated that the pathway of metabolism of *p*-hydroxybenzaldehyde was similar to that occurring in bacteria, according to which one would expect that breaking of the ring would take place after the formation of protocatechuic acid, with the subsequent formation of β-ketoadipic acid (Evans, 1947; Evans, Parr & Evans, 1949).

Recently (Henderson, unpublished), using trace element-deficient cultures of *Aspergillus niger*, it has been found that iron plays an important part at this stage. Dagley & Patel (1957) have already shown that protocatechuic acid oxidase in *Pseudomonas* sp. is dependent on ferrous ions, and we obtained confirmation of this when we found that there was a definite accumulation of protocatechuic acid when iron-deficient cultures of *A. niger* were incubated over a solution of *p*-hydroxybenzoic acid. Also, with *o*-hydroxybenzoic acid and iron-deficient mycelium, an accumulation of catechol was obtained. Walker & Evans (1952) found that catechol is an intermediate in the breakdown of *o*-hydroxybenzoic acid by *Ps. fluorescens*, and, like protocatechuic acid, catechol is the product which immediately precedes rupture of the aromatic ring.

Since this technique was proving successful, it was also utilized in a study of demethoxylation (Henderson, 1957). It is a well-known fact that in soil a significant feature associated with the decomposition of lignin is the reduction in methoxyl content (Sowden & Atkinson, 1949).

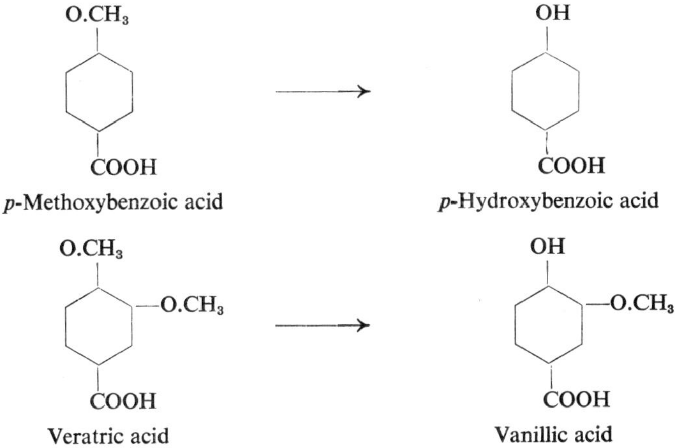

O.CH₃   OH

——→

COOH   COOH
p-Methoxybenzoic acid   *p*-Hydroxybenzoic acid

O.CH₃   OH
        —O.CH₃   —O.CH₃
——→

COOH   COOH
Veratric acid   Vanillic acid

Fig. 4.

Mono- and di-methoxybenzoic acids were used for this work, and the decomposition of the acids was followed by taking samples from the flasks at intervals of a few days and analysing the samples by U.V. spectrometry. The formation of intermediates was studied by paper chromatography of ether extracts of culture solutions. The three mono-methoxybenzoic acids were all attacked by *Hormodendrum* sp., the para form disappearing most quickly, while the ortho form was attacked very slowly. Three fungi, *Haplographium* sp., *Hormodendrum* sp., and *Penicillium* sp., were used for the chromatographical analyses, and in each case they produced the corresponding mono-hydroxybenzoic acid from the mono-methoxybenzoic acids (Fig. 4). Demothoxylation was also demonstrated in veratric acid (3:4-dimethoxybenzoic acid). From it vanillic acid was produced, i.e. the methoxyl group in the para position had been converted to a hydroxyl group.

Thus, it has been shown that soil micro-fungi are capable of deme-thoxylating and breaking down constituent units of lignin. However, this property could be of importance in the decomposition of lignin in soil only if these units can exist there in the free state.

Release of lignin-related molecules from wood sawdusts by fungi

Evidence that other fungi may release such acids was obtained by using *Polystictus versicolor*, a white rot (Henderson, 1955). When grown on a rich medium in the presence of spruce sawdust over a period of 6 months it released vanillic acid, which could be isolated on extraction of the sawdust with alkali. Similarly, on birch sawdust this fungus released vanillic and syringic acids. Soil micro-fungi were inactive in this respect. It is worth noting that the macro-fungus released from the soft-wood (spruce) and the hardwood (birch), the same units as are obtained on nitrobenzene oxidation of the lignins obtained from these woods. Since similar treatment of soils and peats has also been shown to release these units, it seems possible that, if there exist in soil basidiomycetes possessing enzyme systems similar to that present in the wood-rotting basidiomycete, lignin in the soil could similarly be broken down and its constituent units released.

Remarks on the tannic acid method as a means of detecting soil-fungi decomposing lignin

It was mentioned that the ability to colour tannic acid was used as a criterion in the isolation of fungi from soil samples. In the course of the experimental work, no evidence was obtained which indicated any correlation between the possession of enzymes which oxidize tannic acid and the ability to attack lignin-related compounds. This is not altogether surprising since the oxidation of phenolic compounds in-volves quinone formation and polymerization, while the attack on the phenolic compounds studied involved breaking of the ring, two entirely different processes. It, therefore, appears that the use of the tannic-acid method for isolating lignin-decomposing fungi has little foundation in the light of these results. After all, when lignin is removed by white rots from wood, the remaining product is lighter in colour than the original!

Conclusions

A surprising feature arising from the work is the widespread ability of soil micro-fungi to decompose aromatic compounds. The sixty fungi used in the preliminary survey with *p*-hydroxybenzaldehyde, ferulic acid, syringaldehyde, and vanillin belonged to some 30 different genera, all of which exhibited some ability to decompose the compounds. Certain genera were more active than others and removed all traces of the four compounds from the media, while others could decompose completely only some of the compounds.

The approach to the problem of lignin decomposition which we are using at the Macaulay Institute gives, it is believed, for the first time one way in which lignin can be broken down under natural conditions by fungi. It is thought that it takes place by a primary release of the aromatic units of lignin, e.g. vanillin, etc., by macro-fungi followed by further breakdown of these compounds by soil micro-fungi. It is still not known how the basic units are released, but their further breakdown involves demethoxylation and hydroxylation followed by ring rupture, along paths probably leading into one of the common metabolic systems; for example, the Krebs Cycle.

REFERENCES

BAVENDAMM, W. (1928). Über das Vorkommen und den Nachweis von Oxydasen bei holzzerstörenden Pilzen. *Z. PflKrankh.*, **38**, 257–76.

BRAUNS, F. E. (1939). Native lignin. I. Its isolation and methylation. *J. Amer. chem. Soc.*, **61**, 2120–7.

BRAUNS, F. E. (1952). *The chemistry of lignin.* New York: Academic Press Inc.

CREIGHTON, R. H. J., GIBBS, R. D., & HIBBERT, H. (1944). Lignin and related compounds. LXXVI. Alkaline nitrobenzene oxidation of maize stalks. Isolation of *p*-hydroxybenzaldehyde. *J. Amer. chem. Soc.*, **66**, 37–8.

DAGLEY, S., & PATEL, M. D. (1957). Oxidation of *p*-cresol and related compounds by a Pseudomonas. *Biochem. J.*, **66**, 227–33.

DAVIDSON, R. W., CAMPBELL, W. A., & BLAISDELL, D. J. (1938). Differentiation of wood-decaying fungi by their reactions on gallic- or tannic-acid medium. *J. agric. Res.*, **57**, 683–95.

DION, W. M. (1952). Production and properties of a polyphenol oxidase from the fungus *Polyporus versicolor. Canad. J. Bot.*, **30**, 9–21.

ERDTMAN, H. (1949). The chemical nature of lignin. *Tappi.*, **32**, 71–4.

EVANS, W. C. (1947). Oxidation of phenol and benzoic acid by some soil bacteria. *Biochem. J.*, **41**, 373–82.

EVANS, R. A., PARR, W. H., & EVANS, W. C. (1949). The bacterial oxidation of aromatic compounds. *Biochem. J.*, **44**, VIII.

GOTTLIEB, S., & HENDRICKS, S. B. (1945). Soil organic matter as related to newer concepts of lignin chemistry. *Proc. Soil Sci. Soc. Amer.*, **10**, 117–25.

HENDERSON, M. E. K., & FARMER, V. C. (1955). Utilization by soil fungi of *p*-hydroxybenzaldehyde, ferulic acid, syringaldehyde, and vanillin. *J. gen. Microbiol.*, **12**, 37–46.

HENDERSON, M. E. K. (1955). Release of aromatic compounds from birch and spruce sawdusts during decomposition by white-rot fungi. *Nature Lond.*, **175**, 634.

HENDERSON, M. E. K. (1956). A study of the metabolism of phenolic compounds by soil fungi using spore suspensions. *J. gen. Microbiol.*, **14**, 684–91 .

HENDERSON, M. E. K. (1957). Metabolism of methoxylated aromatic compounds by soil fungi. *J. gen. Microbiol.*, **16**, 686–95.

HOBSON, R. P., & PAGE, H. J. (1932). Studies on the carbon and nitrogen cycles in the soil. VII. The nature of the organic nitrogen compounds of the soil: 'non-humic' nitrogen. *J. agric. Sci.*, **22**, 516–26.

KLUYVER, A. J., & VAN ZIJP, J. C. M. (1951). The production of homogentisic acid out of phenylacetic acid by *Aspergillus niger*. *Leewenhoek ned. Tijdschr.*, **17**, 47–56.

KONETZKA, W. A., PELCZAR, M. J., & GOTTLIEB, S. (1952). The biological degradation of lignin. III. Bacterial degradation of α-conidendrin. *J. Bact.*, **63**, 771–8.

LEOPOLD, B. (1952). Studies on lignin. III. Oxidation of wood from *Picea abies* with nitrobenzene and alkali. *Acta Chem. Scand.*, **6**, 38–48.

MORRISON, R. I. (1958). The alkaline nitrobenzene oxidation of soil organic matter. *J. Soil Sci.*, **9**, 130–40.

SMITH, D. C. C. (1955). *p*-Hydroxybenzoate groups in the lignin of Aspen (*Populus tremula*). *J. chem. Soc.*, 2347–51.

SOWDEN, F. J., & ATKINSON, H. J. (1949). Composition of certain soil organic matter fractions. *Soil Sci.*, **68**, 433–40.

WAKSMAN, S. A. (1916). Soil fungi and their activities. *Soil Sci.*, **2**, 103–55.

WAKSMAN, S. A. (1926). The origin and nature of the soil organic matter or soil 'humus'. III. The nature of the substances contributing to the formation of humus. *Soil Sci.*, **22**, 323–33.

WAKSMAN, S. A., & IYER, K. R. N. (1932). Contribution to our knowledge of the chemical nature and origin of humus: I. On the synthesis of the 'humus nucleus'. *Soil Sci.*, **34**, 43–69.

WALKER, N., & EVANS, W. C. (1952). Pathways in metabolism of mono-hydroxy-benzoic acids by soil bacteria. *Biochem. J.*, **52**, XXIII–XXIV.

OBSERVATIONS ON *STREPTOMYCES SCABIES* (THAXT.) WAKSMAN & HENRICI OF SIGNIFICANCE IN THE STUDY OF ACTINOMYCETE ECOLOGY

E. H. GARRARD

Department of Bacteriology, Ontario Agricultural College, Guelph, Canada

INTRODUCTION

IN 1948 a committee was appointed by the Ontario Department of Agriculture to conduct research on potato scab caused by *Streptomyces scabies*. This committee consisted of personnel from various departments at the Ontario Agricultural College, the Botany Department, University of Western Ontario, and the Division of Plant Pathology and Bacteriology, Science Service Laboratories at St. Catharines, Ontario, and was under the chairmanship of Dr. G. H. Berkeley of the St. Catharines laboratories. Since that time a great deal of worth-while information relating to potato-scab infection has been obtained, much of which was unknown before.

The main task of our department was to conduct fundamental studies on the causal organism. These included biochemical reactions, influence of soil microflora on *S. scabies*, serological studies, actinophages, effects of dithiocarbamates on *S. scabies*, and cytological and genetic studies. This report deals briefly with certain aspects of this work, the results of which have not only been of assistance in better understanding *S. scabies*, but are thought to be of significance in the study of actinomycete ecology in general.

BIOCHEMICAL STUDIES

There are many problems involved in attempting to classify the actinomycetes; one of these is their extreme variability, particularly noticeable in the genus *Streptomyces*. For instance, nine distinct types of variability for *S. griseus* have been described, many of them considerably affected by environmental conditions (Waksman, 1957). In other studies

(Douglas & Garrard, 1954) variations in *S. scabies* have made it extremely difficult to differentiate between scab-producing and non-scab-producing strains from tuber lesions and soil. The ability to cause scab on tubers generally has been used as a characteristic of the species; this is not only time consuming but use of this property as a species determining criterion has been questioned (Waksman, 1950).

Brown-ring test

Many biochemical tests have been suggested to distinguish between actinomycetes from tubers and soil, but most have proved unreliable. The most promising of these is the brown-ring test described by various workers (Lutman & Cunningham, 1914; Taylor & Decker, 1947; Vaisey *et al.*, 1955). This test is supposed to separate non-scab producing from scab-producing strains of streptomycetes on the premise that the latter are capable of forming a brown pigment on protein medium in the presence of air. This brown colour formation is considered to be owing to the action of tyrosinase on tyrosine, or tyrosine-containing compounds with the formation of melanin pigment (Skinner, 1938). Further work with mutational techniques (Gregory & Vaisey, 1956) proved fairly conclusively that the enzyme tyrosinase is not associated with the virulence of *S. scabies*, as highly stable virulent mutants incapable of producing tyrosinase were isolated from tyrosinase positive parents; while on the other hand certain avirulent forms produced tyrosinase. As with other microbial groups, the lack of differential physiological characteristics has led to the use of serological methods to detect subtle differences between closely related forms. The serological studies herewith reported have been under the direction of Dr. R. J. Douglas of our laboratory.

SEROLOGICAL

Serological methods have been used in attempts to characterize actinomycetes, and modifications of conventional serological procedures have been devised to overcome the difficulties imposed by the filamentous nature of the organisms. These have included the testing of actinomycetes from various sources by the agglutination method (Ludwig & Hutchinson, 1949; Slack *et al.*, 1951) and numerous strains of *S. scabies* from soil and tubers by the precipitin and a newly devised flocculation test (Douglas & Garrard, 1954). While results of the latter test indicated a striking similarity between scab-producing strains, which similarity was not evident in the non-scab-producing forms, there were certain cross reactions, and a few isolates in each group did not follow the serological pattern of the majority, thus making it impossible to separate the two groups by this method.

Hemagglutination tests

In recent years the technique of passive hemagglutination has been a widely used procedure (Neter, 1956). Basically, the method involves the adsorption of soluble antigens on to red washed blood cells, a process which modifies the cells in such a way that they become agglutinable by antisera to the adsorbed antigen. With these modified red blood cells antisera may be titrated in a reaction comparable to, but more sensitive than, the agglutination test. The technical simplicity of this procedure prompted its application to strains of *S. scabies*, at which time attempts also were made to assess the occurrence of cross reactivity among a number of *Streptomyces* cultures.

The cultures of *S. scabies* were obtained from tuber lesions and soil, and were subjected to pathogenicity and biochemical tests described elsewhere (Douglas & Garrard, 1954). The named cultures included *S. griseus*, *S. albus*, *S. fradiae*, *S. olivaceous*, and *S. ipomoeae*. Preparations for the test consisted of immunizing mature rabbits with mycelial suspensions disrupted in a Raytheon sonic oscillator, the purification of crude sonic extracts by phenol extraction, and sensitizing prepared rabbit red blood cells with sonic extracts. Attempts were made to isolate the red blood cell sensitizing antigen. Using the lysozyme technique of other workers (Romano & Nickerson, 1956; Romano & Sohler, 1956), it was found possible to remove the cell walls of young mycelium of *S. scabies* and *S. fradiae* and separate the protoplasts. Subsequent phenol extractions showed that the red blood sensitizing substance was absent from the protoplast extract, but could be obtained from the extra-protoplastic supernatant. This was strong evidence that the red blood cell sensitizing agent was a cell wall constituent, and probably polysaccharide in nature (Romano & Nickerson, 1956; Romano & Sohler, 1956).

Results

In previous work (Douglas & Garrard, 1954) with precipitin and agglutination tests, serological cross reactions were frequently encountered. Attempts to exclude such reactions are generally based on serum absorption procedures. In these studies absorptions were carried out using red blood cells modified with acetone dried powders as the absorbing agent.

Although the numbers of cultures tested to date have been limited-
the results have been encouraging. They support the suggestion of anti,
gens of different specificities, and that the crossing antigen(s) may be of
quite widespread distribution. The test is simple, requiring spot-plate
reactions instead of tube titrations, and requiring only prepared
antisera, carrier red blood cells, and antigen extracts of the organisms.
It has been possible to remove certain antibodies and to retain those of
more restricted activity. Strong cross reactions were noted between
certain species, e.g. *S. fradiae* and *S. scabies*, and between *S. albus* and
S. scabies, and yet it was found possible to absorb the sera so that
heterologous reactions are removed but homologous reactions still are
in evidence. These reactions are shown in the following table:

TABLE 1

*Slide agglutination tests with sensitized red blood cells before and after
serum absorption*

Serum	Red blood cells modified with antigens derived from:					
	S. ipomoeae	*S. fradiae*	*S. albus*	*S. scabies*	*S. griseus*	*S. olivaceous*
Anti-ipomoeae	+	+	−	+	−	−
Absorbed with *S. scabies*	+	−	−	−	−	−
Anti-fradiae	−	+ +	+	+	?	+
Absorbed with *S. scabies*	−	+ +	−	−	−	−

To assess more accurately the validity of the absorption procedure,
it will be necessary to investigate a larger group of organisms in order
to obtain more complete information on the extent to which common
antigens may be distributed, and also to investigate further the nature
of the red blood cell modifying material. However, this has been the
most promising of the serological methods attempted to distinguish
between various strain of streptomycetes.

ACTINOPHAGES

In studying the function of soil streptomycetes, especially *Streptomyces
scabies*, and ecological factors influencing this population, of particular

interest has been the isolation of actinophages and their possible use to separate various species of *Streptomyces*. Such an actinophage has been reported as possessing some value as a typing method for streptomycin-producing strains of *S. griseus* (Reilly *et al.*, 1947), and more recent studies (Newbould & Garrard, 1954) have demonstrated that while an actinophage for *S. scabies* would lyse scab-producing strains, several non-scab-producing strains of streptomycetes were similarly lysed. Lack of specificity of the actinophage was attributed to the variability of the *Streptomyces*.

While soil is acknowledged to be the source of bacteriophages and actinophages, there has been relatively little work on the distribution, frequency, and ecological importance of these forms. Studies have been conducted on bacteriophages associated with the root nodule bacteria (Kleczkowska, 1950; Vandecaveye *et al.*, 1940), and data on the distribution of actinophages in soil and manure have been accumulated (Gilmour & Buthala, 1950; Welsch *et al.*, 1955; Welsch, 1956). Preliminary work by Professor J. B. Robinson and Dr. C. T. Corke of our department suggested that further studies of the actinophage populations of soil and their significance might be of interest, and also might lead to the isolation of an actinophage suitable for typing purposes.

Methods

The perfusion apparatus formerly used by Chase (1948) was employed to demonstrate the presence of both bacteriophages and actinophages in soil. Soil was perfused in these units with distilled water, and the perfusates, after filtration through a membrane filter, were plated on a solid medium with spore suspensions of a number of streptomycete isolates. In this way an estimate of the number of actinophage particles active against specific strains was obtained. Any increase of actinophage titre in the perfusate was presumed to be due to the presence in the soil of host cells in the right physiological state to allow actinophage proliferation.

Earlier experiments had shown that soil perfusates differed markedly in their actinophage content against *S. scabies*, which may have been owing to increased adsorption of the actinophage where the perfusate had a low titre, or it might reflect a difference in the number of host cells in the soil. To test this latter hypothesis an experiment was designed in which 12 streptomycete cultures were isolated at random from each of 3 different soils. Perfusates of these soils were then plated against the 36 streptomycetes and 8 named species, including *S. lavendulae*, *S. violaceus*, and the 6 species used in former serological tests.

Results

The results are shown in Table 2. It was apparent that two of the soils contained more actinophages for the homologous isolates, i.e. there was a greater number of cultures affected and a high apparent titre for strains isolated from that particular soil than for cultures isolated from the other soils. It also was apparent that the heavier clay loam contained more actinophages active against named and unnamed strains than the other soils. With a few exceptions, the greatest concentration of actino-phage particles active against the majority of cultures occurred at 48 hr. A marked difference in the numbers of actinophages for each isolate was noted, and the daily fluctuations in actinophage titre were not the same for each isolate, suggesting that the perfusates contained many actinophages.

TABLE 2

Average number of plaques and percentage of isolates affected by actinophages

Perfusate from soil	G.P.S. isolates		L.S.L. isolates		C.L. isolates		Named species	
	Av. No. plaques	% affected	Av. No. plaques	% affected	Av. No. plaques	% affected	Av. No. plaques	% affected
G.P.S.*	11	75	3	56	8	56	5·5	50
L.S.L.	10	50	60	80	8·5	66	26	62
C.L.	14·5	91	20	60	179	91	47·5	75

* G.P.S.—High organic greenhouse potting soil.
  L.S.L.—Light sandy loam.
  C.L.—Heavier clay loam.

While the indirect evidence suggests the presence of many actino-phages, experiments to demonstrate the multiplicity of actinophages have only recently been undertaken. A preliminary experiment in which newly isolated actinophages were tested against certain *Streptomyces* species indicated that at least two different groups of actinophages were present. This confirms former studies (Welsch *et al.*, 1955; Welsch, 1956) where different actinophages isolated from manure were found to be active against specific strains of *Streptomyces*, suggesting a fairly large population of actinophages in their natural environment.

In another series of experiments, selected strains of soil bacteria were used to determine the bacteriophage present in soil perfusates. To date surprisingly few bacterial cultures have been found to be affected by bacteriophages. In one experiment where 9 named species and 8 unidentified species of soil bacteria were tested, only two named species of *Arthrobacter* and one unidentified soil isolate were found to be sensitive to bacteriophages from the same soil. On the other hand, in all experiments at this laboratory, actinophages have been obtained for a high percentage of named and unnamed strains of *Streptomyces* tested. In one experiment, 29 of 33 strains of streptomycetes were found to be susceptible to actinophages. It is difficult to explain the apparent difference in numbers of actinophages and bacteriophages isolated from soil in these experiments, unless in freshly moistened soil, the actinomycetes reach a state of active growth more readily than do the bacteria. Also it is possible that bacteriophages are more readily adsorbed on the soil colloids than are actinophages, and do not appear in the perfusates. More evidence will be necessary before such suggestions can be validated.

While no single actinophage has yet been isolated which was specific enough to be used for typing purposes, it has been demonstrated that actinophages are extremely plentiful in soils, and more so in some soils than others, and that they may be separated into various groups according to host specificity. How much the presence of these actinophages affect actinomycete populations is yet to be determined, but the isolation of large numbers of actinophages active against the majority of named and unnamed cultures indicate the highly active state of actinomycetes in the soil.

GENETIC STUDIES

Former studies have shown that *S. scabies*, in common with other *Streptomyces* species, shows a great variation in the characteristics of strains isolated from nature and strains continually sub-cultured in the laboratory. While environmental conditions may affect such variation, it has been suggested that the streptomycetes may alternate between haploid and diploid phases (Klieneberger-Nobel, 1947); if such should prove to be the case it would represent a mechanism for the combination and segregation of characteristics. Recent studies have shown that while variations may be due in part to mutation, nuclear reactions may occur between strains of *Streptomyces*, and heterokaryosis has been reported in several species (Alikhanian & Mindlin, 1957; Bradley, 1957; Bradley & Lederberg, 1956; Braendle & Szybalski, 1957; Sermonti & Spada-Sermonti, 1956).

Studies with *S. scabies*, under the direction of Dr. K. F. Gregory, have shown this species to possess the features necessary for the establishment of heterokaryosis; namely, an ability to undergo hyphal anastomosis and a mycelium composed of multinucleate cells. Anastomosis was frequently observed as the joining of two hyphae by multiple hyphal bridges. A membrane stain (tannic acid followed by dilute crystal violet) confirmed that anastomosis had occurred, since hyphae touching each other without fusing showed a darkly stained interface between them.

While it has been claimed that in general the mycelium of *Streptomyces* appears to be coenocytic (Erikson, 1949) in both young and old hyphae, there also has been revealed the presence of regularly spaced discoid structures interpreted as septa. Recent confirmation that at least some of the mycelia of *S. scabies* appear to be partitioned by septa has been provided by the demonstration by Douglas that lysozyme acting upon *S. scabies* mycelia in the presence of sucrose results in the formation of many stable protoplasts. It is difficult to conceive of protoplast formation in the absence of septate mycelium. The range in size of protoplasts would suggest that this septation could occur at somewhat irregular intervals in the filaments, although a great number of the protoplasts appeared to be of similar size. As each of these cells confined by observed septa contain several bodies which stain with the acid Giemsa stain technique, the cells were considered to be multinucleate.

Methods

Studies on genetic interaction in *S. scabies* were dependent on the development of nutritionally deficient mutant strains. Although several methods were used, including the penicillin-screening method and the replica-plating procedure, the filtration enrichment technique formerly described (Braendle & Szybalski, 1957; Fries, 1947) was adopted and the presence of auxotrophic and prototrophic forms established. Briefly, this method consisted of growing a culture from ultra-violet irradiated spores of *S. scabies* on a liquid minimal medium (Gregory & Vaisey, 1956). This was followed by shaking and filtering through sterile No. 1 Whatman filter-paper. Nutritionally deficient spores did not develop in the minimal medium, and therefore passed through the paper, whereas most of the parental-type spores formed a filamentous growth which was removed by filtration.

Results

Mutants with certain nutritional requirements were encountered relatively frequently. The growth-factor requirements encountered most frequently were those for arginine, histidine, biotin, and a reduced form of sulphur. Mutant strains having the following double requirements have been found to be suitable for genetic studies: arginine and biotin, arginine and methionine, niacin and biotin, arginine and uracil.

Mixed platings of spores or macerated mycelium of strains with double complementary nutritional requirements resulted in the formation of colonies capable of slow growth on minimal medium. These colonies would subsequently grow on minimal medium only if mycelial fragments were transferred, but not if spores were transferred. The great majority of the conidia formed by these colonies possessed the nutritional requirements of one or the other parent. These prototrophic colonies were thus considered to be heterokaryons, possessing the nuclei of the two parental strains associated in the same hyphae.

One recombinant class in which two nutritional deficiencies occurred, one deficiency inherited from each of the two parents, was found to occur quite frequently. Where spores from a heterokaryon derived from a parent incapable of synthesizing niacin and biotin and a parent deficient in arginine and methionine, 1% of the spores developed into colonies, almost half of which required biotin and methionine. No mechanism other than genetic recombination is apparent to explain this occurrence of a new combination of two nutritional deficiencies from two parents. The data are insufficient to allow conclusions to be drawn relative to the significance of heterokaryon formation and genetic recombination in nature. They do suggest that genetic interaction between *Streptomyces* should be considered as a factor involved in the relationship between *S. scabies* and perhaps other streptomycetes and their environment, and that such genetic interactions may be one of the principal causes of variation encountered in these studies.

Acknowledgments

This work is part of the programme of the Potato Scab Research Committee in Ontario. The support of this committee and the assistance of Dr. F. E. Chase, Department of Bacteriology, O.A.C., are gratefully acknowledged.

REFERENCES

ALIKHANIAN, S. I., & MINDLIN, S. (1957). Recombinations in *Streptomyces rimosus. Nature, Lond.,* **180,** 1208–9

BRADLEY, S. G. (1957). Heterokaryosis in *Streptomyces coelicolor. J. Bact.,* **73,** 581–2.

BRADLEY, S. G., & LEDERBERG, J. (1956). Heterokaryosis in *Streptomyces. J. Bact.,* **72,** 219–25.

BRAENDLE, D. H., & SZYBALSKI, W. (1957). Genetic interaction among strepto-mycetes: heterokaryosis and synkaryosis. *Proc. Nat. Acad. Sci.*, **43**, 947–55.

CHASE, F. E. (1948). A preliminary report on the use of the Lees and Quastel soil perfusion technique in determining the nitrifying capacity of field soils. *Sci. Agr.*, **28**, 315–20.

DOUGLAS, R. J., & GARRARD, E. H. (1954). A simple serological test for certain actinomycetes. *Canad. J. Bot.*, **32**, 38–9.

DOUGLAS, R. J., & GARRARD, E. H. (1954). Serological observations on the actino-mycetes associated with potato scab. *Canad. J. Bot.*, **32**, 480–5.

ERIKSON, D. (1949). The morphology, cytology and taxonomy of the Actino-mycetes. *Ann. Rev. Microbiol.*, **3**, 23–54.

FRIES, N. (1947). Experiments with different methods of isolating physiological mutations of filamentous fungi. *Nature, Lond.*, **159**, 199.

GILMOUR, C. M., & BUTHALA, D. (1950). The isolation and study of actinophage from soil. *Bact. Proc.* (1950), 17.

GREGORY, K. F. (1956). Hyphal anastomosis and cytological aspects of *Strepto-myces scabies*. *Canad. J. Microbiol.*, **2**, 649–55.

GREGORY, K. F., & VAISEY, E. B. (1956). Pathogenicity of tyrosinase-deficient mutants of *Streptomyces scabies*. *Canad. J. Microbiol.*, **2**, 65–71.

KLECZKOWSKA, J. (1950). A study of phage-resistant mutants of *Rhizobium trifolii*. *J. gen. Microbiol.*, **4**, 298–310.

KLIENEBERGER-NOBEL, E. (1947). The life cycle of sporing Actinomyces as revealed by a study of their structure and septation. *J. gen. Microbiol.*, **1**, 22–32.

LUDWIG, E. H., & HUTCHINSON, W. G. (1949). A serological study of selected species of Actinomycetes. *J. Bact.*, **58**, 89–101.

LUTMAN, B. F., & CUNNINGHAM, G. C. (1914). Potato Scab. *Vermont Agr. Expt. Sta. Bull.*, **184**.

NETER, E. (1956). Bacterial hemagglutination and hemolysis. *Bact. Rev.*, **20**, 166–88.

NEWBOULD, F. H. S., & GARRARD, E. H. (1954). Studies on actinophage for *Streptomyces scabies*. *Canad. J. Bot.*, **32**, 386.

REILLY, H. C., HARRIS, D. A., & WAKSMAN, S. A. (1947). An actinophage for *Streptomyces scabies*. *J. Bact.*, **54**, 451–86.

ROMANO, A. H., & NICKERSON, W. J. (1956). The biochemistry of the Actino-mycetales. Studies on the cell wall of *Streptomyces fradiae*. *J. Bact.*, **72**, 478–82.

ROMANO, A. H., & SOHLER, A. (1956). Biochemistry of the Actinomycetales. 11. A comparison of the cell wall composition of species of the genera *Streptomyces* and *Nocardia*. *J. Bact.*, **72**, 865–8.

SERMONTI, G., & SPADA-SERMONTI, I. (1956). Gene recombination in *Streptomyces coelicolor*. *J. gen. Microbiol.*, **15**, 609–16.

SKINNER, C. E. (1938). The 'tyrosinase reaction' of the actinomycetes. *J. Bact.*, **35**, 415–24.

SLACK, J. M., LUDWIG, E. H., BIRD, H. H., & CANBY, C. M. (1951). Studies with Microaerophilic Actinomycetes. 1. The agglutination reaction. *J. Bact.*, **61**, 721–35.

TAYLOR, C. F., & DECKER, P. (1947). A correlation between pathogenicity and cultural characteristics in the genus *Actinomyces*. *Phytopath.*, **37**, 49–58.

VANDECAVEYE, S. C., FULLER, W. H., & KATZNELSON, H. (1940). Bacteriophage of Rhizobia in relation to symbiotic nitrogen fixation by alfalfa. *Soil Sci.*, **50**, 15–28.

VAISEY, E. B., CARPENTER, J. A., & ATKINSON, R. G. (1955). Pigment production in skim milk by actinomycetes in relation to potato scab. *Canad. J. Microbiol.*, **1**, 574–8.

WAKSMAN, S. A. (1957). Species concept among the Actinomycetes with special reference to the genus Streptomyces. *Bact. Rev.*, **21**, 1–29.

WAKSMAN, S. (1950). *The Actinomyces.* Waltham, Mass.: Chronica Botanica.

WELSCH, M. (1956). Actinophages dans les milieux naturels. *C.R. Soc. Biol.*, **150**, 1496–9.

WELSCH, M., MINON, A., & SCHONFELD, J. K. (1955). Isolation of Actinophages. *Experientia.*, **11**, 24–8.

DISCUSSION

Dr. E. Grossbard. As Dr. Harley said that very little is known about translocation in fungi, it is not fair to expect a straightforward and clear answer, but could he speculate as to what may be the agent of translocation in fungi?

Dr. J. L. Harley. The sheath tissue of ectotrophic mycorrhizal roots consists of a fungal pseudoparenchyma which encloses the root tissues completely. The absorbing parts of the root system of plants so infected are mainly composed of rootlets ensheathed in this way. Substances absorbed from the soil must therefore somehow pass through the fungal tissue into the host tissue. It has been shown experimentally that there is not only a movement of phosphorus through the living fungal tissue of beech mycorrhizas, but also that phosphorus which has been accumulated in the fungus may pass into the host. The rate of this latter movement from sites of previous accumulation was found to be dependent upon temperature and oxygen supply. Using P^{32} as a tracer, it was shown that transport by this means was most rapid when an external phosphate supply was withheld from the mycorrhizal roots. In the presence of adequate phosphate in the external solution, a proportion of the phosphate being absorbed passed to the host, but none of that previously accumulated in the fungal hyphae moved. During the process of absorption from dilute solutions ions do not seem to move through the absorbing layer of fungal sheath or cortex by way of the sites of accumulation, but by a more direct path presumably through the protoplasts. Other experiments with beech have suggested that yet another path through the fungal sheath may exist which becomes important when high external salt concentrations are applied. This is a direct diffusional path through the interhyphal spaces of the fungal layer, and it has its counterpart in the intercellular diffusion path in uninfected roots or tissue slices.

There appear to be, then, three paths of movement of phosphate through the sheath tissue of beech mycorrhizas; through the protoplasmic layer, via the accumulation sites, and through the interhyphal spaces. It is only in very high phosphate concentrations, too high to be expected ecologically, that the direct diffusional path is significant. My colleagues and myself have concluded that in ecologically probable conditions phosphate passes to the host through the living hyphae of the sheath.

HARLEY, J. L., McCREADY, C. C., & BRIERLEY, J. K. (1958). The uptake of phosphate by excised mycorrhizal roots of the beech. VIII. Translocation of phosphorus in mycorrhizal roots. *New Phytol.*, **57**, 353–62.

Prof. A. Burges. One of the very surprising things is that in litter accumulation or decomposition, where you do have abundant carbohydrate supply, you do not often get an accumulation of organic acids. Admittedly the humus goes acid, but if you extract from that and examine chromatographically you have difficulty in finding much organic acid. Fumaric acid is one of the few that we have picked up. Do you think that this is leaching away or that other things are keeping the metabolic balance?

Dr. J. L. Harley. Well, the fact that fumaric acid is one of the acids you find solves a problem raised earlier in the symposium. It must mean that the Phycomycetes are active in the decay of litter, for the only organisms recorded (I think I am correct) as producing fumaric acid in any significant quantity are the Mucorales.

Now, the reason you do not find organic acids, I should have thought, is that they are highly reactive substances, and a number of organisms are greatly stimulated in activity by the addition of small quantities of acids which may enter into their Krebs Cycle mechanism. So they are likely to be taken up right away.

Prof. A. Burges. We got Overell [Melbourne] to examine *Casuarina* litter, and the only acid he could find in any amount was fumaric, which was as much as 0·06% (w/w) of the dry weight in the litter.

Dr. H. Katznelson. With regard to the importance of CO_2 for the growth of certain fungi, I would imagine that such a condition would obtain in the rhizosphere where, owing to the intense microbial activity, the CO_2 tension is higher than in the soil away from the root. This might permit development of fungi near the root, which would not develop away from the root.

Dr. A. G. Morton. A question of great importance is how far the physiology of fungi in the rather unnatural experimental conditions of the laboratory can be related to fungal behaviour in their normal habitat. Can studies of the physiology of soil fungi throw light on what they do in the soil? Some work in our laboratory suggests that the data of physiology can be very relevant.

We have studied the factors affecting sporulation (formation of asexual conidia) in *Penicillium griseofulvum*, which is a soil-inhabiting species. Some other soil *Penicillia* show a general similarity in sporulation response. Sporulation is found to be induced by three main factors. Firstly, by exhaustion (absence) of assimilable nitrogen in the medium, whilst available carbohydrate is still present. Secondly, by increasing the osmotic pressure of the medium or (in some conditions) by partial desiccation of the mycelium. Thirdly, by exposure of the mycelium to aerial conditions after previous submerged growth. Since these observations have already been reported in detail (Morton, England, & Towler, 1958), I only mention them now as exemplifying physiological responses clearly correlated with the probable habitat of such fungi on 'islands' of limited nutrient capacity in the soil. Induction of sporulation precisely in these general physiological conditions would be advantageous to the fungus and tend to be established by natural selection.

The most powerful stimulus to sporulation in these *Penicillia* seems to be the emergence of growing hyphae from submerged to aerial conditions, and I should like to describe very briefly some observations on this point. When young growing mycelium of *Penicillium griseofulvum* is transferred from full nutrient medium (in which is does not sporulate) to a nitrogen-free medium containing a high concentration of glucose (10% (w/v)), the mycelium proceeds to form numerous conidiophores and conidia after 10–12 hr. in submerged conditions. As early as 5 hr. after transfer to nitrogen-free 10% glucose the mycelium can be shown to be 'induced' (i.e. capable of sporulation). In submerged conditions sporulation is only completed, however, if the mycelium is maintained in the high concentration of glucose. If such induced mycelium is transferred (after 5 hr. in 10% glucose) to phosphate buffer solution without glucose, in submerged conditions scarcely any conidiophores or conidia are formed, nor is there vegetative growth. The mycelium is full of reserve carbohydrate (glycogen) and fat, but these reserves are not mobilized in submerged conditions in buffer alone, even when the oxygen supply is increased by injection of air and vigorous stirring.

If the same mycelium in buffer is exposed to aerial conditions, however, by spreading a little of the suspension on a porous plate or sintered glass filter, its behaviour is very different. Within 2 or 3 hr. aerial hyphae grow up and project above the substratum. The tips branch repeatedly, and rapidly form many conidiophores which bear long chains of conidia. Thus aerial conditions permit mobilization of mycelial reserves and the completion of sporulation (accompanied by some vegetative development and differentiation), whilst these processes are almost completely prevented when the mycelium remains submerged.

The physiological basis of this striking difference in behaviour of the organism in submerged and aerial conditions requires further investigation, but it is encouraging and significant that it corresponds to what appears to be observed in soil conditions. Several reports in this symposium have suggested that conidia are formed by fungi only in air-spaces in the soil, not within the substrate (i.e. in submerged conditions).

One other point I would like to mention. Our work has shown that many fungi secrete complex peptide-like nitrogen compounds into the surrounding medium during growth. Whether fungi do this when growing in the soil I do not know, but peptide-like substances can be detected in the soil water (after passage through a bacterial filter) and constitute a significant proportion of the nitrogen in solution in it. The existence of this supply of soluble organic nitrogen in the soil deserves consideration in studies of soil ecology.

MORTON, A. G., ENGLAND, D. J. F., & TOWLER, D. A. (1958). The physiology of sporulation in *Penicillium griseofulvum* Dierclex. *Trans. Brit. mycol. Soc.*, **41**, 39–51.

Dr. H. Katznelson. Apropos of studying the activity of fungi in soil, we have often wondered how to separate the activities of different groups of organisms in the soil as a whole. One method tried was the use of selected antibiotics. With chloramphenicol there was a reduction of oxygen uptake by soil in a Warburg vessel. Now, this substance has no anti-fungal effect that I know of and no anti-protozoan effect, and may be considered to have been active therefore against bacteria. Actidione was not effective in these experiments. Another method which effectively cut off oxygen uptake by soil was the reduction of pH to 3·5–4·0. We think that this may be due to inhibition of bacterial respiration, but of course one cannot be certain as various indirect effects may have been involved. I quite agree that one must not be too reckless about interpreting results based on isolated organisms be they fungi or bacteria, and that the soil as a whole should be studied.

CO_2 supply in the rhizosphere soil is greater than in non-rhizosphere soil, and may be important in the growth of various types of fungi as well as of bacteria.

Dr. M. Witkamp. We estimated reduction of CO_2 production after the addition of antibiotics to soil. The reductions were rather low, and combinations of anti-fungal and anti-bacterial substances were not able to check CO_2 evolution, even when additional insecticides was mixed in.

The relative activity of fungi or bacteria in various types of soil could, however, be demonstrated by adding cycloheximide or chloromycetin separately to various types of soil, and comparing the resulting reduction in CO_2 production.

Dr. J. L. Harley. How much material do you suppose was in the bacterial bodies that you killed? There might be a significant release of material. I ask this because it always worries me that people do analyses, for instance, of rhizosphere soil, and they show higher amounts of ammonia and amino acids than in normal soil; but in extraction of the soil since one had a very much higher population, it is possible that these amino acids arose from the dead bodies of the organisms extracted and are not in the soil. To what extent are we getting the same sort of thing here?

Dr. H. Katznelson. The amount of nitrogenous material produced in such a way would be extremely small.

I should like to ask Dr. Hurst if there is any evidence of an oxidative shunt pathway in *Neurospora*? Martin and co-workers at the N.R.C., Ottawa, for instance, have demonstrated a shunt pathway in *Aspergillus*.

Dr. H. M. Hurst. We do not know whether *Neurospora crassa* has an isocitritase shunt, but isocitritase has been shown to be present in at least one mould (KORN-BERG & KREBS, *Nature, Lond.*, **179,** 1957).

Dr. J. L. Harley. Perhaps I might ask how widespread has Dr. Boulter found CO light-reversed inhibition in the fungi? I ask this because I have heard it said that if the cytochrome oxidase system is widespread in fungi they are unlikely to be inhibited by low-oxygen concentrations in the soil.

Dr. D. Boulter. We have at various times demonstrated a CO light-reversed inhibition of the respiration of about a dozen fungi, and it is our feeling that probably the main oxidative mechanism of fungi is by the cytochrome system provided the fungus is young. As the fungus ages, oxidations other than those directly relating to energy requirements may occur, and it is then much more difficult to demonstrate a CO light-reversed inhibition because the cytochrome system may carry a smaller part of the total oxygen uptake. Of course, there are certain difficulties in all selective inhibitor studies; these apply to CO as well which does not always reach the desired site of action.

AUTHOR INDEX

(Contributors to discussions included)

MICRO-ORGANISM INDEX

SUBJECT INDEX

324   SUBJECT INDEX

Temperature as an ecological factor, 66–
    67, 94–97, 109, 120, 142–144, 195,
    307
Tidal muds, 202–208, 220
Toxicity, 116, 118, 124, 134, 145, 152,
    162, 217
Translocation in hyphae, 51, 60–62, 271,
    307
Tropics, 134, 186

Vitamin precursors, 269
    production, 269
    requirements, 196, 225, 260, 274

Washing techniques, 17–18, 22–27, 51–
    52, 226–227
Water as an ecological factor, 15, 38–39,
    67, 108, 109, 195
Wood, decomposition, 260, 286–296